ACADEMY OF SCIENCES OF THE USSR
Zelinskii Institute of Organic Chemistry

PROBLEMS OF KINETICS AND CATALYSIS
XI

SCIENTIFIC SELECTION
OF CATALYSTS

Edited by A. A. Balandin, B. A. Kazanskii, V. E. Vasserberg
G. V. Isagulyants, and G. I. Levi

Translated from Russian
by A. Aledjem

Israel Program for Scientific Translations
Jerusalem 1968

This book is a translation of

NAUCHNYE OSNOVY PODBORA KATALIZATOROV
Seriya: "Problemy kinetiki i kataliza"
Izdatel'stvo "Nauka"
Moskva 1966

IPST Cat. No. 2187

Printed and Bound in Israel

Printed in Jerusalem by S. Monson
Binding: Wiener Bindery Ltd., Jerusalem

TABLE OF CONTENTS

EXPLANATORY LIST OF ABBREVIATIONS OF USSR INSTITUTIONS
AND JOURNALS APPEARING IN THIS TEXT

Abbreviation	Full name (transliterated)	Translation
DAN SSSR	Doklady Akademii Nauk SSSR	Proceedings of the Academy of Sciences of the USSR
FMM	Fizika Metallov i Metallovedenie	The Physics of Metals and Metallurgy (Journal)
GEOKhi	Institut Geokhimii i Analiticheskoi Khimii imeni V. I. Vernadskogo (Akademii Nauk SSSR)	Institute of Geochemistry and Analytical Chemistry imeni V. I. Vernadskii (of the Academy of Sciences of the USSR)
IAN	Izvestiya Akademii Nauk SSSR	News of the Academy of Sciences of the USSR (periodical)
IKhF	Institut Khimicheskoi Fiziki	Institute of Chemical Physics
IL	Izdatel'stvo Inostrannoi Literatury	Foreign Literature Publishing House
OKhN	Otdelenie Khimicheskikh Nauk (Akademii Nauk SSSR)	Department of Chemical Sciences (of the Academy of Sciences of the USSR)
SO AN SSSR	Sibirskoe Otdelenie Akademii Nauk SSSR	Siberian Department of the Academy of Sciences of the USSR
VNIINP	Vsesoyuznyi Nauchno-Issledovatel'skii Institut po Pererabotke Nefti i Gaza i Polucheniyu Iskusstvennogo Zhidkogo Topliva	All-Union Scientific Research Institute for Oil and Gas Processing and Production of Synthetic Liquid Fuel
ZhETF	Zhurnal Eksperimental'noi i Teoreticheskoi Fiziki	Journal of Experimental and Theoretical Physics (periodical)
ZhFKh	Zhurnal Fizicheskoi Khimii	Journal of Physical Chemistry
ZhNKh	Zhurnal Neorganicheskoi Khimii	Journal of Inorganic Chemistry
ZhPKh	Zhurnal Prikladnoi Khimii	Journal of Applied Chemistry

FROM THE EDITORS

   The eleventh collection in the series "Problems of Kinetics and Catalysis"
is based on the reports presented at the All-Union Conference on the
Scientific Principles of the Selection of Catalysts for Heterogeneous
Chemical Reactions, organized by the N.D. Zelinskii Institute of Organic
Chemistry of the Academy of Sciences of the USSR, for the section
Scientific Principles of Catalyst Selection and Preparation of the
Scientific Council on Catalysis and Its Industrial Applications, and the
Section for Catalysis of the Scientific Council for Structural Theory,
Kinetics, Reactivity, and Catalysis. The Conference was organized by a
commission headed by Academician A.A. Balandin; the vice-chairman
of the commission was S.L. Kiperman (Candidate of Chemical Sciences).
The Conference took place in Moscow, July 1—5, 1964.
   The reports in the collection give an indication of the active work of
Soviet scientists towards the development of the scientific principles of
catalyst selection and methods for the determination of the best catalysts
for existing processes, and the discovery of new catalysts for new, as yet
unknown, reactions. The solution of the above problems, which are of
tremendous economic and scientific importance, is the aim of the research
work of catalysis chemists belonging to different schools and with different
lines of thought. The simultaneous application of the principles of structural
and energy correspondence of the multiplet theory, the modern electronic
concepts of solid-state physics, and comprehensive experimental investigations
with the use of kinetic, thermochemical, and chemical methods have all
led to the accumulation of many valuable results (as shown by the reports
presented at the Conference), and give promise of even greater advances
in the future.
   This collection comprises all the reports presented at the Conference,
except the report of L.Ya. Margolis, A.V. Krylova, O.V. Isaev, and
Z.S. Aleksandrov on "The Electronic Properties and Activity of Complex
Catalysts for the Oxidation of Hydrocarbons", the report of I.I. Ioffe,
Z.I. Ezhkova, and A.G. Lyubarskii on "Some Problems of the Selective
Oxidation of Organic Compounds on Non-metallic Catalysts", the report
of A.A. Ponomarev and A.S. Chegol on "Some Experimental Data
Concerning the Catalytic Properties of Ruthenium in Hydrogenation
Processes", and the report of Z.G. Zul'fugarova, T.A. Adamskii, S.G.
Agaev, and A.G. Efendiev on "The Effect of Lanthanides and New Clay
Binders on the Activity of Chromoaluminum Catalysts and Zeolites". The
authors of these reports did not submit their manuscripts.
   We hope that this Collection will be read with interest and be of
assistance.

I. GENERAL PROBLEMS OF THE SCIENTIFIC SELECTION OF CATALYSTS

A.A. Balandin

STRUCTURAL AND ENERGY FACTORS IN THE THEORY OF CATALYST SELECTION

In the present state of the science of catalysis it is important to determine the possible contribution of each of the existing theories of catalysis toward the establishment of the scientific principles of the choice of catalysts, and to define the recommendations of each theory for further experimental work.

We shall deal with the main points of the multiplet theory and its uses; we shall list the facts and relations that have been explained on the basis of this theory; we shall recall the predictions made by the multiplet theory and to what extent these predictions were confirmed by experiment; and finally what recommendations could be made on the basis of this theory for the further development of the theory of catalyst selection. Our task is simplified by the appearance of two review papers on the multiplet theory /1, 2/ and of a monograph whose first part was published in 1963 /3/, and second part in 1964 /4/.

It is universally accepted that catalysis is a chemical phenomenon. It is known from the science of the structure of matter that chemical valence forces have a very small radius of action. Hence, the atoms react only upon contact. This is the main basis of the multiplet theory. From the known values of the valence angles, and bond lengths and energies, the multiplet theory makes it possible to build models of the intermediate multiplet complex, to calculate the energy of formation and decomposition of this complex, and from these to predict the occurrence of specified reactions. The bond energy and length are stable properties of the complex; they may be determined experimentally, and in this way they are more readily available than by the cumbersome and complicated quantum-mechanics calculations of the interaction of nuclei and electrons, although such a calculation also leads, in principle, to the determination of the bond energy and length. In addition to the electronic theory, the multiplet theory of catalysis is related to the theory of absolute reaction rates. However, while the latter theory develops in a deductive way, the multiplet theory develops by an inductive approach, correlating the factual data on the basis of the theory of the structure of matter. The multiplet theory established two principles — the structural and energetic correspondence between the reacting molecules and the catalysts.

The multiplet theory has been applied successfully to a branch of organic catalysis including many hydrogenation, dehydrogenation, hydrogenolysis, deuterium-exchange, dehydration, dehalogenation, and other reactions;

1

this has been accompanied by the establishment of the laws describing the effects of conjugation and ring formation. At present, the above theory should not be applied to reactions involving a change in valence (and in particular to oxidation reactions) and to acid-base catalysis, although we cannot exclude the possibility that it might be developed to apply to the above fields, too. For instance, K.V. Topchieva and A.P. Ballod have found that a certain relationship exists between the interatomic distances in hydrocarbons and in catalysts for cracking /5/. According to R. Hansford, the carbonium ion on the surface of aluminosilicate is not free, but is a strongly polarized part of the catalytic complex /6/. M.I. Temkin and N.V. Kul'kova have established the existence of a relationship between the metal-oxygen bond energy and the activity of oxides as oxidation catalysts /7/. This is in close agreement with the multiplet theory, but the exact relation between this theory and the above cases needs further clarification.

In the doublet reaction

$$
\begin{array}{ccc}
\text{A} \quad \text{D} & \text{A---D} & \text{A—D} \\
| \quad | \rightarrow & | \quad | \rightarrow & \\
\text{B} \quad \text{C} & \text{B---C} & \text{B—C} \\
& (M) &
\end{array}
\tag{1}
$$

two vertical bonds are broken and two horizontal bonds are created between the A, B, C, and D atoms lying on the surface of the catalyst when passing through the stage of formation of a multiplet complex with the catalyst (M). Atoms A, B, C, and D may be replaced by other atoms, and the bonds may be simple, double, triple, or even non-existent [i.e., decomposition rather than double decomposition in the first stage]. By replacing the A, B, C, and D atoms by C, N, O, S, H, and Cl and using different bond configurations, it is possible to derive a classification involving about 2,000 types of reactions, most of which are unknown and have to be discovered. Some of these reactions have, in fact, been discovered at our laboratory by guided research. This classification is of the same importance as the Fedorov classification in crystallography, since it comprises all possible types of duplet reactions. It extends also to the four-atom intermediate cyclic complexes (Syrkin complexes) in homogeneous reactions. Naturally, in addition to the structural feasibility, the thermodynamic feasibility of the reaction must also be taken into account.

The above classification [probably structural] and thermodynamic requirements do not take into account the role of the catalyst. They are discussed on the basis of the principles of structural and energetic correspondence, which affect the reaction kinetics but not the reaction equilibrium.

The structural correspondence has several aspects. In the first place, it explains several general characteristics of catalytic processes: the occurrence of the reaction in an adsorbed monolayer, the orientation of molecules of the reacting atoms in the direction of the catalyst, the special effect of the boundary between solid phases, the poisoning of catalysts and the orientation of molecules of the poison, the activation by small amounts of poisons, the limiting cases of bond deformation on the surface with the formation of free atoms and radicals and the initiation of chain reactions, the transfer of metal over the surface due to the migration and decomposition of the multiplet complexes, the laminar structure of the intermediate complex, etc.

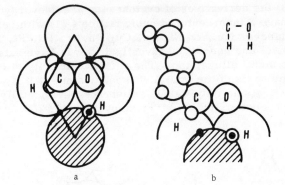

FIGURE 1. Model of the active complex in duplet dehydrogenation. Dehydrogenation of the n-butanol on nickel:

a- view from above; b- view from the side.

In the second place, the complex M in formula (1) may be represented
to scale by a three-dimensional model, e.g., for the dehydrogenation of
n-butanol (Figure 1). It can be shown that such models must obey the rule
of conservation of the valence angle in the following cases (see Figure 2):
a) for the hydrogenation of olefins, where rhodium is the most active
catalyst; b) for the hydrogenation of acetylene bonds, where the calculations
of Harrington show that nickel should be the most active catalyst, which
has been confirmed by experimental data; c) for the hydrogenation of
carbonyl bonds. On the above basis, the author, N.A. Vasyunina et al.,
have predicted that ruthenium would be the best catalyst for a new reaction
of great practical importance — the hydrolytic hydrogenation of cellulose
to sorbitol; this prediction has been confirmed by experimental data.

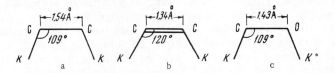

FIGURE 2. Location of molecules on the catalyst surface during
the hydrogenation of:

a- olefin bonds; b- acetylene bonds; c- carbonyl bonds.

In the third place, doublet schemes similar to those in Figure 1, and
especially sextet models, require an extremely accurate superposition of
the molecules on the catalyst lattice. As an example of doublet reaction we
may cite the recent work of Rienäcker and Porubskii** who found /1, 2/
that binary Ni — Fe alloys are active catalysts in the hydrogenation of propylene
only when the alloys have the structure of nickel (A 1) and thus satisfy the
model in Figure 1. The author has found that in agreement with the sextet

* [Throughout the book, the catalyst is denoted by "K".]
** In order to limit the size of the list of references, here and below only two reviews are referred to /1, 2/,
in which the complete references can be found according to the authors' names.

3

model (Figure 3) the derivatives of cyclohexane are dehydrogenated only on metals that have a face-centered cubic lattice (A 1) with certain definite interatomic distances, i.e., on Ni, Co, Cu, Rh, Ir, Pd, Pt, Ru, Os, and Re. Several Soviet and non-Soviet investigators [1] have extended the above results to metal alloys, too. The catalytic activity of rhenium was anticipated on the basis of the multiplet theory, since it lies within the "activity square"; its activity was established experimentally by the author, E.I. Karpeiskaya and A.A. Tolstopyatova [1, 2].

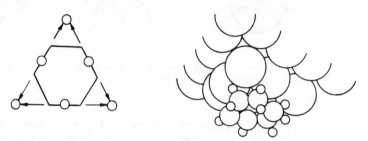

FIGURE 3. Planar sextet model of the dehydrogenation of cyclohexane on metals.

A similar behavior is observed in the deuterium exchange of cyclohexane on metallic films. On Pt, Pd, and Ni (metals with the A 1 lattice) the number of deuterium atoms introduced into the cyclohexane has a maximum at the sixth D atom, which indicates a sextet configuration, while on W, Mo, and Fe (with a different lattice) no maximum is observed up to the twelfth D atom (according to data of the author, B.S. Gudkov and R.M. Fedorovich [1, 2] based on the results of mass spectrographic analyses).

On the other hand, decahydroazulene is not dehydrogenated satisfactorily on palladium (in spite of the fact that the dehydrogenation would yield an aromatic compound) since it has no common symmetry elements with the Pd lattice and the sextet mechanism of dehydrogenation is not possible. The multiplet theory is in good agreement with the stereochemical data of Linstead on the hydrogenation of diphenic acids [1, 2], etc.

In the fourth place, several observations indicate that at low temperatures substituents at the A, B, C, and D atoms may also be adsorbed on the surface (V.E. Vasserberg, the present author) [1, 2]. Such planar adsorption may be attributed to asymmetric catalysis and (at least in part) to the high selectivity of the enzymes. The present author, E.I. Klabunovskii and Yu.I. Petrov [1, 2] have shown that the adsorption of gelatine on Skitas catalyst is of the W-type.

Future research in the development of the principle of structural correspondence should be in the direction of X-ray diffraction and electron-diffraction measurements of the lattice parameters of various catalysts, including hitherto unexamined (in this respect) oxides, sulfides, nitrides, carbides, borides, etc., as well as mixed catalysts; the structures of the reactant molecules are usually known.

The principle of energetic correspondence is even more important than the principle of structural correspondence. Let us denote the heat of formation of the intermediate complex from the starting substances, according to scheme (1), by E', and its decomposition into reaction products by E''. Then

$$E' = -Q_{AB} - Q_{CD} + (Q_{AK} + Q_{BK} + Q_{CK} + Q_{DK});\}$$
$$E'' = Q_{AD} + Q_{BC} - (Q_{AK} + Q_{BK} + Q_{CK} + Q_{DK}), \quad \} \qquad (2)$$

where K is the catalyst and Q_{XY} is the $X-Y$ bond energy.

The activation energy ε of the reaction is related to E by the expression

$$\varepsilon = A - \gamma E, \qquad (3)$$

where E is the smaller among E' and E'', $A \approx 0$, and γ has a value of $3/4$ for endothermic and $1/4$ for exothermic reactions.

Equations (2) and (3) are the energetic equations of the multiplet theory, and equation (2) has been derived also by M.I. Temkin /2/, while equation (3) has been derived (for the case of free radicals) by N.N. Semenov /2/. Similar equations have been applied by Polanyi to the particular case of para-ortho transitions in hydrogen. Equation (3) is analogous with the Bronsted equation. Thus, equations (2) and (3) which have been derived by the present author are in good agreement with the results of other authors. The derivation of (2) and (3) is based on some simplifying assumptions, but an analysis reported in 1956 /9/ has established their validity in certain cases.

According to the principles of energetic correspondence

$$E' = E''. \qquad (4)$$

A graphical plot of equation (2) yields the so-called volcano-shaped curves (see Figure 4 for the specific case of alcohol dehydrogenation (I) and dehydration (II); the curves are drawn to scale). The adsorption potential $q = Q_{AK} + Q_{BK} + Q_{CK} + Q_{DK}$ is plotted on the abscissa, and E is plotted on the ordinate. Each reaction has a specific volcano-shaped curve; the maximum on such a curve corresponds to the most active catalyst which satisfies the following condition (derived from equation (4)):

$$q_0 = Q_{AK} + Q_{BK} + Q_{CK} + Q_{DK} = \tfrac{1}{2}(Q_{AB} + Q_{CD} + Q_{AD} + Q_{BC}). \qquad (5)$$

On both sides of the maximum (i.e., for a decrease or increase in the adsorption potential) there is a decrease in activity.

The use of equation (5) for the selection of catalysts by additive computation of the optimum adsorption potentials q_0 from the bond energies is (in principle) not more complicated than the conventional computation of molecular refractions from atomic refractions. In addition to atomic refractions, the computation of molecular refractions takes into consideration some other terms, e.g., increments for multiple bonds, exaltation for conjugated bonds, etc. By analogy, the additive computation of energy barriers from the bond energies between the reactant atoms must take into account terms for the effect of adjacent atoms, effect of substitutions (conjugation energy σ, the sublimation term λ, etc.).

The values of Q_{AK} and the other terms in equation (5) yield the sum of Q^0_{AK} (the bond energy in the standard state in the three-dimensional lattice)

5

and λ (the sublimation term):

$$Q_{AK} = Q^{\circ}_{AK} + \lambda. \qquad (6)$$

Such constitutive effects in catalysis have been studied to a lesser extent than in the theory of refraction. However, it is possible even now to discuss them in part.

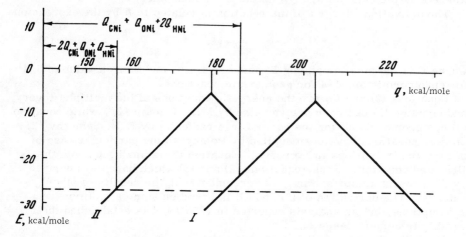

FIGURE 4. Volcano-shaped curves for the dehydrogenation (I) and dehydration (II) of alcohols.

Thus, the influence of substituents on catalytic reaction rates must be less pronounced than on the thermal effect or on the bond energy, since in equation (2) the respective terms (e.g., Q_{AB} and Q_{AK}) have opposite signs. Hence, the substitution may have no observable effect on the rate (when $\delta Q_{AB} = \delta Q_{AK}$), or the substitution may either increase the rate of the first stage of reaction (1) (at $\delta Q_{AB} < \delta Q_{AK}$) or reduce it (when $\delta Q_{AB} > \delta Q_{AK}$). This explains the apparent disagreement between the data of Constable [F.H. Constable], S.V. Lebedev, B.A. Kazanskii, A.V. Lozovoi, A.Kh. Bork, A.A. Tolstopyatova, O.K. Bogdanova, and others /1, 2/. Thus, contrary to the case of conventional organic chemistry, in catalytic reactions all considerations concerning the electron density distribution, its effect on the reaction rate, etc., must be discussed twice — once for Q_{AB} and once for Q_{AK}.

The effect of the conjugation energy has been discussed in the papers of the present author with M.L. Khidekel, with O.K. Bogdanova, and others /1, 2/.

Some data are also available for the sublimation term λ whose value depends on the mode of preparation of the catalyst. Thus, an equation has been derived for the dependence of λ on the heat of sublimation (from the bulk of the catalyst), on the positions of atoms on the surface, on the effect of the number of neighboring atoms, etc. This indicates that for catalysts of the same nature but prepared in different ways the changes in the activation energy should be smaller than half the heat of sublimation (from the bulk of the catalyst). This prediction of the multiplet theory has been confirmed by the present author, A.I. Kukina, and others.

The existence of volcano-shaped curves has been confirmed experimentally by Sachtler, Fahrenfort, van Reyen, V.A. Roiter, and G.I. Golodets (see /4/) for many reactions and catalysts. The last two authors have obtained volcano-shaped curves for some non-doublet oxidation reactions, too.*

What has been achieved by the method based on the use of equations (2) and (3) of the multiplet theory? In the first place, it became possible to determine the relative ease of occurrence of different reactions. The values of the activation energy ε determined from equations (2) and (3) may be substituted in the Arrhenius equation, taking into account the compensation effect:

$$k = \varkappa e^{\varepsilon\left(h - \frac{1}{RT}\right)}, \tag{7}$$

where k is the rate constant of the reaction studied, h is the active centers dissipation parameter whose value is fairly constant for reactions of a given type, and $\varkappa$ is usually close to unity. The series expanded with respect to k would be reversed as compared with the series expanded with respect to ε or, in other words, k would change in parallel with E [sic, probably ε].

The problem of catalyst selection has two aspects: 1) finding catalysts for a given reaction; 2) finding reactions that would occur on the given catalyst. The second aspect of the problem is solved satisfactorily by the multiplet theory. Thus, the laws governing the hydrogenolysis of different bonds in polyfunctional molecules on nickel, and the comparative ease of occurrence of such reactions, were determined for the first time by using the multiplet theory. A reference to the actual data is given in the book /4/. It shows that calculations based on the multiplet theory are in agreement with the data in hundreds of cases, almost without exception. This is evident not only from the literature data, but also from data collected in our laboratory in subsequent studies of many types of reactions: hydrogenation of olefin and carbonyl bonds, hydrogenolysis, ring rupture, dehydrogenation of hydrocarbons, amines, and alcohols, deuterium exchange, etc. We studied both simple and more complex compounds such as derivatives of triptycene, furan, monosaccharides, polyhydric alcohols, etc. In some cases we were able to achieve reactions that were predicted by the multiplet theory: dehydrogenation of fatty amines into ketimines, hydrogenolysis of tert-butyl chloride, N-bromoacetamide, organic peroxides and hydroperoxides, etc.

Thus, the multiplet theory predicted the possibility of hydrogenolysis of the peroxide bond $O-O$, and in particular the possibility of preparation of α-decalol by hydrogenation of decaline peroxide on nickel. Calculations showed that these hitherto unknown reactions should occur readily. The hydrogenation of various peroxides was studied by the author together with N.V. Nikitorova and L.Kh. Freidlin. The experimental results were in good agreement with the calculations /1, 2/. The activation energy was close to the calculated. Moreover, it was shown that in polyfunctional compounds the hydrogenolysis of $O-O$ bonds lies (in order of ease of occurrence) between the hydrogenation of $C \equiv C$ bonds and the reduction of the NO_2 group, in agreement with the predictions of the multiplet theory.

---

* [No reference is given in the text; the paper of Golodets and Roiter was published in Ukrainskii Khimicheskii Zhurnal, Vol. 29: 667. 1963.]

As another example of the predictions of the relative ease of occurrence of reactions we shall cite a series of 45 hitherto unknown transformations of various furan derivatives, which have been studied recently on nickel by A.A. Ponomarev, Z.V. Til', et al. From the standpoint of their relative rates, all these reactions conformed with the series predicted on the basis of the general rules established in 1956 by the author and A.A. Ponomarev /1, 2/ and derived on the basis of the multiplet theory.

In the case of catalysis on carbon, the bond energies Q_{AK} are also known and the theory may be applied. An investigation was made of the reduction by hydrogen of halogenated derivatives (by the author and V.V. Patrikeev), and of cyclohexanol (by the author with G.I. Levi and L.M. Broude) /1, 2/. The theory describes correctly the differences in the rate-determining stages (adsorption in the first and desorption in the second of the above cases), and predicts almost exactly (as compared with the experimental data) the sequential order of occurrence of the various reactions of those compounds.

At present it is more difficult to predict the catalysts for a given reaction. This difficulty will undoubtedly be eliminated with time, since it is caused by the fact that data on the bond energies between the reactant atoms and the catalyst are available for only a few cases. As our knowledge in the above field expands, this difficulty will be eliminated.

Nevertheless, some predictions have already been made and their validity has been established. Thus, confirmation has been obtained for the predicted catalytic activity of cadmium in the dehydrogenation of hydrocarbons and piperidine. Another example is zinc, which was found (in agreement with the theory) to have catalytic activity for the hydrogenation of olefin and carbonyl bonds in a sequence different from the sequence of these reactions on nickel.

Experiments have also confirmed that in the case of reactions with conjugation energy in their energy balance it would be possible to choose a catalyst with a lower adsorption potential. For instance, cadmium (but not zinc) is a suitable catalyst for the dehydrogenation of cyclohexane, and both cadmium oxide and zinc oxide are adequate catalysts for the dehydrogenation of butylene while alkaline-earth oxides cannot be used for that purpose.

The above brief survey (which, naturally, could not cover all available data) indicates that for the prediction of catalytic activities it is of importance to know the bond energies between the reactant atoms, and between these atoms and the catalyst. Hence, the determination of bond energies is a very important problem. In the opinion of the author, systematic studies in that direction are imperative. In most cases the mean values of Q_{AB} for molecules have already been established. However, it is necessary to determine the separate bond energies in order to assess the effect of substituents. Such measurements and calculations have been made (mainly by thermochemical methods) in the case of hydrocarbons by M.Kh. Karapetyants, V.M. Tatevskii, V.V. Voevodskii, and others /1, 2/.

The mean energies of atom-catalyst bonds Q_{AK} are known in far fewer cases. However, important data are available even for such bonds. Thus, the five known bond energies with nickel (namely, for hydrogen,

8

oxygen, nitrogen, and single and double carbon bonds) are used to calculate the correct sequence of energy barriers for twenty reactions types which accurately describe the sequential order of occurrence of hundreds of reactions. This indicates an extensive range of additivity, in agreement with equations (2) and (3) of the multiplet theory. Data for some other metals have also been collected.

Extensive experimental data on Q_{AK} for oxides have been obtained by A.A. Tolstopyatova, the present author, and their collaborators. The results and the observed general rules are discussed in more detail by A.A. Tolstopyatova (this collection, p.36).

In view of the fact that the properties of the whole surface and catalytically active centers are not uniform, kinetic and related methods are the most suitable for the determination of bond energies with catalysts. Two variants of kinetic methods have been developed in our laboratory (one variant with Tolstopyatova and the other with Kiperman). The method is based on the use of equations (2) and (3) of the multiplet theory. In using the above method one measures the activation energy of as many reactions as are required to determine the unknown bond energies in the equations, and the required bond energies are then determined by using those equations. Adequate methods for the determination of activation energies taking into account the adsorption coefficients have been described by the present author /10/. In addition, it is convenient to use a combined comparative-thermochemical method which also uses equation (2) of the multiplet theory, but the energy barriers are determined not on the basis of the activation energies but by comparing the rates of different doublet reactions, e.g., dehydrogenation, dehydration, etc. This gives a series of inequalities, which define the top and bottom limits of the energy barrier. In combination with thermochemical data, this makes it possible to determine the value of the bond energy.

Several considerations indicate that the values of the bond energies with the catalysts, assessed by the above methods, are correct.

In the first place, the values of bond energies between nickel and hydrogen, carbon or oxygen obtained by the combined thermochemical and comparative method are close to the values of the bond energies of these elements with chromium oxide, as determined by using the first variant of the kinetic method (Table 1). At the same time, since nickel and chromium oxide catalysts have a different chemical composition, the above values are not exactly the same, which also agrees with the theory.

TABLE 1. Bond energies with Ni and Cr_2O_3 catalysts

K	$H-K$	$C-K$	$O-K$
Ni	55	14	48.5
Cr_2O_3 (precipitation with NH_3) .	60.9	22.7	51.8

In the second place, values of the bond energies of nickel with hydrogen, carbon or nitrogen determined by the second variant of the kinetic method are virtually identical with the values collected much earlier and independently by the combined thermochemical and comparative method (Table 2).

9

TABLE 2. Bond energies with Ni (comparison between two methods)

Method	H−Ni	−C−Ni	=C−Ni	O−Ni	N−Ni
Kinetic, second variant	50.1	16	28.1	57.5	29.3
Comparative-thermochemical .	55	14	27	48.5	27

In the third place, it was found that the bond energies of hydrogen, carbon, and oxygen with the catalyst changed in agreement with the magnetic moment μ of the corresponding rare-earth element (for Q_{HK} — Figure 5), and this is a very important confirmation of the correctness of the bond energies determined by using the energetic equations of the multiplet theory.

In the fourth place, an agreement is observed between the changes in the bond energies of oxygen with the oxide catalysts as determined by the kinetic method $Q^K_{O-Me_nO_m}$ and the changes in the bond energies of oxygen with the metals in these oxides, as determined by the thermochemical method Q^T_{OMe} (see Figure 6).

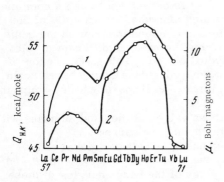

FIGURE 5. Effect of the atomic number of rare-earth elements on the bond energy Q_{HK} (1) and the magnetic moment μ (2).

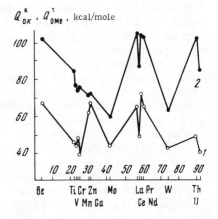

FIGURE 6. Correspondence between the bond energies of oxygen with the surfaces of oxide catalysts as determined by the kinetic method $Q^K_{O-Me_nO_m}$ (1) and the bond energy of the metal with oxygen in the solid oxide, as determined by a thermochemical method from the heat of formation of the oxide from the elements Q^T_{OMe} (2).

In the fifth place, an agreement exists between the bond energies with the oxide catalysts and a number of other properties of elements in the whole periodic system; an especially good agreement exists between the bond energies with the catalysts and the ionic radii (for example, see Figure 7).

Finally, in the sixth place, on the basis of the obtained, bond energies it is possible to determine the correct sequence of occurrence of hundreds of organic reactions, as mentioned above.

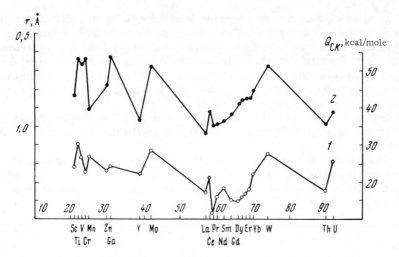

FIGURE 7. Correspondence between the changes in the bond energy of carbon with the catalyst Q_{CK} (1) and the ionic radii (2).

It is evident that the general rules described above could not be based on coincidence, and the measured bond energies thus correspond to the actual values.

Other methods for the determination of Q_{AK} either need further development or refer to the properties of the whole rather than the active surface of the catalyst. Of the above, the electrochemical methods and the method of adsorption-chemical equilibria are of interest. Moreover, some data may be obtained by infrared spectroscopy of adsorbed molecules, magnetic methods, mass-spectrometric methods, and other new physical methods in conjunction with kinetic studies. The development and use of such indirect methods is very desirable.

Emphasis should be placed upon works for the determination of the heats of formation of metal hydrides, borides, nitrides, sulfides, and analogous compounds, as well as of organic acid esters and salts (as a function of their structure and the nature of the metal), i.e., of all those substances that are considered (by the theory of intermediate compounds) as indermediates in catalytic reactions. The above data, with appropriate corrections, may be used to determine the bond energies with the metals, and the values obtained used in calculations based on the equations of the multiplet theory.

It is also necessary to carry out a systematic study of the general features of the so-called sublimation term, i.e., the rules governing the relationship between the crystallization factors, the bond energy on the surface of the solid body, and the catalytic activity.

In conclusion, we shall make a brief evaluation of the prospects of future research in the directions outlined in this paper.

The research on catalysis would undoubtedly expand in the direction of studies of the mechanism of catalytic reactions and the properties of catalysts, with the use of all modern methods. To this end, it is necessary to improve the existing methods and to develop new methods for the determination of bond energies with the catalysts, to make a systematic collection of new data on bond energies (and especially of individual bond energies), to extend organic catalytic reaction to molecules containing heteroatoms (boron, nitrogen, phosphorus, sulfur, selenium, tellurium, halogens, etc.), with determination of the respective bond energies within the molecules and with the catalyst, to find the laws governing the reactions in the above field, and to extend the calculations to other catalysts, especially to mixed and promoted ones.

It is necessary to strengthen the association of the multiplet theory with the electronic theory in organic chemistry and with the electronic theories of catalysis.

The above extensive program requires much time and labor, but it can be expected that the results will be of great importance for the development of a theory of catalyst selection; the need for such a theory is very urgent.

BIBLIOGRAPHY

1. BALANDIN, A. A. —Uspekhi Khimii, Vol. 31: 1265. 1962.
2. BALANDIN, A. A. —Uspekhi Khimii, Vol. 33: 549. 1964.
3. BALANDIN, A. A. Mul'tipletnaya teoriya kataliza (The Multiplet Theory of Catalysis). Part 1. Structural factors.—Moskva, Izd. MGU. 1963.
4. BALANDIN, A. A. Mul'tipletnaya teoriya kataliza (The Multiplet Theory of Catalysis). Part 2. Energetic factors.—Moskva, Izd. MGU. 1964.
5. TOPCHIEVA, K. V. and A. P. BALLOD. —Uspekhi Khimii, Vol. 20: 161. 1951.
6. HANSFORD, R. "Catalysis. Catalysts for Organic Reactions". —Collection of translated papers, p. 27. Moskva, IL. 1955.
7. KUL'KOVA, N. V. and M. I. TEMKIN.—ZhFKh, Vol. 31: 2017. 1957.
8. BALANDIN, A. A., N. A. VASYUNINA, S. V. CHEPIGO, and G. S. BARYSHEVA.—DAN SSSR, Vol. 128: 141. 1959.
9. BALANDIN, A. A. and A. A. TOLSTOPYATOVA.—ZhFKh, Vol. 30: 1636. 1956.
10. BALANDIN, A. A.—ZhFKh, Vol. 31: 745. 1957.

S. Z. Roginskii

SELECTION OF CATALYSTS AND CONSTRUCTION OF CATALYTIC SCHEMES

I. SELECTION OF CATALYSTS AND PREDICTION OF CATALYTIC PROPERTIES

1. The concept of selection, and the role of theory in it. Soviet chemists working in the field of catalysis have realized the need for concentrating considerable efforts towards the development of the scientific principles of catalyst selection. In dealing with the above problem, one should bear in mind the existence of a wide variety of problems of different degrees of complexity, which are unified by the concept of "selection of catalysts". The simplest of them (Table 1) involves the selection of the best (under the given conditions) catalyst among a number of known catalysts for the given reaction. The most complex problem involves the synthesis and the construction of "schemes" for processes of new types, which cannot be realized with a sufficient degree of effectiveness (or even cannot be realized at all) by using existing catalysts, and for which it is impossible to apply analogies to other mastered catalytic processes.

TABLE 1. Problems of catalyst selection in order of increasing complexity

A. Selection among known catalysts			B. Search for new catalysts			C. Synthesis of catalysts and construction of catalytic systems with prescribed properties
Best for the given reaction (among known catalysts)	For reactions analogous to known catalytic reactions	For new reactions	For mastered catalytic reactions	For reactions analogous to the mastered	For reactions of new types, having no analogs among mastered reactions	(A problem for the future)

The farther we depart from known and mastered catalysts and catalytic reactions, the more important becomes the prediction of catalytic properties (of single substances and more complex catalytic systems) for the selection of catalysts.

In cases in which the problem is confined to an expansion of the number of known catalysts for relatively simple reactions for which there exists even a single satisfactory catalyst, it would be very useful to use: a) analogies based on the periodic system of the elements and other general laws of chemistry and physics; b) empirical or theoretically predicted laws relating the catalytic properties of solid bodies to their electronic physical properties, the chemical composition, and the structure /1, 2/. By the above methods it has been possible not only to improve some already known catalysts, but also to discover extensive groups of new catalysts. The following examples of achievements made at our laboratory will be cited here: 1) the discovery of the oxidation-reduction catalytic activity of simple semiconductors and semiconducting compounds containing no transition elements /2—4/; 2) the discovery of the oxidation-reduction catalytic activity of refractory compounds and alloys of the transition elements with N, S, P, C, Si, and other non-metals /5/. In both cases the existence of such an activity was predicted on the basis of the already established rules governing the selection of catalysts, i.e., the predominance of solid bodies with electronic conductivity (metals and semiconductors) among catalysts for oxidation-reduction reactions (according to the classification of the present author) /2/. In the second case the prediction was even more definite due to the use of the second selection rule — the favorable effect of transition elements in the composition of a catalyst. A great increase was also made in the number of known solid inorganic catalysts for acid-base reactions /6/, and new large groups of organic and organometallic catalysts were developed for reactions of various types.

2. **The importance of chromatography for the selection.** The more complicated the process, and the stricter the requirements with respect to the polyfunctionality and selectivity of the catalyst needed for this process, the smaller is the possible contribution of the theory of catalysis (in its current form) towards the selection of catalysts. Hence, in addition to work on the further development of this theory, it is of great importance to improve the existing experimental methods for the study of catalytic properties and the rules governing the selection, as this is necessary for the rapid collection of more detailed information. We should stress the great possibilities offered by the use of gas and vapor chromatographic methods. These methods make it possible to detect and investigate catalytic phenomena at very low degrees of conversion; to determine rapidly the composition of all reaction products; to prepare the starting substances in a very pure state; to study the adsorption of reactants on the catalyst during the course of the reaction; and, finally, to carry out experimental studies of the kinetics of catalytic processes, of specific surfaces, and other important characteristics of the reaction and the catalyst /7/. Radiochromatography is especially effective in the study of mechanisms of complex catalytic reactions /8/. Great promise is offered by reaction studies under chromatographic conditions /9/, which make it possible to overcome the thermodynamic limitations, etc.

Even today the correlated use of gas chromatography in research on catalyst selection results in a considerable acceleration of the study of catalytic properties of solids. The importance of chromatography in such research will increase in the near future with the development of automatic chromatographic equipment and devices for the testing and study of catalysts and, in particular, of equipment that presents directly, in a processed form, the main kinetic and adsorption characteristics of the substances.

3. **Relationship between catalytic and other properties of a solid.** In the future, investigations of such relationships (in the study of the mechanism of catalytic action) should serve as the basis for the prediction of catalytic properties. Unfortunately, the available tabulated data on the structure and main properties of substances are often insufficient for this purpose. In some cases such data should not be used because of the specific properties of the phenomenon of catalysis. For this reason, in the development of research on the selection of catalysts there are many gaps to be filled, even in the case of the most thoroughly studied main bulk properties of individual substances, whether single crystals or massive polycrystalline bodies. The surface properties of such substances have been studied in much less detail and are reproducible to a lesser extent. This is attributed to the marked differences of the surface properties (physical and catalytic) on different faces /10/, and the influence exerted upon these properties by structural imperfections and by microchemical surface phenomena, including adsorption, which cannot be avoided in catalytic processes*. However, most catalysts are two- or three-phase (or even more complicated) systems with a high degree of porosity. Some of those phases are of variable composition; most of them contain stabilizers and modifying additives. Thus, in addition to the main properties of the separate substances, data should be available also on their structure-sensitive properties and the properties of the actual catalysts. At the same time, the respective properties should be determined by the fastest possible method, and, if possible, during the catalytic process or at least under conditions that resemble most closely the conditions existing during the process.

II. THE FUNCTIONS OF A CATALYST

The theory of the search for new catalysts should not be separated from the functions of such catalysts. As is evident from Table 2, these functions may be very varied. The reactions in group 1 (see Table 2) comprise systems in which the catalyst has the ability (from the standpoint of thermodynamic conditions) to initiate or accelerate only a single process which occurs under the given conditions (together with the reverse process in cases of a noticeably reversible reaction). In some reactions belonging to group 1 the above requirements are satisfied only partially, and not under all conditions. Thus, under certain conditions, oxygen atoms yield not only molecular oxygen but ozone too; the formation of H_2O_2 is observed occasionally in the oxidation of hydrogen. The low-temperature hydrogenation of benzene and its homologs may also be regarded as belonging to group 1. The seemingly simple hydrogenation of acetylene to ethylene and ethane may be complicated by side reactions: polymerization to kupren [sic], dehydrogenation to carbon, and destructive hydrogenation into CH_4. The above process has been classified by us as belonging to group 2. In

---

* Related problems have been reviewed at the Discussions of the Faraday Society (Liverpool 1966), in the reports of Ehrlich, Homer, and Sachtler.

15

many catalytic processes involving systems with a high free energy it must be taken into account that large amounts of various active species: radicals and atoms, ions, labile associative complexes, etc., are formed and that these species are formed not only on the surfaces of the solids but also within the bulk of the gas or liquid. In all cases cited above the starting substances and final products are stable.

TABLE 2. Catalyst functions in order of increasing complexity

Action of the catalyst	Examples
1. Initiation or acceleration of the only possible or strongly predominant reaction	$H_2 + D_2 \xrightarrow{Cr_2O_3} 2HD$; $2H \xrightarrow{W} H_2$; $2O \xrightarrow{MgO} O_2$; $2SO_2 + O_2 \xrightarrow{Fe_2O_3} 2SO_3$; $N_2 + 3H_2 \xrightarrow{Fe} 2NH_3$; $2H_2O_2 \xrightarrow{MnO_2} 2H_2O + O_2$; $2H_2 + O_2 \xrightarrow{Pd} 2H_2O$
2. Selective acceleration of some reactions (among several possible)	$CH_3-CHOH-CH_3$ $\nearrow CH_3-CO-CH_3 + H_2$ $\rightarrow CH_3CH=CH_2 + H_2O$ $\searrow (C_3H_7)_2O + H_2O$ $CO + H_2 \rightarrow$ Synthine $\nearrow CH_4$ $\searrow CH_3OH$ $C_2H_2 + H_2$ $\nearrow C_2H_4 \rightarrow C_2H_6$ $\rightarrow 2C + 2H_2$ $\searrow 2CH_4$ $(C_2H_2)_n$
3. Providing for the concurrence of processes	"Irreversible" Zelinskii catalysis Divinyl from ethanol according to Lebedev Coupling of oxidation reactions and endothermic synthesis in biocatalysis
4. Morphological functions (providing for a prescribed structure of the products)	Regulation of three-dimensional and configurational structures (l, d, cis-, trans-, etc.). Regulation of the branching and ring-formation in carbon chains Arrangement of monomers in the molecule in copolymerization, etc. Matrix biosynthesis

The functions of catalysts belonging to group 2 are more complicated and less direct. The selectivity may be based on the control of the relative velocities of independent parallel reactions or certain stages of the complicated process, or on the simultaneous control of the rate ratios of processes of both types.

The first type involves syntheses based on $CO + H_2$. Under certain conditions (Fischer-Tropsch synthetic fuel) the reaction product is almost completely composed of normal alkanes, from CH_4 to alkanes with tens and even hundreds of C atoms, comprising almost all alkanes in the series. By measuring the distribution of radioactive carbon from labelled initiators (olefins, alcohols, ketenes) between the various compounds in the series it has been found that those compounds are formed by independent, parallel reactions, from CO and H_2 /11, 12/. By changing the catalyst and the process conditions it is possible to change (within wide limits) the composition of the product — from virtually pure methane to liquid mixtures containing almost no CH_4 and even to parafins with a high melting point. In cases in which compounds belonging to a certain series are not clearly predominant, it is often impossible to ascertain whether the compounds belonging to different homologous series are formed independently and simultaneously (directly from the CO and H_2) or in some consecutive order.

The simultaneous and independent formation of different products is favored by catalytically non-homogeneous surfaces. The validity of the above statement has been confirmed in the particular cases of acetylene hydrogenation on nickel /14/, and of the decomposition of alcohols on oxides of metals belonging to group II of the periodic system /15/, by using the isotopic methods developed at the laboratory of the present author /13/. In both cases, each of the reaction products was formed from molecules adsorbed on specific sections of the surface, having different ranges of the heat of adsorption and different reactivities. Thus, reduction of the [surface] non-homogeneity either during the preparation or by selective poisoning of certain sections is one of the possible ways of increasing the selectivity. Evidently, this should not lead to the conclusion that in all cases the different products are formed only on different sections and hence no successive formation takes place. Successive formation of products having different molecular weights has been observed in particular in some polycondensation and polymerization reactions. The work of Kembell and others has shown that the successive formation of deuterium-containing products (of various degrees of substitution) from some hydrocarbons and amines is the predominant process in catalytic isotopic exchange with deuterium, while simultaneous [parallel] formation of such products is predominant in the case of other hydrocarbons and amines (see /16/).

No strict separation of parallel and consecutive reactions is possible in catalytic processes, due to the following reasons. a) There are many processes in which parallel reactions are superimposed on successive reactions. For example, this has been shown (by using radioactive carbon as a tracer) in the case of the catalytic oxidation of organic compounds by oxygen /17/ (Figure 1). b) Even in cases in which the various stable products (e.g., various oxygen-containing organic compounds) that can be separated are formed virtually independently and simultaneously, the synthesis of each of these products on any catalyst passes through a series of consecutive, hidden stages, most of which involve the participation or formation of active labile substances /18/. Our knowledge of the nature and properties of these products is expanding rapidly with the use of modern physical methods of research. In heterogeneous catalysis, a decrease in the number of independent parallel processes should be expected when the microchemical and energetic non-homogeneity of the surface is increased. Parallel independent reactions should be less frequent in homogeneous catalysis (as compared with heterogeneous catalysis), all other conditions being equal.

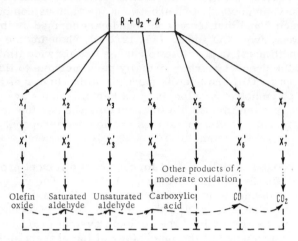

FIGURE 1. Idealized scheme of the catalytic oxidation of olefins in cases in which parallel processes are predominant:

R— olefin; K— catalysts; X_1, X_1', X_2', etc. — labile intermediate forms. The continuous-line arrows indicate independent transformations of stable molecules, while the dotted lines indicate successive transformations. (The predominance of a certain product is determined by the catalyst and the process conditions).

Conjugation and correlation reactions are classified as belonging to group 3. Apparent or hidden conjugation of stages is characteristic of any catalytic process. Otherwise no possibility would exist even for simple repetition and resumption of the process on the same centers of a heterogeneous catalyst (or on the same ions or molecules of a homogeneous catalyst), while the stability of any catalytic process necessitates exact correlation of the conjugated stages. The conjugation may be simple and trivial, as in the catalytic recombination of atoms (e.g., H and O) or in the homomolecular exchange between diatomic molecules involving competition for a given site (scheme 1):

$$K + A \rightarrow K \cdot A_{chemis}\{\equiv A_{chemis}\}$$
$$A_{chemis} + A \rightarrow A_{2\,ads} \rightarrow K + A_2$$
$$\nearrow$$
$$2A_{chemis}$$

Scheme 1. K— catalyst; A_{chemis}— chemisorbed substance; $\equiv$ symbol of identity.

The conjugation may be electronic-chemical, as in the decomposition of H_2O_2 with the reduction of $2H^+$ to H_2 on electron donor centers and the oxidation of O_2 into $O_{2(gas)}$ on acceptor centers (Figure 2). Finally, more complicated and specific conjugation is also possible, as in the case /19/

18

of redistribution of hydrogen between cyclohexane (or cyclohexadiene) molecules in the irreversible Zelinskii catalytic process (scheme 2,a), or in the synthesis of butadiene from ethanol by the method of Lebedev (scheme 2,b). In the second case, the following stages are correlated and conjugated: dehydrogenation of two molecules of the starting compound (ethanol), condensation dimerization of acetaldehyde, two dehydration stages, hydrogenation of ethanol, and adsorption-desorption stages /20/. This has been shown in experiments with molecules labelled with carbon-14 /21/.

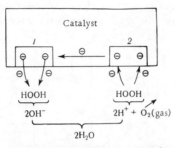

FIGURE 2. Electronic conjugation of stages in the catalytic decomposition of aqueous solutions of H_2O_2 on a catalyst with n-type conductivity:

1- donor section; 2- acceptor section.

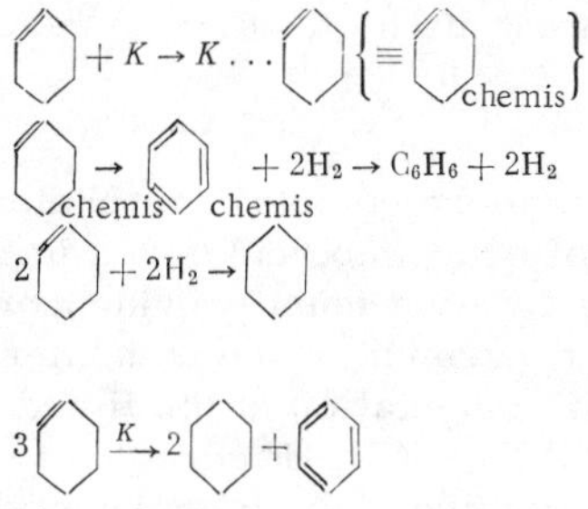

$$2C_2H_5OH \xrightarrow{K} 2CH_3CHO_{chemis} + H_2$$
$$2CH_3CHO_{chemis} \rightarrow CH_3CH(OH)CH_2CHO_{chemis}$$
$$CH_3CH(OH)CH_2CHO_{chemis} \rightarrow$$
$$\rightarrow CH_3CH = CHCHO_{chemis} + H_2O$$
$$CH_3CH = CHCHO_{chemis} + C_2H_5OH_{chemis} \rightarrow$$
$$\rightarrow CH_3CH = CH-CH_2OH + CH_3CHO$$
$$CH_3CH = CHCH_2OH_{chemis} \rightarrow C_4H_6 + H_2O$$

_____

$$2C_2H_5OH \xrightarrow{K} C_4H_6 + 2H_2O + H_2$$

Scheme 2.   a   b

Even the above cases include conjugation of exothermic and endothermic stages;* much more complicated cases of such coupling of stages and whole complex cycles is observed in biological catalysis. It is characterized by the strictly correlated action of several (many) catalysts, the whole process being controlled by a method similar to the "feedback" in automatic control. The most important life processes are based on such coupling. Providing for the correlation of stages and effective coupling is one of the most important functions of catalysts.

Morphological catalysis is classified as belonging to group 4 /22/. Recently special attention has been given to the catalytic synthesis of substances with strictly defined chemical and spatial structures. For a

_____

* In fact, such coupling occurs in all cases in which the reaction passes through endothermic intermediate stages.

long time it was assumed that such synthesis is a specific property of living matter. More recently techniques have been mastered by which such reactions are carried out artificially on isolated enzymes in the presence of coenzymes. Certain advances have been made also in the modelling of the action of enzymes and in the synthesis of their analogs.

In the catalytic synthesis of compounds of low molecular weight the concept of morphology includes the selective production of: a) isomers with normal or iso-structures; b) ring and linear isomers; c) predetermined optical and conformation isomers; d) prescribed sequence or spatial distribution of substituents, such as ortho-, para- or meta- substitutions, etc. The planar projection of the simplest configuration isomers of polypropylene are shown below, as an illustrative example:

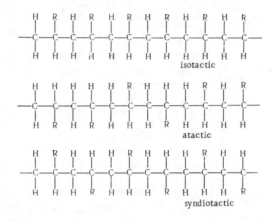

New morphological variants and new, more complex morphological problems are created in the synthesis of macromolecules and in their chemical reactions. In many cases the catalyst must provide a prescribed mutual orientation or some order of arrangement of the monomers in the macromolecules, for instance, a certain orientation of the H and the R groups in the polymerization of olefins $RCH = CH_2$ (Figure 3), a certain correlation and order of arrangement of amino acids in polypeptides or synthetic copolymers, the formation of molecular spirals of the dextro- or levo- types, and other complex secondary spatial structures. The number of different structural morphological variants is very large. Morphological catalysis is predominant in the biochemistry of living cells. The most complicated and perfect example of such catalysis is the enzymatic control of the synthesis of single proteins, which takes place in the cell ribosomes, and the control of cell division and the transfer of hereditary properties concentrated in the chromosome apparatus of the cell nucleus.

At present morphological catalysis has no theoretical basis sufficiently developed for a deductive approach to the selection of new catalysts. The experience gained by the scientific schools of N.D. Zelinskii, B.A. Kazanskii, A.A. Balandin, and others indicates that in the catalytic chemistry of hydrocarbons it is often possible to control the structure of the products by using conventional hydrogenation-dehydrogenation and isomerization catalysts, by changing the microchemistry of the catalysts, the conditions of their preparation, the carriers, and the process conditions. Morphological syntheses of polymers are carried out mainly on dissolved organometallic catalysts and solid oxide catalysts.

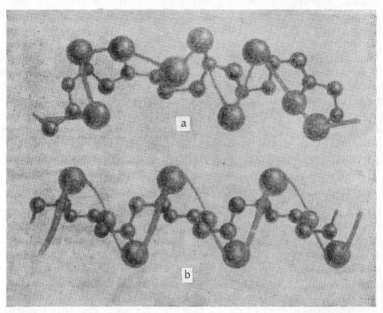

FIGURE 3. Model of the atactic (a) and isotactic (b) sections of molecular poly-propylene spirals.

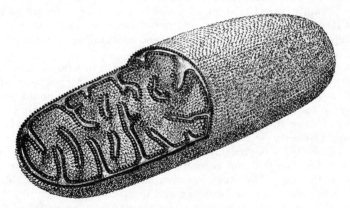

FIGURE 4. Structure of a single mitochondria (cross-section). Length 1—2 microns, diameter 0.3—0.6 microns.

The particles lying on the outer surface of the external shell and the inner surface of the second shell (of the mitochondria walls) carry out different enzymatic reactions, which are conjugated by means of electron transfer and transformations of adenosine phosphate molecules.

The different functions of catalysts (acceleration, control of selectivity, conjugation, and morphology) in complex catalytic reactions must be interrelated and in correspondence. The more complex the catalyst functions, and the stricter the requirements with respect to the accuracy of process control, the smaller is the probability of securing the prescribed effect by a single acceleration act. This increases the importance of complex systems with a combination of active centers or different catalysts, and especially of systems that ensure correlation.

It is not by chance that most enzymes in living bodies are concentrated within the dense organelles of cells. The ultramicroscopic structure of such a formation — ribosomes — is shown in Figure 4. This is the center of the cellular synthesis of proteins — a complex catalytic system comprising many enzymes, coenzymes, and other biologically active substances.

III. NEW RULES GOVERNING THE SELECTION OF CATALYSTS WITH SIMPLE FUNCTIONS

1. Ideal and real selection. An ideal selection theory in heterogeneous catalysis should make it possible: a) to predict the properties of solids (systems) that may catalyze certain prescribed reactions (including new, as yet impossible reactions) from some starting substances, the prediction being based on the known chemical structure and physical properties of these starting substances; b) to assist in the determination of the required catalysts (for the above purpose) among known solid systems, and to indicate the most promising methods for the synthesis of catalysts and catalytic systems, even in cases in which no such systems exist among the known catalysts.

The existing theories cannot be used for such a radical approach to the problem, but recent advances in the theory of selection show a trend towards the consideration of new mechanisms of catalysis and towards the clearest possible specification of models and laws. At present, great attention is paid to the selection of monofunctional catalysts for relatively simple processes in which conjugation and morphology do not play a predominant role.

2. The periodic table and catalyst selection. In assembling and developing his periodic table of the elements, D.I. Mendeleev did not consider the catalytic properties of the elements. This could probably be attributed to the scarcity of data on catalysis in nineteenth-century chemistry. Since the main chemical and physical properties of a substance are related (directly or indirectly) to the electron-shell structure of its atoms, and exhibit a periodicity for any possible mechanism of catalysis, it could be expected that the selection of catalysts would also be governed by the periodic law. The first observations on the validity of this law in catalysis were made in the twenties and thirties of this century /23/. More recent systematic research has provided further proof of the existence of analogous properties in elements that are analogs in the periodic table (in the composition of catalysts, modifiers, and carriers). This is true for simple substances as well as for binary and more complex compounds. For instance: a) oxides of the elements belonging to each subgroup in group II of the periodic table, and their binary compounds with other non-metals in group VI, have properties similar to those of catalysts for the dehydrogenation and dehydration of alcohols, and their catalytic properties change in a regular manner in the transition from compounds of the light metals in the subgroup to compounds of the heavier metals /24, 14/; b) the same is observed in the substitution of one non-metal for another, e.g., for oxidation-reduction reaction the activity increases in the transition from oxides to tellurides /3/; other experiments conducted at the laboratory of the authors also indicate regular changes in the catalytic activity as a result of changes of the non-metallic component, and that such changes may probably be used in the selection and modification of catalysts; c) all alkali metals act as promoters in the catalytic synthesis of ammonia and, by analogy, in the catalytic polymerization of butadiene; d) finally, there are simple periodic regularities in the case of semiconductors with a diamond-like structure (for more details see the paper of O.V. Krylov, in this collection, p.82).

One of the most important general features of catalyst selection is related to the existence (in transition elements and their compounds) of common catalytic properties with respect to reactions of certain types (especially oxidation-reduction and free-radical reactions), and common differences between the catalytic activity of those elements and the activity of non-transition elements. The catalytic properties of metals of group VIII and their neighbors (in the same series) are well known. The nearest neighbors of elements of group VIII — copper and silver — often behave (from the standpoint of their catalytic properties) as the transition elements, in both conventional homogeneous and heterogeneous catalysis. In cases in which the transition properties are of decisive importance, these properties govern the behavior of the elements as well as of some of their compounds (e.g., oxides, sulfides, nitrides, etc.). Recent advances in the catalysis on organic polymers and chelates show that the above rule is valid in the case of organic compounds, too. In homogeneous catalysis the above rule is valid in cases of the so-called "catalysis by ions of variable valence". With some reservations, the above rule may be applied also to biological catalysis. In particular, the active prosthetic groups in oxidation-reduction enzymes (oxidoreductase and the transferase, lyase, ligase series) contain Fe, Mo, and Mn ions, and, less frequently, Co and Cu ions.*

In heterogeneous catalysis, the difference between transition and non-transition metals becomes especially marked if the surface is purified very thoroughly, by activating and treating in ultra-high vacuum (of the order of 10^{-10} torr). As an example we may cite the data of I.I. Tret'yakova et al., obtained at our laboratory in experiments on the chemisorption of H_2 and O_2 during the interaction of hydrogen and oxygen.

3. **Selection of catalysts and the crystalline field theory.** The development of quantum chemistry and of the electronic theory of solids resulted in many attempts to explain the special role of transition elements in catalysis (the theory of d-zones, the theory of ds- and dp- bonds, etc.); however, no substantial results were obtained in the above field until the sixties.

---

* It appears that chlorophyl is the only oxidation-reduction enzyme containing a typical non-transition element (Mg). However, its function as a photocatalyst differs from the functions of other enzymes.

Great promise is shown by a new trend based on the application (to heterogeneous catalysis) of the quantum-mechanical concepts of crystalline field and ligand field /25/. D. Dowden /26/ was the first to apply the above concepts to the problem of catalyst selection. The "semiconductor" electronic theories of chemisorption and catalysis are based on the macroscopic characteristics of solids, and in particular on the concentrations of electrons and holes (as expressed by the position of the Fermi levels), and the electron work functions. In contrast, according to the new concepts, the activation of molecules in catalytic reactions is associated with the formation of complexes, resulting from attachment to separate metal ions (and less frequently — to anions) in the lattice, by the same forces that bind the ligands to complex ions in solution or in a crystal lattice. According to the above approach, the chemisorption bonds and the activation are localized, while the macroscopic electronic properties are of secondary importance. At the same time, great importance is attached to the number of d-electrons in the ionic shell of the metal, which has the role of an active center, since this number determines the complex-formation energy and the spatial distribution of ligands. The above concept will not be treated by us in detail in the present paper; we shall mention only that it explains:

1) the similarity in the catalytic action of the same elements as simple solids (metals), as solid compounds of certain types (oxides, sulfides, etc.), and as solvated ions in solutions;

2) the role of chemisorption in catalysis (thus creating new possibilities for explaining the selectivity of catalysis and morphological effects by the spatial structure of ligand fields);

3) the special importance of transition elements in oxidation-reduction catalysis, without using the controversial d-zone model.

In addition, the above concept creates new models for the intermediate forms of catalysis (including also intermediate complexes) and makes it possible to apply to studies on chemisorption and catalysis the laws of the well-known and important branches of chemistry — the chemistry of complexes and chelates and crystallochemistry. However, a simple application of these laws to chemisorption and heterogeneous catalysis would be as inadequate as the sole use of the collective macroscopic characteristics of solids (Fermi levels, zone bending, electric conductance, etc.) in many derivations of the electronic theory of catalysis on semiconductors /27, 28/. Doubts exist on the validity of universal series of catalytic activity for metals, alloys, and oxides of elements at different valence states, with extremums for a given number of d-electrons in the atom (or ion) of the complex-forming element (e.g., for one or five d-electrons). These doubts are based on the following considerations: a) usually it is not certain whether the "bulk" number of d-electrons per atom is maintained also in the surface ions of the metal; b) even if the evaluation of the valence and the number of d-electrons in the element on the surface of the given sample is accurate, it does not necessarily mean (as is usually believed) that the extremal catalytic activity appears at the same number of d-electrons associated with an extremal value of the ionization energy (affinity) or ligand bond energy (with the central ion); c) direct experiments have shown that in some oxides the active centers are formed by ions in which the metal valence differs sharply from the

24

stoichiometric. Hence, it is easy to understand the contradictory results of some recent research works /29/, which cannot be used as reliable proof of the predictions based on an analogy with complex stability. In particular, it should be mentioned that one of Dowden's maxima (for NiO and Co_3O_4) is apparently associated with partial reduction to the metallic state.

4. **The role of geometric factors.** The importance of geometric factors in the theory of catalysis is expressed in the most general form by the principle of geometric correspondence in the multiplet theory of Balandin. A similar principle serves as the basis of the theory of matrix effects, which is generally accepted in modern molecular biology for the explanation of the effect of enzymes, nucleic acids, and other biochemical process controlling agents. However, the use of geometric characteristics for evaluating the possibility of accelerating relatively simple fractions requires considerable care. The difficulties start with the selection of the geometric characteristics of the surface. In the first place, there are differences between these parameters for the ideal planes with different indices (in the same single crystal), which usually exist simultaneously on the surface. In the second place, direct slow-electron diffraction studies show that differences in both the lattice parameters and the type of the lattice may exist between the surface and the bulk of the crystal. For instance, Ge and Si have a diamond-type structure in the bulk, but their surfaces are hexagonal; the Si —Si (or Ge —Ge) distances in the bulk and on the surface differ very substantially (as is well known). In the third place, electron diffraction and emission microscopy data show that the surface atoms of many transition metals (Cu, Pt, Pd, W, Mo, Ti, Ni) and semiconducting elements (Si and Ge) exist in the "bare" state only when in contact with the light inert gases (He and Ne). In contact with other gases and vapors the surface is rapidly covered with a stable two-dimensional [sic, probably monomolecular] film of a chemisorption compound /30/ (oxide, nitride, etc.)*. The lattice parameters of these surface compounds differ markedly from the parameters of the cleavage surface of the metallic (semiconductor) crystal. Similar effects probably take place in the case of alloys and, under certain conditions, in the case of oxides. Furthermore, in addition to the data that indicate the existence of a distinct relationship between catalytic activity and lattice parameters, there are data that indicate the absence of such a relationship. For instance, no correlation between the catalytic activity and the lattice constants exists in the case of diamond-like semiconductors. In particular, pure Si and Ge, with a = 5.420 and 5.658 Å , respectively, have virtually identical activities. When arranged in a series in order of ascending activity, the semiconductors based on elements from different series in the periodic table show no direct correlation with the changes in a, and no optimum values exist as a function of a.**

The above notes refer only to the role of the simplest geometric characteristics in reactions in which the catalyst has no specific morphological functions and there is no mutual conjugation of processes.

---

* Even at pressures of about $10^{-8}-10^{-6}$ torr.

** In cases in which different authors observed sharp maxima in the parameter a in different samples of the same catalyst, it could be assumed that there were microchemical differences, since noticeable changes in the crystal lattice parameters occur mainly in the formation of solid solutions.

However, such reactions are affected by geometric factors of other types.

Thus, when the solid has a frame structure on the molecular scale one observes a marked preferential acceleration of the reactions involving non-branched organic molecules (as compared with the analogous reactions with branched molecules). Marked differences exist also in the rates of formation of normal, iso-, and cyclic reaction products. In the latter case the nature of the porosity affects the direction of the process and its selectivity (see the paper of Kh.M. Minachev et al., in this collection, p.239). The geometric structure peculiarities do not allow the adsorption of molecules of certain structural types (or having rather large dimensions) on the greatest part of the surface. On the other hand, molecules with an appropriate geometric structure are subject to the collective effect of several adjacent atoms (ions) of the catalyst, i.e., the reactant molecule may exist in a state resembling that of a solid solution.

Another limiting case of the formation of a solid solution of the catalyst and the substrate is observed in the action of cations during the decomposition or rearrangement of complex anions in the solid phase (e.g., in the break-up of NO_3^-, ClO_3^-, ClO_4^-, MnO_4^-):

$$Me^{n+}(MnO_4)_n^- \rightarrow Me^{n+}(MnO_2)_n^- + nO_2.$$

The catalytic action of transition metal ions (exhibited as a decrease in the process temperature and the energy of activation) is enhanced by increasing electric field intensity $E = ne/R$ (where ne is the ionic charge in electron units, and R is the ionic radius) /31/. The effect of transition element ions is not sufficiently well known.

It is of interest to consider the influence of the zeolitic surface structures formed on many solids and in particular on glasses. Zeolites (with certain definite size and shape of the micropores and the channels joining them) show promise as carriers for metallic ions (Ag^+, Ni^{2+}, Mg^{2+}, etc.) with specific catalytic activities, and for the metallic atoms and microcrystals formed upon the reduction of these ions. The "spongy" structure of zeolites and other inorganic framework structures is stable and does not change as a result of moderate changes in the external conditions.

The organic framework structures of macromolecular catalysts are of great importance in biocatalysis. Such structures change readily as a result of changes in the pH, temperature, and other factors, and this could be of great importance from the standpoint of morphological effects in biocatalysis.

The geometric arrangement of chemical bonds within the lattice and on its surface is another more general factor in catalysis. It is based on the peculiar geometric arrangement of the atomic orbitals of s-, p-, and d-electrons (taking into account hybridization, conjugation, and other specific quantum-mechanical effects). These atomic orbitals lead to more complicated molecular orbitals that differ in their shape and spatial arrangement.

5. Non-classical active forms. A discussion of the geometric factors and energy relationships in catalysis on smooth surfaces should be based, as a first approximation, on the electronic structure of the respective surface atom (ion) (which is directly bound to the chemisorbed molecule) in the free state. The type of bonds and coordination characterizing the

same ion in the crystal lattice must also be taken into account. A similarity with the bonds and coordination of the same ions in solutions is possible, but is not certain. Investigations of EPR spectra show that a difficulty arises due to the fact that the main carriers of the catalytic activity may be single surface ions (atoms) of anomalous valence, possessing unpaired electrons (e.g., Cr^{5+} in the aluminum-chromium [oxide] catalysts for the polymerization of ethylene) /32/. The concentration of such ion-radicals on the surface is very low (0.1 − 0.01%). The similarity between heterogeneous catalysis processes and homogeneous catalytic reactions of complex ions in a solution makes it necessary to take into account the possibility of preferential activated chemisorption on one surface ion (atom). At the same time, data on catalysis in solutions indicate that in certain cases (e.g., in the hydrogenation of C_2H_4) the active center must contain two or more complexable metal ions* /33/.

It is very probable that π-complexes with multicentered orbitals play an important role in catalysis (and not only in reactions of unsaturated and aromatic compounds). In chemisorption the active center reacts with the collective electronic cloud of several π-electrons (two in olefins, four in diolefins with conjugated double bonds, and six in benzene and pyridine) that either exists in the starting substance or is formed in the process. A flat array of molecules on the surface probably exists in the case of the π-complex. From the point of view of its orientation, such a configuration resembles the doublets, quadruplets, and sextets of the multiplet theory. The probable participation of several other complex types with non-classical bonds has been indicated by Ya.K. Syrkin /34/. Each such form has a specific geometric configuration, that may differ markedly from the geometric structure based on the angles and distances of classical bonds. The crystalline field theory may be applied both to oxidation-reduction and to acid-base catalysis.

6. Catalyst selection and thermodynamics; radiation-induced reactions. In addition to the kinetic requirements (realization of new reaction methods or acceleration of reactions) the selection of catalysts must take into account thermodynamic limitation — the use of catalysts cannot lead to yields greater than the equilibrium yield. In modern catalysis the above limitation is less strict, due to the following considerations.

Because of the continuous separation of substances in a chromatographic column /8/ it is possible to achieve high degrees of conversion in reactions characterized by inadequate equilibrium constants. This poses new problems in the selection, since for full utilization of the possibilities offered by such conditions it is necessary to use catalysts with a high activity; this is accompanied by a decrease in the probability of catalyst poisoning.

Furthermore, the thermodynamic limitations affecting isolated reactions resulting in an increase in free energy may be eliminated by combining such a reaction with other processes involving a decrease in free energy. Such a conjugation of processes, which is of great importance in the biochemistry of living bodies, is encountered (in a less apparent form) also in conventional catalysis. However, no notice is usually taken of the above phenomenon. One of the main problems in catalysis is the mastering

---

* Hydrogenation in solutions occurs only on Hg_2^{2+}-, and Cu_2^{2+}-, but not on Cu^{2+}- and Hg^{2+}-ions.

of conjugation and the selection of effective catalysts and conditions for such conjugation.

The thermodynamic conditions change markedly and the kinetic requirements (with respect to the catalyst) become less strict when catalysis is applied to an extensive range of radiation-induced and plasma reactions, and to reactions of single active species — free atoms, radicals, ions, and excited molecules. In such reactions the problem of activation is usually eliminated or is of secondary importance. The thermodynamic limitations are also eliminated in most cases. Hence, the achievement of more-or-less complicated reactions stricter for the requirements with respect to the catalytic control of the selectivity and morphology are necessary. Thus, it is easily understood that the rules governing the selection of catalysts for such reactions may be the opposite of the selection rules in conventional thermal catalysis /35/. In particular, the data of G. M. Zhabrova et al. /36/ show that in the radiation dehydrogenation of adsorbed cyclohexane and methanol molecules the degree of conversion has a maximum on insulators (e.g., SiO_2) containing no transition elements, and a minimum on the transition metals, Ni, and semiconducting oxides (NiO).* This could probably be attributed to the fact that the radiation-catalytic activity depends on the recombination rate of free electrons.

7. **Correlation of the activity and selectivity of catalysts with the collective electronic characteristics of a solid.** The establishment of the semiconductor nature of oxidation-reduction reactions led to the formulation of concepts according to which the electrons and holes in a solid play a direct part in catalytic processes. Chemisorption with electron transfer is regarded as the determining stage of the catalysis. According to the so-called electronic theory of catalysis, the catalytic activity is a typical structure-sensitive property; this makes the theory of little interest from the point of view of catalyst selection, which is affected most strongly by the inherent properties of the substances. Experimental studies (carried out at our laboratory) of diamond-like semiconductors have shown that within that extensive group of semiconductors there exists a distinct correlation between the tabulated forbidden zone width Δu of a substance and its catalytic activity in oxidation-reduction reactions /37/. A subsequent systematic analysis of data from the literature (see the paper of O. V. Krylov, p. 82 in this collection) indicates that such a correlation is much more general. The fact that a correlation exists between Δu and the activity makes rather improbable the existence of a systematic correlation between the activity and the electric conductivity in the doped junction, and throws doubt on the determining influence of the type of conductivity (n or p) in catalysis.

In catalysis involving stages with electron transfer a dependence could be expected between the catalytic properties of a solid (for oxidation-reduction reactions) and the electron work function (φ). A general check of this assumption is difficult, because of the great sensitivity of φ to several factors and the difficulties in its measurement during the catalytic process. In some cases we may assume that proofs exist of a distinct relationship between the changes in the catalyst activity in simple reactions or its selectivity in complex reactions and the changes in the work function

---

* It should be mentioned that in low-temperature experiments the semiconductors behaved as insulators, and the forbidden zone width (rather than the conductivity) was the determining factor.

upon the addition of additives, either nonvolatile or difficult to volatilize /38/. Earlier, it has been mentioned /39/ that such a correlation should be expected when there are differences between the charges of the starting substances and the intermediate reaction complex,* since the charging energy is part of the free energy of formation of the complex. This makes it possible to explain the effect of several additives of different valency on the rate of oxidation of CO on MnO_2 and NiO, and the effect of added alkali and alkaline-earth metals on the activity of iron in ammonia synthesis. Under the influence of any factor causing surface charging, the above electrostatic mechanism may cause either an increase or a decrease in the catalytic activity of semiconductors as well as of metallic catalysts, depending on the sign of the charge of the intermediate complex.

In the oxidation of ethylene to ethylene oxide on Ag and in the oxidation of propylene to acrolein on mixed oxides there exists a distinct correspondence between the changes in the selectivity of the catalyst under the effect of additives and the changes in the electron work function /18/. This may be caused by differences in the charges of the intermediate complexes at independent stages, or in the directions of the reactions determining the rates of the partial and complete oxidation. A classification of additives according to the signs of their charge and to the changes in the electron work function may be of great value for the choice of selective catalysts for oxidation-reduction reactions. According to the data of the authors, alkali and alkaline-earth metals (in the free state and as oxides) cause a sharp increase, in the electron work function, while halogens, oxygen, and sulfate ions cause an increase.

The importance to catalysis of the fact that the transition metal ions have isoelectronic valence shells has been postulated frequently, and stress has been placed upon the significant fact that binary semiconductors and semiconducting elements belonging to group IV are isoelectronic; this is of importance for the possible creation of the peculiar crystallochemical and electronic properties characteristic of semiconductors belonging to this group. This leads, naturally, to the conclusion that the fact that they are isoelectronic with Ge, Si, and α-Sn is of importance for the exhibition of a catalytic activity. The range of semiconductors in this group has been extended recently as a result of the inclusion of binary compounds and more complex systems in which the average number of valence electrons (n) attached to one atom in the lattice may differ markedly from 4. At the same time, a tetrahedral coordination may be maintained due to the appearance of holes or excess electrons in one of the partial sublattices. Several systems of the above type, and in particular Ga_2Se_3 and Ga_2Te_3 with $n = 4.8$, were among the systems investigated at our laboratory. The data for these systems conformed, without great deviations, to the general (for the whole group) relationship between the catalytic activity and the forbidden zone width. This may be regarded as an indication that the catalytic activity is affected only slightly by n and by lattice imperfections. The authors believe that this result is not incidental, and that it may be of great importance for the understanding of the mechanism of catalysis by semiconductors and the laws governing [catalyst] selection.**

---

* I.e., in electron transfer during the formation of this complex.

** In this way the investigation of the effect of n in catalysis becomes of great importance.

8. Other relationships. In many cases, and especially in reactions of the acid-base type, there exists a similarity in the catalytic action of compounds having a similar composition and a similar crystalline lattice. Hence, data on the catalytic activity of a compound of the Me_mX_n type in a given catalytic process may often indicate that similar properties could be expected in other Me_mX_n compounds, even if the other Me and X belong to different groups and different rows in the periodic table. Thus, with respect to dehydration reactions and many other acid-base type reactions, there are many common features in the catalytic activities of Al_2O_3, In_2O_3, Sc_2O_3, La_2O_3, Cr_2O_3, and Fe_2O_3, in spite of the fact that Al and In are non-transition elements, while Sc, La, Cr, and Fe are transition elements, and in spite of the fact that Al, In, La, and Sc exist only in the trivalent state; in the case of Fe the trivalent state is the higher of two, while in the case of Cr it is one of the lower-valence states. If all other conditions are the same, the catalytic properties of solids become more similar when the solids have the same or approximately the same crystal lattice.

To conclude this section, let us mention another general characteristic of the selection, which may often simplify it — the far-reaching similarity between chemisorption and catalysis. It is not surprising since, as a rule, the catalytic process begins and ends with chemisorption. This rule is often valid for the deactivation and activation of catalysts. A complication is introduced by the existence of several types of chemisorption (even in the case of the simplest gases — H_2, O_2), associated in different ways with the possibility of conducting the catalytic process* and with the surface nonhomogeneity. In spite of these facts, an extraordinarily good correlation often exists between the chemisorption and catalysis processes. The meaning of this correlation is the simplest in cases in which the only starting substance, or one of the starting substances (e.g., CH_4, N_2, cyclohexane, organofluorine compounds) reacts with difficulty. In such cases the "activation" of the respective substances could be regarded as the main problem to be solved for a certain type of chemisorption** on the catalysis. Other cases may require simultaneous chemisorption of two substances, etc.

Chemisorption studies are usually simpler than the study of catalytic processes, and yield more unequivocal results; hence, they may be used in the study of catalytic processes in cases in which it is impossible to determine which is the leading activation process (for the molecules of one of the substances).

IV. PROBLEMS IN THE SELECTION OF CATALYSIS WITH CYBERNETIC FUNCTIONS

In any catalytic process the catalyst has, to a certain extent, some cybernetic functions. These functions become predominant in reactions

---

* Chemisorption of a molecule does not always lead to creation of the state required for a catalytic process; some types of chemisorption may even cause a loss of the catalytic activity of solids.

** The above treatment is somewhat simplified. Actually, in the interaction of two or more substances a catalyst may initiate the reaction by increasing the reactivity of the more active component or by creating new reaction paths in which two or even three components are activated simultaneously.

with complex conjugation, and in which the structure of the product is controlled by the catalyst. The greater the importance of the cybernetic functions, the lesser is our knowledge of the rules governing the selection. Thus, the space devoted to the last section of the present paper does not correspond, in any way, to the importance of the problems discussed in it.

1. **The simplest reaction conjugation mechanisms.** Some suggestions concerning the possible rules governing the selection of conjugation catalysts may be derived from the existing incomplete qualitative concepts of the possible mechanism of the conjugation process. In general terms, it is possible to distinguish between two limiting conjugation types:

a) conjugation involving the coupling of two (or several) simpler reactions of which one, two (or all) are catalytic, without the existence of any additional, special mechanisms;

b) conjugation that is not a simple summation of independent processes, and that involves special mechanisms.

The first case is characterized by the same activation mechanisms that act in the absence of apparent conjugation, while the second case is characterized by special, specific mechanisms. These mechanisms may differ substantially for reactions between gases and those between liquids.

The redistribution of hydrogen in irreversible Zelinskii catalysis (see scheme 2a, p.19) is a good example of conjugation of the first type in heterogeneous catalysis. In this case the problem of conjugation is simplified, in the first place because the two conjugated processes belong to the same group (hydrogenation and dehydrogenation), and in the second place because in the most simple case the two reactions involve the participation of the same compound — cyclene or cyclodiene. Hence, the two conjugated processes may take place on the same catalyst, and even on the same [active] centers, and there is no need to use more complex catalytic systems. The specific selection requirements are related usually to the ratio of the adsorption coefficients of hydrogen and the aromatic product. The first should not be too low, while the second should not be too high. The conjugation takes place through a component common for the two processes — the chemisorbed hydrogen ions:

$$C_6H_{10\,chemis} \rightarrow C_6H_{6\,chemis} + 4H_{chemis}$$
$$\downarrow \qquad \downarrow$$
$$C_6H_6 \qquad 2H_2$$
$$C_6H_{10\,chemis} + 2H_{chemis} \rightarrow C_6H_{12\,chemis} \rightarrow C_6H_{12}.$$

Evidently, the conjugated redistribution of hydrogen between the molecules of different substances may occur in a similar way. In such a case the choice of new catalysts involves no difficulties. A conjugation mechanism with the participation of active intermediate products is often encountered in homogeneous catalysis, where free atoms, radicals, and ions may serve as such intermediate products.

More complicated, and of greater interest, is the problem of the conjugation of processes (or stages) belonging to different types, e.g., oxidation-reduction and acid-base processes. Such is the conjugation of hydrogenation and dehydrogenation on the one hand, and of simple and condensation dehydration on the other, in the synthesis of divinyl (see

31

scheme 2b). S.V. Lebedev based the development of the above process on a concept according to which it is necessary to use two catalysts: one for dehydrogenation and the other for dehydration.

The extensive and interesting group of hydropolymerization and hydrocondensation reactions,* discovered and intensively studied by Ya.T. Eidus et al. /40/, is apparently based on conjugation. In these reactions, impurities (CO and other substances, including oxygen) cause the polymerization of over-stoichiometric amounts of olefins. Experiments with labelled CO show that it is included in the polymer /41/. Hence, some product of its interaction with the olefin or with the hydrogen takes part directly in the reaction (initiates the process). In catalysis, initiation is often a certain form of conjugation.

Several mechanisms may be envisaged of the simultaneous action of two catalysts in conjugation, e.g.: a) by direct interactions of intermediate products from reaction stages of different types adsorbed on contiguous crystallites (or grains) of catalysts having different functions; b) by the motion of adsorbed intermediate products from catalyst to catalyst by means of surface diffusion; c) through the gaseous phase, involving desorption from one catalyst and adsorption on another.

The first two mechanisms probably exist in the case of a single catalyst having centers of different types, or in the case of a mixed catalyst containing in its grains microcrystallites of different types. The third mechanism may exist also in the case of coarser mixed systems. As has been mentioned by the authors, escape into the bulk is most probable for liquid-phase catalytic reactions /42/, although the diffusion in a liquid is much slower /43/.

2. **Special conjugation mechanisms.** Of the various special mechanisms, let us discuss firstly conjugation with the participation of conductivity electrons and excitons. In its simplest form, the above type has been discussed previously for the decomposition of H_2O_2 (see Figure 2). The oxidation stage, involving the loss of electrons and the formation of H^+ and O_2, occurs on catalytic centers of the acceptor type. Reduction occurs on donor centers; the electrons passing to the peroxide transform the latter into two OH^- ions. The process is facilitated by the hydration of ions. The continuity of the process is maintained by a flow of electrons from acceptor to donor centers along the conductor. Oxidation and reduction reactions between hydrogen peroxide and other substances may also have a similar mechanism. Further conjugation possibilities are opened by the formation of neutral and charged radicals (HO_2, O_2^-, and OH) in chain reactions in the bulk. Chain reactions in the bulk are observed on low- and moderate-activity catalysts.

In connection with the new concepts of the role of excitons in chemical processes, it would be natural to examine the possibility of exciton conjugation of catalytic processes. This problem has not been investigated in connection with heterogeneous catalysis, but exciton conjugation is known in photochemistry. Electron and exciton transfer is of great importance in the conjugation of catalytic processes in biochemistry.

The second specific type of conjugation involves the participation of special carriers. Such is the role of hydrogen in the homogeneous

---

* Hidden conjugation takes place also in Fischer-Tropsch synthesis.

oxidation of CO and in the hydropolymerization of olefins, and the role of adenosine phosphate and nucleotide phosphate in complex biocatalysis, and in particular in photosynthesis. The energy of the single processes (mainly the catalytic or primary photosynthesis processes) is stored in the phosphate bonds; catalytic hydrolysis along these bonds causes the liberation of this energy, which is used for the conjugated processes of the synthesis. In this case we deal with two types of conjugation: indirect (assuming arbitrary bond ruptures in time and space), and more direct. In direct conjugation the conventional chemical mechanisms are associated with purely electronic mechanisms, and the whole set of processes requires the participation of systems of several enzymes and coenzymes.

3. **Selection and "building" of catalysts.** It is quite probable that in many cases in conventional catalysis the preference for mixed catalysts (as compared with simple catalysts) and the need for carriers and modifiers are associated with the necessity of providing the means for a hidden conjugation of processes, which is necessary for the formation of a certain product. Until now the above possibility has been neglected by the theory of catalyst selection, and in particular in the author's paper on the classification of complex catalysts /44/. The mechanisms discussed above show that, as a rule, complex catalytic systems are required for effective conjugation. Such systems have been selected empirically. Their guided selection, and the "building" of such systems are important problems of this theory. With respect to the mechanisms discussed above, one direction in this search is already clear, namely, the attachment to one catalyst (or a mixture of catalysts) of the functions required for the realization of a conjugated process of the required type.

In some cases the "building" may be based on available data on the oxidation-reduction and acidic activity of various solids, their acceptor-donor properties, their ability to form radicals and ionize molecules, etc. In such cases it is often possible to apply the principle of "similarity between the activator and the active form". In fact, a free radical is readily formed in the reaction between a normal molecule and the radical centers in a catalyst with an unpaired electron or a free orbital; the reaction of free positive ions and neutral molecules yields new positive ions, etc. The above principle may be applied also to some variant of morphological catalysis. There are other activation mechanisms for which the similarity principle is not valid.

The selection must take into account some other conjugation mechanisms that have not been discussed here, in particular conjugation through the formation of common active complexes (conventional or transitional) that contain the molecules participating in the two conjugated processes and the active centers of the catalysts. In many cases it is difficult to distinguish between conjugation and the effect of the gradual modification and poisoning of the catalyst on the reaction.

4. **The mechanism of action of morphological catalysts and their selection.** We shall confine ourselves to a few notes concerning the least studied and most difficult problem of the selection. In conventional catalysis, the mechanism through which catalysts fulfill their morphological functions has been studied to a lesser extent than other mechanisms, and these studies have been concerned chiefly with the problem of asymmetric synthesis. A more thorough study of these problems has been carried out in

biocatalysis, in view of the biological importance of the exact duplication of separate proteins in intracellular syntheses and in reproduction.

Of great interest is the "matrix" principle, according to which there are certain structures (e.g., single free segments of the double spirals of desoxynucleic acids) that, in the synthesis of an additional segment, serve as a chemical "matrix" that stores a "print" of the detached, missing segment. The "matrix" principle resembles the geometric correspondence and similarity principles, and may be applied to the synthesis of most complicated biomolecules. In asymmetric synthesis the "matrix" nature is associated with the existence of spatial asymmetry in at least one of the components of the reacting system — reactant, catalyst, solvent. Works on the synthesis of optically-active polymers of propylene oxide are of interest in this respect. Such polymers may be prepared on conventional optically-inactive catalysts, from the optically active oxide monomer, and on optically active catalysts from a racemic mixture of the asymmetric isomers.* This is related to the model of three-point adsorption of a substrate on the active centers of a catalyst, which is applied to many enzymatic processes and, in particular, to all cases in which one observes the effect of a hidden isotopic Ogston asymmetry (see /45/).

Biosynthesis is governed by a strict morphological control of each stage, with the use of stationary matrixes and matrix carriers (information-bearing nucleic acids, hormones, etc.). In conventional catalysis a part of the morphological effects should be of a different nature. This is evident even from the fact that there are cases in which complex regular structures may be formed catalytically on homogeneous catalysts (and in particular on complex ions) as well as on heterogeneous catalysts of a different structure. Some examples are the Ziegler catalysts, oxide-chromate catalysts, and certain metallic catalysts. In the case of processes that take place in solution, the solvent may have a morphological influence, by causing configurational changes and acting as an elastic, labile matrix as well as a medium (phase) for the continuous creation of small quasicrystalline regions in which there exists close-range order. The importance of such effects and of the already existing ordered configuration of starting monomeric molecular groups is indicated by the occurrence of effective catalytic polymerization of crystalline monomers, with frequent preservation of the external shape of the starting crystal. Thus, we may assume the possible existence of an autocatalytic effect of seeds of substances having a similar macrostructure, in the presence of centers that activate the monomers in accordance with one of the main primary polymerization processes.

A more detailed analysis of the theory and experimental data of morphological catalysis is outside the scope of this paper.

BIBLIOGRAPHY

1. ROGINSKII, S. Z. —Problemy Kinetiki i Kataliza, Vol. 8: 110. 1955.
2. ROGINSKII, S. Z. —Ibid, Vol. 6: 9. 1949; Vol. 10: 13. 1960.

* Another possibility is asymmetric synthesis from a racemic mixture, with the adsorption of asymmetric extraneous molecules on the optically inactive catalyst.

3. KRYLOV, O.V., S.Z. ROGINSKII, and V.M. FROLOV.—DAN SSSR, Vol. 111: 623. 1956; Problemy
Kinetiki i Kataliza, Vol. 10: 102. 1960.

4. ROGINSKII, S.Z.—Kinetika i Kataliz, Vol. 1: 15. 1960; S.Z. ROGINSKY. Actes du 2-me Congrès
International de Catalyse, Vol. 2: 1527. Paris, Technip. 1960.

5. GAZIEV, G.A., O.V. KRYLOV, S.Z. ROGINSKII, G.V. SAMSONOV, E.A. FOKINA, and M.I.
YANOVSKII.—DAN SSSR, Vol. 140: 863. 1961; S.Z. ROGINSKII. Sbornik materialov po
metallovedeniyu i tekhnologii izotopnykh metallokeramicheskikh tverdykh splavov tugoplavikh
metallov i soedinenii na ikh osnove. Part 2.. Moskva, Metallurgizdat. 1963.

6. IOFFE, I.I. and S.Z. ROGINSKII.—ZhFKh, Vol. 31: 612. 1957.

7. ROGINSKII, S.Z., M.I. YANOVSKII, G.M. ZHABROVA, B.M. KADENATSI, and O.M.
VINOGRADOVA.—In: Sbornik "Gazovaya khromatografiya". Trudy I Vsesoyuznoi Konferentsii,
p. 135. Moskva, Izd. AN SSSR. 1960.

8. YANOVSKII, M.I. and G.A. GAZIEV.—Vestnik AN SSSR, No. 5: 27. 1960.

9. ROGINSKII, S.Z., M.I. YANOVSKII, and G.A. GAZIEV.—DAN SSSR, Vol. 140: 1125. 1961; Kinetika
i Kataliz, Vol. 3: 529. 1962; In: Sbornik: "Gazovaya Khromatografiya". Trudy II
Vsesoyuznoi Konferentsii, p. 27. Moskva, Izd. "Nauka". 1964.

10. ROGINSKII, S.Z., I.I. TRET'YAKOV, and A.B. SHEKHTER.—DAN SSSR, Vol. 100: 487. 1955; A.T.
GWATMEY and R.E. CUNNINGHAM. Adv. Cat., Vol. 10: 57. 1958; SOSNOWSKI. J.
Phys. Chem. Solids, Vol. 8: 142. 1959.

11. KUMMER, J.T., P.H. EMMETT, et al.—J. Am. Chem. Soc., Vol. 73: 564. 1951; HALL, W., R.
KOKES, and P.H. EMMETT. J. Am. Chem. Soc., Vol. 82: 1027. 1960.

12. GOLOVINA, O.A., S.Z. ROGINSKII, M.M. SAKHAROV, Ya.T. EIDUS, and E.S. DOKUKINA.—
Problemy Kinetiki i Kataliza, Vol. 9: 76. 1957; GOLOVINA, O.A., S.Z. ROGINSKII, M.M.
SAKHAROV, and E.S. DOKUKINA.—ZhFKh, Vol. 33: 2451. 1959.

13. ROGINSKII, S.Z.—ZhFKh, Vol. 32: 737. 1958; Vol. 31: 2381. 1957.

14. KEIER, N.P. and S.Z. ROGINSKII.—IAN SSSR, OKhN, p. 27. 1960.

15. KRYLOV, O.V. and E.A. FOKINA.—Kinetika i Kataliz, Vol. 1: 421, 542. 1960.

16. ROGINSKII, S.Z. Teoreticheskie osnovy izotopnykh metodov izucheniya khimicheskikh reaktsii
(Theoretical Principles of Isotopic Methods for the Study of Chemical Reactions). Chapter 5.—
Moskva, Izd. AN SSSR. 1956.

17. MARGOLIS, L.Ya. and S.Z. ROGINSKII.—IAN SSSR, seriya khimicheskaya, p. 281. 1956; Problemy
Kinetiki i Kataliza, Vol. 9: 107. 1957.

18. MARGOLIS, L.Ya. Geterogennoe kataliticheskoe okislenie uglevodorodov (Heterogeneous Catalytic
Oxidation of Hydrocarbons).—Moskva, Gostoptekhizdat. 1962.

19. GRYAZNOV, V.M. and V.I. SHIMULIS.—Kinetika i Kataliz, Vol. 2: 534, 894. 1961; GRYAZNOV,
V.M. Uspekhi Khimii, Vol. 32: 433. 1963.

20. GORIN, Yu.A.—ZhOKh, Vol. 16: 2839. 1946; KOGAN, M.Ya., G.D. LYUBARSKII, and O.M.
PODGURSKAYA.—IAN SSSR, OKhN, p. 173. 1947.

21. VINOGRADOVA, O.M., N.P. KEIER, and S.Z. ROGINSKII.—DAN SSSR, Vol. 112: 1075. 1957;
Problemy Kinetiki i Kataliza, Vol. 9: 175. 1957.

22. SEIFERT, H. Actes du 2-me Congrès International de Catalyse, Vol. 2: 1881. Paris, Technip. 1960.

23. ROGINSKII, S.Z.—Acta physicochim. URSS, Vol. 1: 651. 1934; ROGINSKII, S.Z. ZhFKh, Vol. 6:
334. 1935.

24. KRYLOV, O.V., S.Z. ROGINSKII, and E.A. FOKINA.—IAN SSSR, OKhN, p. 668. 1956; p. 421. 1957.

25. SATURO SUGANO.—J. Appl. Phys., Vol. 33: 303. 1962; BAL'KHAUZEN, K. Vvedenie v teoriyu
polya ligandov (Introduction to Ligand Field Theory). Moskva, "Mir". 1964; ORGEL', L.
Vvedenie v khimiyu perekhodnykh metallov (Introduction to Transition Metal Chemistry).
Moskva, Izd. "Mir". 1964.

26. DOWDEN, D.A. and D. WELLS. Actes du 2-me Congrès International de Catalyse, Vol. 2: 1499. Paris,
Technip. 1960.

27. VOL'KENSHTEIN, F.F. Elektronnaya teoriya kataliza na poluprovodnikakh (The Electronic Theory of
Catalysis on Semiconductors).—Moskva, Fizmatgiz. 1960.

28. HAUFFE, K. Reactions in Solids and on Solid Surfaces. [Russian translation. 1962.]; GARRETT,
C.G.B. J. Chem. Phys., Vol. 33: 966. 1960; LEE, V.J. and J.R. MASON. Bull. Am.
Phys. Soc. ser. II, Vol. 8: 337. 1963.

29. McYVER, D.S. and H.H. TOBIN.—J. Phys. Chem., Vol. 65: 1665. 1961; STONE, S.D. Nature,
Vol. 195: 570. 1962; DIXON, G.M., D.N. NICHOLLS, and H. STEINER. Proceedings of
the 3rd. International Congress on Catalysis, Vol. 2: 815. Amsterdam, North-Holland Publ.
Co. 1965.

30. ROGINSKII, S. Z. and I. I. TRET'YAKOV.—ZhFKh, Vol. 30: 2539. 1956; ROGINSKII, S. Z. and V. A. SHISHKIN.—DAN SSSR, Vol. 130: 577. 1960; GOMER, H. Field Emission and Field Ionization. London. 1961; HAYWARD, D. O. and B. M. W. TRAPNELL. Chemisorption. London, Butterworth. 1964.

31. ELOVICH, S. Yu., E. I. SHMUK, and S. Z. ROGINSKII.—IAN SSSR, OKhN, p. 469. 1950.

32. BUKANAEVA, F. M., Yu. I. PECHERSKAYA, V. B. KAZANSKII, and V. A. DZIS'KO.—Kinetika i Kataliz, Vol. 3: 358. 1962; ANUF'EV, V. V., et al., Ibid, Vol. 3: 353. 1962.

33. HALPERN, J.—Advan. Catalysis, Vol. 9: 302. 1957; Vol. 11: 301. 1959.

34. SYRKIN, Ya. K.—Uspekhi Khimii, Vol. 28: 903. 1959; Zhurnal Strukturnoi Khimii, Vol. 1: 189. 1960.

35. HAISSINSKY, M. Actes du 2-me Congrès International de Catalyse, Vol. 2: 1429. Paris, Technip. 1961.

36. ZHABROVA, G. M., V. B. KAZANSKII, et al. —Neftekhimiya, Vol. 4: 753. 1964.

37. KRYLOV, O. V. and S. Z. ROGINSKII.—IAN SSSR, OKhN, p. 17. 1959; KRYLOV, O. V., S. Z. ROGINSKII, and E. A. FOKINA. Problemy Kinetiki i Kataliza, Vol. 10: 117. 1960.

38. ROGINSKII, S. Z.—DAN SSSR, Vol. 126: 817. 1959; Vol. 130: 122. 1960.

39. GORYUNOVA, N. A. Khimiya almazopodobnykh poluprovodnikov (The Chemistry of Diamond-Like Semiconductors).—Moskva, Izd. LGU. 1964.

40. EIDUS, Ya. T. and N. I. ERSHOV.—Problemy Kinetiki i Kataliza, Vol. 10: 404. 1960.

41. ROGINSKY, S. Z. Proceedings of the 3rd. International Congress on Catalysis, Vol. 2: 939. Amsterdam, North-Holland Publ. Co. 1965.

42. ROGINSKII, S. Z.—Problemy Kinetiki i Kataliza, Vol. 10: 373. 1960; In: Sbornik "Mekhanizm i kinetika fermentativnogo kataliza, p. 187. Moskva, Izd. "Nauka". 1964.

43. ROGINSKII, S. Z.—In: Sbornik "Khimicheskaya kinetika i tsepnye reaktsii", p. 483. Moskva, Izd. "Nauka". 1966.

44. ROGINSKII, S. Z.—DAN SSSR, Vol. 87: 1013. 1952; In: Sbornik "Geterogennyi kataliz v khimicheskoi promyshlennosti", p. 29. Edited by G. K. Boreskov. Moskva, ONTI. 1955.

45. ROGINSKII, S. Z. and S. Z. SHNOL'. Izotopy v biokhimii (Isotopes in Biochemistry). Chapter 5.— Moskva, AN SSSR. 1963

A.A. Tolstopyatova

SOME RULES GOVERNING THE SELECTION OF OXIDE CATALYSTS

In connection with the research on the relationship between the catalytic properties of the elements and their position in the periodic table we have studied the dehydrogenation and dehydration properties of oxides of the lanthanides and some rare elements: La, Ce, Pr, Nd, Sm, Eu, Gd, Tb, Dy, Ho, Er, Tu, Yb, Lu, Sc, Y, Ga, Be, Hf, Th, and U, as well as of Mg, Cd, Al, Ti, Zr, Cr, Mn, Mo, and W oxides, the sulfides MoS_2 and WS_2, and three metals: Cu, Re, and Ru.

The comparison was based on the bond energies between the reacting hydrogen, carbon, and oxygen atoms and the active centers on the catalysts (Q_{H-K}, Q_{C-K}, Q_{O-K}), as determined by the kinetic method /1/ from the activation energies of the dehydrogenation and dehydration of alcohols and the dehydrogenation of hydrocarbons.

These values of the bond energies Q_{A-K} of the intermediate surface compounds formed in the course of the catalytic reaction are an important characteristic for the selection of catalysts, since they take into account the effect of both the reacting molecules and the active surface of the catalyst.

In principle, the kinetic method makes it possible to calculate single bond energies Q_{A-K}, but the available data on the nature and type of bonds in catalytic processes, and the absence (in most cases) of values of the separate bond energies for the reacting molecules limit the calculations to average values of Q_{A-K}. An analysis of these average values of Q_{A-K} leads to the clarification of certain very important laws. By using the individual [accurate] values of the bond energies, it would probably be possible to introduce certain complements to these laws.

The kinetic method for the determination of bond energies Q_{A-K} from standard reactions has been discussed in several instances in the literature (for example, see /1—3/).

The dehydrogenation and dehydration of isopropanol and the dehydrogenation of tetralin [tetrahydronaphthalene] and cyclohexane served as the standard reactions for most of the oxide catalysts studied by us. For these reactions we determined the activation energy ε, the relative adsorption coefficients of the reaction products z, and calculated the bond energies Q_{A-K} and the thermodynamic functions of the processes involving adsorptive displacement of the starting compounds by their conversion products: ΔH, ΔS and ΔF (by the method of /4/). The values of ΔH, ΔS, and ΔF are additional characteristics of the catalyst and the catalyzed process.

We also studied the conversions of other alcohols and hydrocarbons (the effect of extraindicial substituents) /1, 2/.

The catalysts were prepared in most cases from the nitrate salts by precipitation with ammonia; the hydroxides formed were dried at 110° and heated in a current of air to 560° (this is the standard method of preparation). We studied also catalysts prepared by different methods (effect of the catalyst preparation method on Q_{A-K}) /2/.

Information on the catalytic properties of the above oxides is of separate interest, but we shall discuss these properties from the point of view of the utilization of such information for the treatment of the problem of catalyst selection. It has been shown /5/ that in the case of the lanthanides there exists a well-defined relationship between the bond energies of the reacting atoms with the catalyst and the magnetic susceptibility of the catalysts μ.

Thus, the changes in Q_{H-K} and Q_{O-K} follow the changes in magnetic susceptibility μ, while the changes in Q_{C-K} are in a direction opposite to the changes in μ; the changes in the activation energy of the dehydrogenation of isopropanol (ε_2) are also in the opposite direction; the activation energy of the dehydrogenation of tetralin (ε_1) follow the changes in the ionic radius r. The above results show that the electronic structure (in the above case — the inner $4f$-level) affects the outer valence electrons (in the above case — the $5d^1$ and $6s^2$ electrons) and changes the chemical and catalytic properties of the elements. It is well known that the properties of the lanthanides change continuously or periodically with changes in the atomic number. The continuous changes are caused by an increase in the charge of the nucleus; for instance, such a change takes place with respect to the ionic radii. The periodic changes are associated with the great stability of 0, 7, or 14-atom configurations — such are the changes in the magnetic susceptibility, the anomalous valences, the atomic radii, etc. The bond energies Q_{A-K} on lanthanide oxides change periodically, like μ, while the activation energy for tetralin changes continuously, like r.

In lanthanides, the catalytic properties could be affected by f-d electron transitions of the $4f \rightarrow 4f^{n-1}d^1$ type, ending in the formation of the d-state.

A parallelism between the hydrogen-catalyst bond energy Q_{H-K} and the magnetic susceptibility of the ions in transition metal oxides has been observed by us in many experiments — see Figure 1 and the table which also contains data for other oxides (for the purpose of comparison). Antiparallelism is observed between the Q_{C-K} bond energy and μ. The Q_{O-K} bond energy depends to a great extent on various factors /2/ and a less distinct dependence on μ is observed in this case. The values for the lanthanide oxides are from /6/; these data are similar to those determined by A.G. Slinkin for our catalysts; the values of μ for the remaining oxides are from /7/.

The above-mentioned relationship between the bond energies and the magnetic susceptibilities shows that the electronic structure of the transition metals affects the catalytic properties as a result of the changes in the bond energies between the reacting atoms and the catalyst.

It has been shown /3/ that the oxygen-catalyst bond energy determined by the kinetic method on oxide catalysts ($Q_{O-Me_nO_m}^{K}$) changes with increasing atomic number, and the changes are parallel to the changes in the bond energy between the oxygen and the metals in the oxide as measured by thermochemical methods ($Q_{O-Me_nO_m}^{T}$). This parallelism is further proof of the fact that in a catalytic process the atoms of the reacting molecules form an adsorption bond primarily with the metals (for more details see /3/), and it shows also that $Q^K_{O-Me_nO_m}$ is a periodic function of the atomic number, since $Q^T_{O-Me_nO_m}$ is a periodic function of n. Moreover, it should be noted that (as it should be expected) $Q^T_{O-Me_nO_m} > Q^K_{O-Me_nO_m}$. The difference is apparently equal to the sublimation term λ, since these values characterize the affinity of the metal for oxygen at the surface (of the catalyst) and in the bulk.

The parallelism becomes even more evident if D_{O-Me} (the bond dissociation energy divided by the metal valence v) is taken instead of $Q^T_{O-Me_nO_m}$. Similar relations should apparently exist also for the bond energies with carbon and hydrogen, but the available data on the heats of formation of hydrides and carbides are too scarce for the calculation of $Q^T_{H-Me_nO_m}$ and $Q^T_{C-Me_nO_m}$.

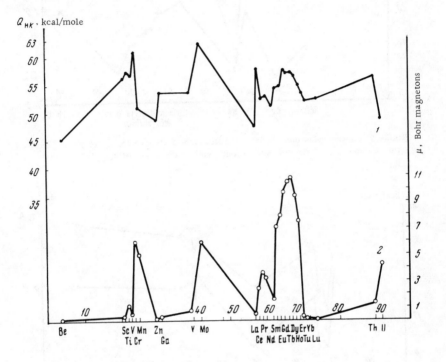

FIGURE 1. Correspondence between the changes of the hydrogen-catalyst bond energies (1) and the magnetic susceptibility of the oxides μ (2).

If the properties of the intermediate surface compounds formed in the course of the catalytic reaction are determined by the chemical nature of the metal atoms (ions) in the oxide lattice, a relationship should exist between the changes of the parameters characterizing the metal ions and the values of the activation energies for the investigated reactions.

Indeed, the activation energy for the dehydrogenation of tetralin ε_1 (Figure 2), the dehydrogenation of cyclohexane ε_1 (Figure 3), the dehydrogenation of isopropanol ε_2 (Figure 4), and the dehydration of isopropanol ε_3 (Figure 5) change in parallel with the ionic radius r /8/.

The ionic radii were taken from /9/, with adequate corrections for the changes in the coordination numbers.

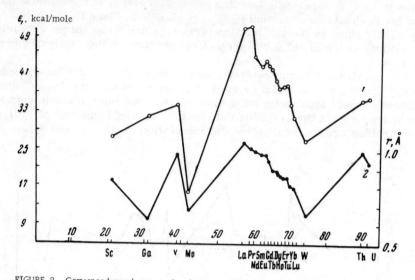

FIGURE 2. Correspondence between the changes in the activation energy for the dehydrogenation of tetralin ε_1 (1) and the ionic radii of metals in the oxides r (2).

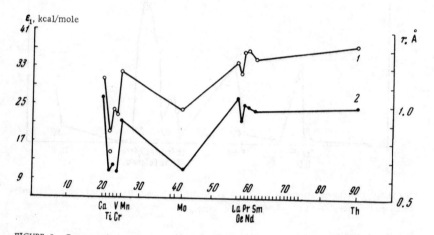

FIGURE 3. Correspondence between the changes in the activation energy for the [dehydrogenation of] cyclohexane ε_1 (1) and the ionic radii of the metals in the oxides r (2).

It is of interest to mention that a similar relationship also exists in the case of metallic catalysts (the data for such catalysts are less extensive than for oxides). A correlation of the metallic radii and the activation energies for the dehydrogenation of isopropanol ε_2 from /10/ (the values for Ru are from /8/ and for Re from /11/) is shown in Figure 6. It is evident that the changes in ε_2 follow the changes in the ionic radius r.

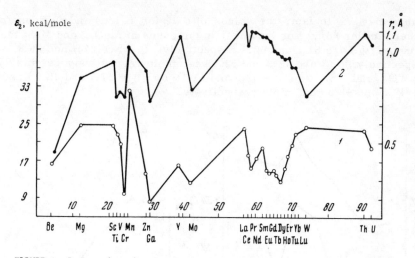

FIGURE 4. Correspondence between the changes in the activation energy for the dehydrogenation of isopropanol ε_2 (1) and the ionic radii of the metals in the oxides r (2).

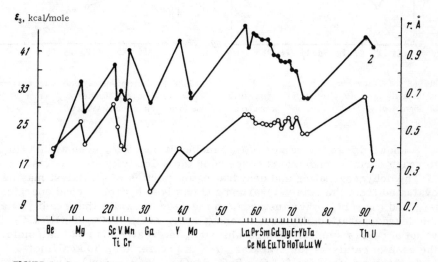

FIGURE 5. Correspondence between the changes in the activation energy for the dehydration of isopropanol ε_3 (1) and the ionic radii of the metals in the oxides r (2).

Figure 7 shows the correlation of the ionic radii of the metals and Q_{C-Me} for Fe, Pt, Pd, Ni, and Cu (taken from /12/) as well as for Ru (the average of several close values was taken from /8/). As is evident from Figure 7, the changes in Q_{C-Me} are in a direction opposite to the changes in the ionic radii. The existence of a relation between the changes in the activation energies on the oxides and the sizes of the metal ions confirms the conclusion that the reacting atoms in a molecule are attracted mainly to the metal atoms (ions) in the oxides.

If the reacting atoms were bound to the oxygen in the oxide, a substitution of the sulfide of the respective metal for the oxide should cause a sharp change in Q_{A-K}. In fact, the values of Q_{A-K} for oxides and sulfides are rather similar /8/. For instance, in the cases of MoO_{3-x} and MoS_2 the values of Q_{H-K} are 61.3 and 60.3 respectively; Q_{C-K} are 27.7 and 26.8, respectively; Q_{O-K} are 42.9 and 52.5 kcal/mole respectively; similarly, for WO_{3-x} and WS_2: Q_{H-K} are 52.6 and 61.1; Q_{C-K} are 27.6 and 25.3; and Q_{O-K} are 43.5 and 49.5 kcal/mole respectively.

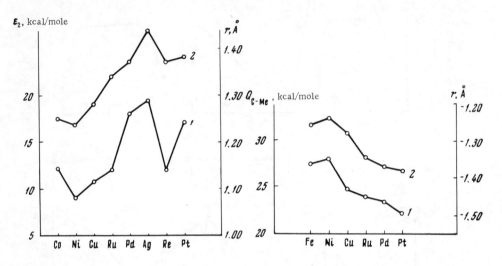

FIGURE 6. Correspondence between the changes in the activation energy for the dehydrogenation of isopropanol ε_2 (1) on metals and the metal radii r (2).

FIGURE 7. Correspondence between the changes in the carbon-catalyst bond energies Q_{C-Me} on metals (1) and the ionic radii of the metals r (2).

A knowledge of the values of Q_{A-K} makes it possible, even at this time, to reach certain conclusions concerning the selectivity of catalysts.

The dehydrogenating and dehydrating properties of a catalyst may be evaluated from the catalyst-carbon and catalyst-hydrogen bond energies Q_{C-K} and Q_{H-K} /13/. For instance, in the case of oxides that readily catalyze the dehydrogenation of hydrocarbons (Cr_2O_3, ZrO_2, CeO_2, ThO_2, V_2O_3) the value of Q_{C-K} is smaller than 20 while Q_{H-K} is greater than 53 kcal/mole. In the case of catalysts for cracking, Q_{C-K} is greater than 30 kcal/mole.

In the case of oxides (Al_2O_3, BeO, MoO_{3-x}, WO_{3-x}, MnO, ZnO) on which the dehydrogenation of hydrocarbons proceeds with difficulty, at least one of the bond energies has a value that is different from the above limiting values. Yttrium oxide $Y_2O_3 \cdot nH_2O$ occupies an intermediate position between the above groups of oxides, and thus the dehydrogenation of hydrocarbons on it should proceed with difficulty. Indeed, it has been shown /14/ that tetralin is the only hydrocarbon (among those studied by us, including ethylbenzene, cumene, cyclohexane, cyclohexene, and tetralin) that is dehydrogenated on $Y_2O_3 \cdot nH_2O$. Apparently, tetralin is dehydrogenated because of the large amount of conjugation energy liberated in the conversion of tetralin to naphthalene.

The ability of a catalyst to assist a given reaction (among several possible) depends on the activation energy ε_1 and the bond energies with the catalyst that are comprised in the expression for ε. Thus, according to the multiplet theory equation /1/, the activation energy for the dehydrogenation of hydrocarbons equals

$$\varepsilon_1 = {}^3/_2 \left(Q_{C-H} - Q_{H-K} - Q_{C-K} \cdots \right). \tag{1}$$

For a given numerical value of ε_1, as calculated from equation (1), a reaction will take place only if the value of each bond energy with the catalyst does not differ sharply from a certain optimum (for the given reaction) value.

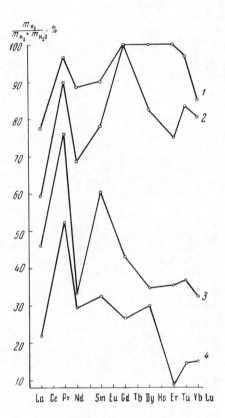

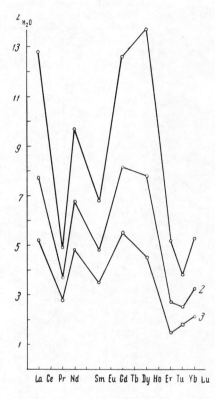

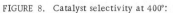

FIGURE 8. Catalyst selectivity at 400°:

1- decomposition of iso-C_4H_9OH; 2- decomposition of n-C_3H_7OH; 3- decomposition of C_2H_5OH; 4- decomposition of iso-C_3H_7OH.

FIGURE 9. Relative water adsorption coefficients z_{H_2O} at various temperatures:

1- 350°; 2- 370°; 3- 390°.

The cracking ability of a catalyst may also be evaluated from the value of Q_{C-K}. In this respect, let us discuss the case of catalyst carbonization.

Carbonization occurs as a result of polycondensation of the starting substance or its conversion products, accompanied by the creation of carbon-carbon bonds. Naturally, the rate of the above reaction should increase if the carbon atoms forming the bond are attached for a longer time (and, hence, by a stronger bond) to the catalyst surface. It has been shown /13, 14/ that Cr_2O_3 is carbonized more slowly than $Y_2O_3 \cdot nH_2O$, while the latter is carbonized somewhat more slowly than TiO_2 /15/ — and, in fact, $Q_{C-Cr} < Q_{C-Y} < Q_{C-Ti}$. It is evident that cracking would be the predominant process for very large value of Q_{C-K}, since in this case the energy barrier for C — C bond rupture (E_{C-C}) is lowered noticeably.

Activation energies for the dehydrogenation of cyclohexane and tetralin (ε_1) and for the dehydrogenation (ε_2) and dehydration (ε_3) of isopropanol (all values are in kcal/mole), the magnetic moments of the atoms (μ, Bohr magnetons) and the ionic radii of the metals in the oxides (r, Å)

Atomic No. of element	Oxide or metal	Ion	r	μ	ε_1 cyclo-hexane	ε_1 tetralin	ε_2 isopropanol	ε_3 isopropanol	Q_{H-K}	Q_{C-K}	Q_{O-K}
4	BeO	Be²⁺	0.34	0	—	57.1	16.4	20.1	45.4	15.3	81.5
12	MgO	Mg²⁺	0.74	0	—	—	24.5*	26.3	—	—	—
13	Al₂O₃	Al³⁺	0.57	0.4	—	—	—	21.0	—	—	—
20	CaO	Ca²⁺	1.04	0	30.5	—	—	—	—	—	—
21	Sc₂O₃	Sc³⁺	0.83	0.14	—	27.6	25.2	30.0	56.1	24.3	39.6
22	TiO₂	Ti⁴⁺	0.64	1.3	19.0	—	22.8	25.0	57.1	29.0	36.0
23	V₂O₃	V³⁺	0.67	0.6	23.8	—	20.6	20.9	56.5*	26.5	42.5
24	Cr₂O₃	Cr³⁺	0.64	6	22.8	—	9.8	19.8	60.9	22.7	51.8
25	MnO	Mn²⁺	0.91	5	32.0	—	31.9	31.0¹	50.8	26.7	38.8
30	ZnO	Zn²⁺	0.78	0	—	—	14.3	—	48.6	23.1	61.7
31	Ga₂O₃	Ga³⁺	0.62	0.3	—	32.0	8.3	11.5	53.5	23.8	67.6
39	Y₂O₃	Y³⁺	0.97	0.67	—	34.5	16.0	20.7	53.6	22.0	58.8
42	MoO₂	Mo⁴⁺	0.68	6	—	16.0	14.0	22.8¹	62.5	28.8	40.3
42	MoO₃₋ₓ	Mo⁶⁺	0.65	0	24.0	14.6	12.1²	18.3	50.5*	28.5	43.6
57	La₂O₃	La³⁺	1.04	0.49	34.3	51.0	24.3	28.0	47.5	17.2	64.9
58	CeO₂	Ce⁴⁺	0.92	2.51	32.0	—	18.3	27.8	57.6	19.8	49.9
59	Pr₂O₃	Pr³⁺	1.00	3.56	36.7	51.6	15.2	27.4	52.4	11.4	72.0
60	Nd₂O₃	Nd³⁺	0.99	3.3	36.8	44.8	17.4	26.0	52.8	16.0	64.7
62	Sm₂O₃	Sm³⁺	0.97	1.74	35.1	42.9	20.0	26.0	51.3	18.0	60.6
63	Eu₂O₃	Eu³⁺	0.97	7.12	—	43.8	15.1	26.0	54.7	14.9	65.2
64	Gd₂O₃	Gd³⁺	0.94	7.95	—	43.3	14.7	25.6	54.8	15.0	65.2
65	Tb₂O₃	Tb³⁺	0.89	9.7	—	42.1	15.2	26.4	57.8	15.2	63.5
66	Dy₂O₃	Dy³⁺	0.88	10.64	—	40.2	13.7	26.5	57.1	14.8	62.2
67	Ho₂O₃	Ho³⁺	0.86	10.89	—	38.4	12.8	24.7	57.1	16.0	62.2
68	Er₂O₃	Er³⁺	0.85	9.5	—	38.6	15.5	26.5	56.5	16.5	59.4
69	Tu₂O₃	Tu³⁺	0.85	7.62	—	38.8	18.3	27.0	54.9	18.0	57.4
70	Yb₂O₃	Yb³⁺	0.81	0.41	—	34.7	20.6	25.1	53.4	22.1	53.0
71	Lu₂O₃	Lu³⁺	0.80	0.21	—	32.0	22.9	27.0	52.0	23.3	52.7
73	Ta₂O₅	Ta⁵⁺	0.66	0.4	—	—	—	23.8	—	—	—
74	WO₃₋ₓ	W⁶⁺	0.65	0	—	26.8	24.4³	23.7	52.6	27.6	43.5
90	ThO₂	Th⁴⁺	0.99	1.3	—	35.7	23.5	31.8	56.3	17.7	48.8
92	U₃O₈	U⁶⁺	0.93	4.28	—	36.3	20.0	18.5	48.9	25.6	40.3
75	Re		1.37	—		7.8	4.8	—	—	—	—
44	Ru		1.34	—	—	11.9	9.3	12.6¹	60.1	22.4	46.1
29	Cu		1.28	—	—	14.9	14.3	11.3¹	55.0	33.7	45.6

* Average values.
¹ Data for trimethylcarbinol.
² Data for formic acid.
³ Data for methanol.

In this way, small values of Q_{C-K} (below 20 kcal/mole) favor the dehydrogenation of hydrocarbons on the given catalyst (provided that $Q_{H-K} >$ 50 kcal/mole). An increase in Q_{C-K} interferes with the dehydrogenation and favors the carbonization. A further increase in Q_{C-K} accelerates the cracking and may cause a decrease in the carbonization rate.

The selectivity of catalysts may be characterized by the ratio $\dfrac{m_{H_2}}{m_{H_2} + m_{H_2O}}$ (in %), i.e., by the ratio of the hydrogen formation rate m_{H_2} to the sum of the formation rates of the olefin m_{H_2O} and hydrogen. Figure 8 shows the changes in the selectivity of lanthanide oxides in alcohol dehydrogenation and dehydration reactions at 400°. As is evident from Figure 8, praseodymium and samarium oxides are more active dehydrogenation catalysts than lanthanum and neodymium oxides; isobutanol is only dehydrogenated on Gd, Dy, and Er oxides.

Figure 9 shows the relationship between the relative adsorption coefficient of water z_{H_2O} and the temperature for isopropanol on lanthanide oxides. It is of interest to note that the curves in Figure 9 show a behavior that is the reverse of that described by the curves in Figure 8 for La, Pr, Nd, and Sm oxides. Thus, Pr and Sm oxides have a greater dehydrogenation activity than La and Nd oxides; the values of z_{H_2O} on these oxides are smaller than on La and Nd oxides. In this way, an increase in the relative water adsorption coefficients favors dehydration and reduces the dehydrogenation rate. Hence, the selectivity of catalysts depends on the value of z for the reaction products.

Thus, the collected experimental data for many oxide catalysts and several metallic catalysts have enabled us to make certain correlations and to derive some rules. With the aid of these rules it is possible, even at the present time, to make approximate predictions concerning the catalytic properties of oxides.

BIBLIOGRAPHY

1. BALANDIN, A.A.—Uspekhi Khimii, Vol. 33: 549. 1964.
2. BALANDIN, A.A. and A.A. TOLSTOPYATOVA.—ZhFKh, Vol. 30: 1367, 1636. 1956.
3. BALANDIN, A.A., A.A. TOLSTOPYATOVA, and V.A. NAUMOVA.—DAN SSSR, Vol. 148: 825. 1963.
4. BALANDIN, A.A.—ZhFKh, Vol. 31: 745. 1957.
5. TOLSTOPYATOVA, A.A. and A.A. BALANDIN.—DAN SSSR, Vol. 138: 1365. 1961.
6. GSHNEIDER, K.L. —Problemy Sovremennoi Metallurgii, No. 2(50): 53. 1960.
7. DORFMAN, Ya. G. Magnitnye svoistva i stroenie veshchestva (Magnetic Properties and the Structure of Matter).—Moskva, GNTI. 1955.
8. TOLSTOPYATOVA, A.A., V.A. NAUMOVA, and A.A. BALANDIN.—ZhFKh, Vol. 38: 1619. 1964.
9. BOKII, G.B. Kristallokhimiya.—Moksva, Izd. MGU. 1960.
10. BALANDIN, A.A. and P. TETENI.—Problemy Kinetiki i Kataliza, Vol. 10: 339. 1960.
11. BALANDIN, A.A., E.I. KARPEISKAYA, and A.A. TOSTOPYATOVA.—IAN SSSR, OKhN, p. 1365. 1959.
12. KIPERMAN, S.L. and A.A. BALANDIN.—Kinetika i Kataliz, Vol. 1: 159. 1960.
13. TOLSTOPYATOVA, A.A., I.R. KONENKO, and A.A. BALANDIN.—Kinetika i Kataliz, Vol. 3: 103. 1962.
14. TOLSTOPYATOVA, A.A., I.R. KONENKO, and A.A. BALANDIN.—Kinetika i Kataliz, Vol. 2: 135. 1961.
15. BALANDIN, A.A., A.A. TOLSTOPYATOVA, and I.R. KONENKO.—IAN SSSR, OKhN, p. 2096. 1960.
16. TOLSTOPYATOVA, A.A.—In: Sbornik "Redkozemel'nye elementy", p. 113. Moskva, Metallurgizdat. 1963.

G.K. Boreskov

OXYGEN MOBILITY AND THE CATALYTIC ACTIVITY OF OXIDES WITH RESPECT TO OXIDATION REACTIONS

This paper deals with the rules governing [catalyst] selection for a relatively narrow group of catalysts and reactions.

In the past, catalysis has been regarded as a peculiar, somewhat mysterious phenomenon with specific laws whose elucidation would solve, at once and in a general form, the problem of [catalyst] selection. It is clear at present that the above is not correct. Catalysis is a chemical phenomenon. The changes in reaction rates by catalytic action are associated with intermediate chemical interactions between the reactants and the catalyst. This means that, in principle, the problem of predicting the catalytic activity does not differ from predictions of chemical reaction rates, but is more complicated because of the participation of an additional component — the catalyst. This explains the difficulties encountered in the selection of catalysts. Even for the simple chemical reactions it is impossible to predict the reaction rates on the basis of theory. It is much less possible to make such a prediction in the case of catalysis. Selection of a catalyst on the basis of theoretical considerations would mean the calculation of the maximum probability of formation of an active complex for the stage (of the reaction considered) involving the participation of one of the possible catalysts. This cannot be done as yet, even with the use of the most modern electronic computers.

Thus, a strict solution of the problem cannot be achieved as yet. The scientific principles of catalyst selection must be based on a combination of particular and approximate relations. However, even narrow-range correlations may be of great value for the development and improvement of catalysts.

The search for such particular correlations in catalytic activity started fairly early. As an example, let us mention the work of W. Ostwald /1/ who, eighty years ago, found that the catalytic activity of dissolved acids is proportional to their electrical conductivity. The above relationship, which played an important role in the development of the physical chemistry of solutions, was the first correlation that could be used to predict the catalytic action of acids. The above correlation was used subsequently (but much later) to obtain some more generalized relationships in the theory of heterogeneous catalysis.

In spite of the wide variety of approaches, there exists a common factor for the particular correlations in the prediction of catalytic activities, namely, the approximate evaluation of the energy of the intermediate reaction between the reactants and the catalyst, and the concept of the optimum values of this interaction. It is clearly evident that very large or very small intermediate interaction energies are not favorable. The optimum value of this energy may be evaluated more accurately by using the well-known equation for the relationship between the change in the activation energy (E) and the heat (q), or the free energy of a chemical interaction:

$$\Delta E = - \varkappa \Delta q.$$

The above equation was derived by J. Brönsted /2/; it was analyzed in detail by M. Polanyi /3/ and was subsequently used with success by M.I. Temkin /4/ in a treatment of the chemisorption and catalysis on non-homogeneous surfaces. N.N. Semenov /5/ found that the above equation is valid for many homogeneous reactions involving the participation of free radicals, and regarded it as one of the most general laws of chemical kinetics. It should be noted that the above equation is not a strict one, and apparently reflects only approximately some more general law. Its accuracy is improved when it is applied to a narrower range of phenomena.

A.A. Balandin made an important contribution when he used the concepts of the optimum energy of intermediate reactions for the solution of the problem of catalyst selection in the form of the principle of energetic correspondence (in multiplet theory /6/). The above principles are not confined to the concepts of the multiplet theory and may be applied to catalytic reactions taking place according to any possible scheme. The main difficulty is the evaluation of the intermediate reaction energy, especially in the case of heterogeneous catalysis.

We shall discuss below a method for such an evaluation in the case of oxidation reactions with the participation of oxygen. It is based on the assumption that it is imposible to calculate the energy of the active complex in the rate-determing stage of the catalytic reaction, but it may be presumed that within a given group of catalysts the changes in the active complex energy are determined primarily by the changes in the energy of one of the bonds ruptured or formed in the transformations of this active complex. It is most probable that, for the reactions discussed here, the above refers to the oxygen-catalyst bond. This approach is exactly the same as the evaluation of the activity of protolytic catalysts on the basis of their acidity, i.e., on the basis of the changes in the free energy of proton detachment.

In the case of oxidation reactions, the energy of the oxygen-catalyst bond is evaluated conveniently by a method based on the study of the isotopic exchange of oxygen. In order to evaluate the bond energy for oxygen on the catalyst surface, we used the following two isotopic exchange reactions:

$$O_2^{16} + O_2^{18} \rightarrow 2O^{16}O^{18}; \tag{1}$$

$$O_2^{18} + O_{surf}^{16} \rightleftharpoons O^{18}O^{16} + O_{surf}^{18} \tag{2}$$

Reaction (1) involves exchange between oxygen molecules, i.e., it is a homomolecular exchange reaction, while reaction (2) involves exchange between molecular oxygen and oxygen from the oxide (heteroexchange).

The rate of each of these reactions may be measured separately (provided that the second reaction has reached equilibrium), or the total rate may be measured, by measuring the changes in the concentrations of molecules with molecular weights of 34 and 36 in the gaseous phase and by measuring the total ^{18}O concentrations.

The isotopic exchange between molecular oxygen and oxygen from the oxide may involve oxygen from both the surface and the bulk. In most cases these two stages show sharp differences in the reaction kinetics /7/. Investigations of the heterogeneous catalytic process are concerned only with the exchange with surface oxygen atoms, and we shall confine our discussion to this case.

In many cases the exchange of surface oxygen occurs in accordance with rather complex kinetic laws. In several transition metal oxides, the surface oxygen is essentially non-uniform from the standpoint of its exchange properties. Data on the course of the exchange on manganese dioxide are shown in Figure 1 /8/. A sharp drop in the [exchange] rate is observed when the degree of exchange reaches a few percent of the amount of oxygen on the surface. In this case, this may be caused in part by the bulk non-homogeneity of the substance, which can be regarded only arbitrarily as a dioxide, in fact, it is a rather complex mixture of various compounds.

Sharp differences in the behavior of the surface oxygen is observed even in the case of homogeneous (in the bulk) oxides — NiO, Co_3O_4, and CuO /9/. This is evident from Figure 2, which shows the variations in the activation energy for the exchange, in the case of the above oxides, until the surface is covered with a monolayer of oxygen.

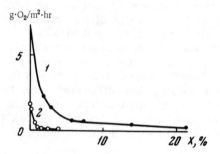

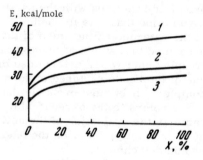

FIGURE 1. Variation in the exchange rate of oxygen (from manganese dioxide) as a function of the degree of exchange of the surface oxgyen:

1- 250°; 2- 203°.

FIGURE 2. Variation in the activation energy for the isotopic exchange of oxygen as a function of the degree of exchange of the surface oxygen:

1- Co_3O_4; 2- CuO; 3- Fe_2O_3; 4- NiO.

In iron oxide and some other oxides the surface oxygen is homogeneous and is exchanged at a constant rate. It is of interest to mention that differences in the bond energies of the surface oxygen are observed in oxides that are characterized by a relatively high catalytic activity. The most labile oxygen may, in such cases, occupy only a small fraction of the surface. This makes it difficult to study its properties by means of heteroexchange, since the process rate must be measured at very low degrees of exchange.

This difficulty is eliminated by using the isotopic exchange in molecular oxygen as a characteristic of the bond energy of oxygen on the surface of catalysts. The measurement of the rate of homomolecular isotopic exchange requires the use of oxygen with a relatively high ^{18}O concentration, and systematic research in this direction was started only recently. The first papers of E. Winter /10/ were published in 1954.

A systematic study of the catalytic properties of transition metal oxides with respect to homomolecular exchange has been in progress for a number of years, under the guidance of this author, at the D.I. Mendeleev Institute of Chemical Technology (Moscow) and, more recently, at the Institute of Catalysis of the Siberian Department of the USSR Academy of Sciences. These studies showed that sharp differences may be observed in the catalytic activity of oxides (with respect to the homomolecular exchange of oxygen) depending on the pretreatment conditions. It was established that the oxides exist in two states. The first state is attained when the oxides are heated in oxygen, and it corresponds to the equilibrium concentration of oxygen on the oxide surface. In this state, the oxides catalyze the homomolecular exchange, with a stable and reproducible activity, but only at relatively high temperatures. The second state is usually attained after heating the oxides to a high temperature, in vacuo. It is characterized by a high catalytic activity even at very low temperatures (75°), but the activity is unstable and is completely destroyed by heating in oxygen. The changes in the activity of zinc oxide at different temperatures are shown in Figure 3 as an example /11/.

The left-hand part of Figure 3 corresponds to the stable, high-temperature activity attained upon the establishment of an equilibrium concentration of oxygen in the surface layer of the oxide. The right-hand part shows the low-temperature activity of samples which have been treated at high temperatures in a vacuum. The activity of such samples decreases continuously at room temperature. The low-temperature activity is completely destroyed by heating in oxygen.

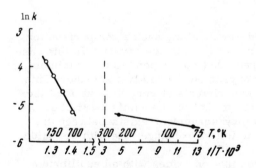

FIGURE 3. Temperature dependence of the isotopic exchange rate of oxygen in zinc oxide.

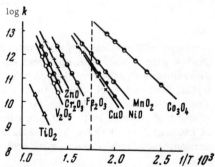

FIGURE 4. Homomolecular exchange rate of oxygen on oxides of elements in the fourth period, with an equilibrium oxygen concentration in the surface layer.

The exchange in the second state, which takes place at very low temperatures and with an especially low activation energy between molecules with very strong bonds and containing fairly heavy atoms, has an interesting mechanism. Nevertheless, in our case we are interested in the exchange at the equilibrium, stable state of the oxide, since it is of importance for our purpose — the evaluation of the bond energy of surface oxygen under the conditions of a steady-state catalytic reaction. Figure 4 shows experimental data /12/ on the activity of oxides of elements of the fourth period with respect to homomolecular exchange at such an equilibrium state. It is noteworthy that the catalytic activity varies within very wide limits (by eight orders of magnitude). The activation energies differ by more than 30 kcal/mole.

Important conclusions may be reached by comparing the exchange rate in molecular oxygen with the exchange rate with oxygen atoms from the catalyst surface (heteroexchange). As is evident from the table, good agreement between these rates is observed for all investigated oxides with an equilibrium oxygen concentration /13/.

Comparison of the exchange rate in molecular oxygen with the isotopic exchange rate with oxide oxygen

Oxide	Temperature, °C	(Exchange rate)$\cdot 10^{11}$, mol/cm$^2\cdot$sec	
		in molecular oxygen	with the oxide oxygen
V_2O_5	550	13.5	13.0
	500	2.4	1.7
Cr_2O_3	525	16	16
	400	0.32	0.61
ZnO	500	29	15
Fe_2O_3	400	6.8	4.7
NiO	300	6.8	6.8
CuO	300	5.7	4.7
MnO_2	300	22	25
	200	5.2	4.2

Some difficulties are encountered when making such a comparison for oxides with a non-uniform bond energy of the surface oxygen. In this case the exchange rate in molecular oxygen must correspond to the maximum, initial isotopic exchange rate of the oxygen on the catalyst surface. This assumption was checked by special experiments at very low ratios of the amount of oxygen in the gaseous phase to that on the catalyst surface. As is evident from Figure 5, a satisfactory agreement exists between the homomolecular exchange rate and the initial exchange rate with the oxide oxygen.

This result leads to the conclusion that on oxides with an equilibrium oxygen content the simplest catalytic reaction (isotopic exchange in molecular oxygen) takes place with the participation of oxygen from the oxide. All the surface oxygen participates in the reaction on oxides with a uniform bond energy of the surface oxygen, while only the most active, "labile" oxygen takes part in the reaction on oxides with a non-uniform bond energy.

This leads to two basic conclusions.

1. In the case of oxides with an equilibrium oxygen content the form of the intermediate reaction between the oxygen and the catalyst coincides with the form of the oxygen bond in the surface layer of the oxide, or at least it resembles it so closely that the conversion from one form to the other is very rapid. Under these conditions, the existence of other species of bound oxygen on the surface is rather improbable; in any case, the rate of formation of such species should be much lower than the rate of binding of oxygen in the surface layer of the oxide, since in the opposite case the exchange of the molecular oxygen would involve the formation of these species, and the rate of formation would be higher than the rate of exchange with oxygen from the oxide.

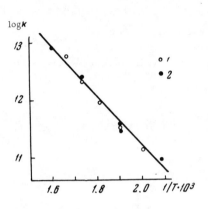

FIGURE 5. Comparison of the homomolecular exchange rate (1) with the initial rate of isotopic exchange with oxygen from the surface of manganese dioxide (2).

2. The catalytic activity with respect to the homomolecular isotopic exchange of oxygen may serve as a characteristic measure of the bond energy and the reactivity of the oxygen from the oxide surface.

The possible schemes of the course of homomolecular exchange are shown in Figure 6.

The fact that an agreement exists between the rates of homomolecular exchange and heteroexchange on oxides with an equilibrium oxygen content shows that in these cases the exchange may occur only by the mechanisms designed as II and III. It is possible to distinguish between these two variants by investigating the kinetics of simultaneously occurring homomolecular and heteromolecular exchange. This is achieved in a most convincing manner by the following approach.

The isotopic exchange with oxygen from the oxide is studied with gaseous oxygen whose composition is such that it is in equilibrium with respect to the homomolecular exchange. If the second mechanism is valid (i.e., one atom of oxygen from the oxide participates in the exchange, tne equilibrium should not change during the heteromolecular exchange process. If, on the other hand, the third mechanism is valid (i.e., if two oxygen atoms from the oxide take part in the exchange), the equilibrium of the homomolecular exchange should be disturbed. The position of the maximum of this disturbance makes it possible to make a quantitative evaluation of the exchange rate according to the third mechanism. The results of such a study of the exchange on vanadium pentoxide /14/ are shown in Figure 7. The position of the maximum indicates that the exchange takes place according to the third mechanism.

The isotopic exchange of oxygen may be used for the characterization of the oxygen bond on the surfaces of metallic catalysts. The first studies of oxygen exchange on metals were made by L.Ya. Margolis et al. /15/.

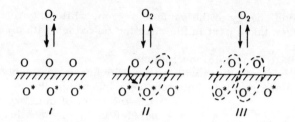

FIGURE 6. Schematic presentation of homomolecular exchange mechanisms:

I- without the participation of oxygen from the oxide; II- with the participation of one oxygen atom from the oxide; III- with the participation of two oxygen atoms from the oxide.

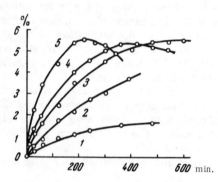

FIGURE 7. Deviations (%) from the equilibrium in the homomolecular exchange of O_2 during exchange with oxygen from vanadium pentoxide:

1- 450°; 2- 463°; 3- 475°; 4- 483°; 5- 500°.

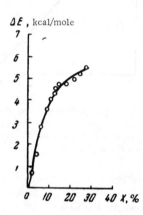

FIGURE 8. Changes in the activation energy of isotopic exchange of oxygen adsorbed on a platinum film, as a function of increasing degree of exchange X.

A.S. Khasin and the present author made a detailed investigation of homomolecular exchange as well as exchange with oxygen adsorbed on platinum films /16/. It was found that the bond energy of oxygen on the platinum surface is very non-uniform, because of surface non-homogeneities. As is evident from Figure 8, the activation energy of the exchange increases by 6 kcal/mole as a result of the exchange of 30% of the monolayer of adsorbed oxygen. The exchange rate in molecular oxygen coincides with the maximum initial exchange rate with adsorbed oxygen. By comparing the activation energies of the homomolecular exchange and the exchange with adsorbed oxygen it was possible to evaluate the heat of adsorption of oxygen on platinum; it is equal to about 13 kcal/mole (on surface sections with a coverage of nearly 0.5, at a pressure of 0.5 mm Hg and at 200°). At degrees of coverage of up to 25% of the monolayer, the heat of adsorption increases to 28 kcal/mole. The homomolecular exchange occurs preferentially on sections that cover about 3% of the total surface of the platinum foil. It is of interest to mention that the nature of the oxygen bond

52

on the platinum surface resembles that of the bond in Co_3O_4 from the point of view of the "mobility" and the degree of non-homogeneity.

A similar study was carried out also for silver films. Contrary to the case of platinum, the oxygen adsorbed on silver was exchanged at a constant rate within the limits of one monolayer, which indicates a uniform oxygen bond energy over the whole surface of the silver (see Figure 9). On silver, the exchange rate is much lower and the activation energy for the exchange is greater than on platinum /17/.

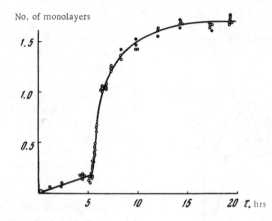

FIGURE 9. Variation in the rate of exchange of oxygen adsorbed on a silver film, with exchange to a thickness of one monolayer or more:

τ is the half-exchange time.

Thus, isotopic exchange in molecular oxygen may be employed for the characterization of the bond energy of oxygen (from oxides) on metallic surfaces.

Let us go back to the problem of the effect of the bond energy of oxygen on the activity of catalysts with respect to oxidation reactions. If the formation of the active complex in the rate-governing stage of the oxidation reaction involves the creation or rupture of an oxygen-catalyst bond, we should expect (within a given series of catalysts) a linear relationship between the activation energies for the oxidation reactions and the changes in the energy of this bond. As a result, there should exist a parallelism in the changes of the catalytic activity with respect to oxidation reactions and homomolecular oxygen exchange.

In order to check the above assumption, we measured the catalytic activities of a series of elements of the fourth period, with respect both to homomolecular oxygen exchange and to a number of reactions involving the participation of oxygen. The activities were measured for all reactions, using the same samples of the catalysts, and under conditions that excluded the effect of processes associated with the transfer of reactants and of heat. The oxidation of oxygen, the exhaustive oxidation of methane (with the participation of oxygen), and the decomposition of nitrogen oxide (yielding oxygen) were used as the model reactions. All these reactions were carried out in oxidizing media, in order to bring the composition of the catalyst surface close to the equilibrium composition corresponding to the conditions existing in the case of isotopic exchange reactions.

The catalytic activity with respect to the hydrogen oxidation reactions was studied by the steady-state circulation method, which has been described in detail in /18/.

The oxidation of methane was carried out in a continuous-flow circulation setup, under atmospheric pressure, at a methane concentration (in the reaction mixture) of $0.7 - 4.0\%$. The course of the reaction was controlled with the aid of a chromatograph /19/.

The catalytic decomposition of nitrogen oxide was studied in a steady-state circulation setup under pressures of $100 - 300$ mm Hg. The oxygen formed in the decomposition reacted with the excess nitric oxide and the product (nitrogen dioxide) was frozen in a trap (cooled by solid carbon dioxide). The reaction rate was calculated on the basis of the accumulation of nitrogen in the reaction mixture, as determined by a chromatographic method in samples that were withdrawn periodically from the setup /20/.

In the investigations, we determined the following parameters for all the above reactions: the specific catalytic activity of the oxides at different temperatures, the activation energies, and the main kinetic relations.

The specific catalytic activities of the oxides for all these reactions are shown in Figure 10; in order to facilitate the comparison, all values are referred to the same temperature $- 573°K$. The uppermost curve represents the changes in the reciprocal heat of formation of the oxides referred to a single oxygen atom. It may be regarded as a very rough characteristic of the ease of detachment of oxygen from the oxide.

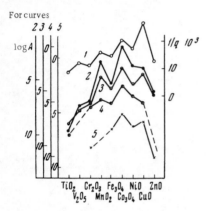

For curves

FIGURE 10. Comparison of the bond energy (q, kcal/g-atom) (1) of oxygen in oxides of elements of the fourth period with the catalytic activity (A, moles/m^{2}hr) of these oxides with respect to various reactions:

2- $^{16}O_2 + ^{18}O_2 \rightleftarrows 2^{16}O^{18}O$; 3- $2H_2 + O_2 = 2H_2O$; 4- $CH_4 + 2O_2 = CO_2 + 2H_2O$; 5- $2NO = N_2 + O_2$.

As is evident from the figure, a distinct parallelism exists in the changes of the specific catalytic activity of oxides of metals belonging to the fourth period with respect to the above reactions. Thus, the activity of oxides with respect to the exchange of molecular oxygen determines also their activity with respect to other oxidation reactions. A similar relationship is observed also for promoted vanadium pentoxide catalysts with respect to the oxidation of hydrogen /21/ and nitrogen dioxide /22/. Data from the literature show that the above sequence of variations in the specific catalytic activities is observed also in the oxidation of carbon monoxide /23/ and ammonia /24/.

In many cases the similarity in the changes of the specific catalytic activity with respect to oxygen exchange and oxidation reactions, in the transition from one oxide [catalyst] to another, is so marked that it could be assumed that the reactions have the same rate-determining stage. In the case of the oxidation of hydrogen, the common rate-determining stage (with the exchange reaction) could be the chemisorption of oxygen. However, the kinetic relations for these two reactions and the activation energies are so different that the assumption of a common rate-determining stage must be disregarded.

This leads to the conclusion that, in spite of the fact that the rate-determining stages of these reactions are different, the catalytic activity is determined by some common property of the oxides that changes gradually from catalyst to catalyst. A natural assumption is that this common property is the bond energy of the oxygen on the catalyst surface. In isotopic exchange this bond energy determines the energy of activation for the adsorption and desorption of oxygen, while in the oxidation of hydrogen it determines the energy of activation for the interaction of hydrogen with the oxygen on the catalyst surface. Similarly, for other oxidation reactions the activation energy for the reaction between the substance to be oxidized and the oxygen on the catalyst surface could depend on the bond energy of the oxygen.

Thus, the bond energy of the oxygen on the catalyst surface is one of the most important factors determining the activity of oxides with respect to oxidation reactions. The isotopic exchange rate in molecular oxygen (which is readily determined by experiment) may serve as a convenient quantitative measure of the reactivity of the oxygen on the catalyst surface.

The problem of predicting the catalytic activity with respect to oxidation reactions remains, nevertheless, quite complicated, since the simple dependence on the bond energy of the oxygen may be obscured by the additional influence of many other factors. Thus, the catalytic activity may be limited by the stability of the oxide or metal phase under the catalytic reaction conditions. As an example, we could cite the catalysts for the oxidation of sulfur dioxide; under the conditions of this process most catalysts have a very low activity because of their conversion into sulfates /25/. If, under the conditions of this reaction, Co_3O_4 were more stable than cobalt sulfate, the cobalt-based catalysts would probably be more active than vanadium-based catalysts (with respect to the oxidation of SO_2).

A complex dependence of the nature of the process on the reactivity of the surface oxygen should be expected also in the case of partial oxidation processes in which the yield of the required product depends on the ratio of the rates of several parallel and consecutive reactions.

In some cases the rate-determining stage in the oxidation reaction might be the interaction of the catalyst with the substance to be oxidized rather than the subsequent reaction with the oxygen from the catalyst surface. The parallelism between the catalytic activity and the activity in oxygen exchange reactions might be absent in such cases, since the conversion of the active complex in the rate-determining stage does not involve the rupture or creation of oxygen-catalyst bonds. Thus, we did not observe such a parallelism in the case of the oxidation of methanol. This indicates that the rate-determining stage does not involve the participation of oxygen from the catalyst and, apparently, dehydrogenation is the rate-determining stage in this case.

It is possible that some oxidation reactions take place through the interaction of the reacting substance with molecular oxygen. Finally, even in cases in which the reaction with oxygen from the catalyst surface is, indeed, part of the rate-determining stage, the simple relationship with the reactivity of this oxygen may be complicated by the fact that the oxidation reaction reduces the oxygen concentration within the surface layer of the catalyst, and this may have a substantial effect on the properties of the surface oxygen. For this reason, the reactivity of oxygen from the catalyst surface could, under the conditions of the reaction, differ substantially from the reactivity in an oxygen atmosphere as measured during the determination of isotopic exchange rates.

In spite of the large number of complicating factors mentioned above, the bond energy of oxygen in the surface layer of the catalyst may still serve as a useful basis for the correlation of experimental data and for the selection of catalysts for a reaction involving the transfer of oxygen atoms between molecules of the reacting substances.

The method may be used also in the study of other systems, for the characterization of the bond of various atoms or molecules on the catalyst surface. Thus, it is of interest to study the reaction between a catalyst and molecules such as CO_2, SO_2, SO_3, etc., by studies of their homomolecular exchange. The range of possible applications of the above method is extended even further by using molecules containing the isotopes of two elements, e.g., $^{15}N^{18}O$, $^{13}C^{18}O$, etc.

The possibilities opened by the isotopic exchange method have not eliminated the need for an extensive and thorough development of all other methods for the evaluation of the energy of intermediate interactions in catalysis, such as chemisorption, especially adsorption calorimetric, adsorption-chemical equilibrium, kinetic, infrared spectroscopic, electrical, electrochemical, emission, and other methods. In view of the present state of the problem, there should be no question of opposition to methods; on the contrary, there should be as many varied data as possible, in order to permit correlation and comparison.

In conclusion, we should deal with the problem of the relationship between the partial functions of the changes in the energy of intermediate interactions in catalysis, namely, the lability of oxygen in different oxides and the electronic structure of catalysts. The existence of such a relationship is evident. Thus, in the case discussed here the binding and detachment of oxygen involves electron transfers in the conversions of molecules into atomic ions and vice versa, and the intermediate interaction energy must depend on the work function of the catalyst. Unfortunately, we were unable to establish an unequivocal relationship between the [electron] work function and the catalytic activity for the catalysts studied by us. Apparently, there exists some general law. The heat of formation of a charged particle on the catalyst surface, e.g., an oxygen ion, may be presented as follows:

$$Q = A - 0.5\,D - \varphi + W,$$

where A is the affinity of oxygen atoms for electrons; φ is the [electron] work function; D is the energy of dissociation of oxygen molecules; W is the energy of interaction of the ion formed and the catalyst; the last value must depend on the position of the adsorbed particle on the surface and cannot be determined as yet within the limitations of the elementary zone theories.

When the composition of a catalyst is changed, the heat of sorption (and hence the energy of activation for the sorption) changes not only as a result of the change in the work function, but also (to a greater or lesser extent) on account of that fraction of the energy of interaction that is independent of the semiconducting properties of the catalyst. Thus, in general, it is impossible to predict the catalytic properties on the basis of the semiconducting properties alone. Only in cases in which the changes in W are so small that they may be neglected as compared with the change in the work function (e.g., upon the introduction of small amounts of additives that hava a great effect on the work function) is it possible to relate the changes in catalytic activity with the changes in the electron work function. It is possible that the the above drawback could be partially removed by taking into account (in the evaluation of the changes in the energy of intermediate interaction as a result of changes in the catalyst composition) not only the changes in the [electron] work function, but also the changes in the energy of the local interaction between the sorbed particle and the catalyst, on the basis of the ligand field theory.

In this way we would probably be able to correlate the experimental investigations in the field of catalytic activity, and to relate the results to the characteristics of the electronic structure of the active catalyst components.

BIBLIOGRAPHY

1. OSTWALD, W.—J. prakt. Chem., Vol. 30: 93. 1884; Vol. 32: 300. 1886; Z. phys. Chem., 2(36): 270. 1888.
2. BRÖNSTED, J.N.—Chem. Rev., Vol. 5: 231. 1928.
3. EVANS, M.G. and M. POLANYI.—Trans. Faraday Soc., Vol. 34: 11. 1938.
4. TEMKIN, M.I.—ZhFKh, Vol. 14: 1153. 1940; Vol. 15: 296. 1941.
5. SEMENOV, N.N. O nekotorykh problemakh khimicheskoi kinetiki i reaktsionnoi sposobnosti (On Some Problems of Chemical Kinetics and Reactivity), p. 43.—Moskva, Izd. AN SSSR. 1958.
6. BALANDIN, A.A.—ZhOKh, Vol. 16: 793. 1946; Uspekhi Khimii, Vol. 33: 549. 1964.
7. BORESKOV, G.K. and V.V. POPOVSKII.—Kinetika i Kataliz, Vol. 2: 657. 1961.
8. KASATKINA, L.A. and G.V. ANTOSHIN.—Kinetika i Kataliz, Vol. 4: 252. 1963.
9. POPOVSKII, V.V. and G.K. BORESKOV.—Kinetika i Kataliz, Vol. 1: 566. 1960.
10. WINTER, E.R.S.—J. Chem. Soc., p. 1522. 1954.
11. GORGORAKI, V.N., G.K. BORESKOV, L.A. KASATKINA, and V.D. SOKOLOVSKII.—Kinetika i Kataliz, Vol. 5: 120. 1964.
12. DZISYAK, A.P., G.K. BORESKOV, and L.A. KASATKINA.—Kinetika i Kataliz, Vol. 3: 81. 1962.
13. BORESKOV, G.K., A.P. DZISYAK, and L.A. KASATKINA.—Kinetika i Kataliz, Vol. 4: 388. 1963.
14. MUZYKANTOV, V.S., V.V. POPOVSKII, and G.K. BORESKOV.—Kinetika i Kataliz, Vol. 5: 624, 745. 1964.
15. MARGOLIS, L.Ya.—IAN SSSR, OKhN, p. 225. 1959.
16. KHASIN, A.S. and G.K. BORESKOV.—DAN SSSR, Vol. 152: 1387. 1963.
17. BORESKOV, G.K. and A.S. KHASIN.—Kinetika i Kataliz, Vol. 5: 956. 1964.
18. POPOVSKII, V.V. and G.K. BORESKOV.—Problemy Kinetiki i Kataliza, Vol. 10: 67. 1960.
19. ANDRUSHKEVICH, T.A., G.K. BORESKOV, and V.V. POPOVSKII.—Kinetika i Kataliz, Vol. 6: 860. 1965.

20. YUR'EVA, T.M., G.K. BORESKOV, and V.V. POPOVSKII.—Kinetika i Kataliz, Vol. 6: 1041. 1965.
21. BORESKOV, G.K., L.A. KASATKINA, V.V. POPOVSKII, and Yu.A. BALOVNEV.—Kinetika i Kataliz, Vol. 1: 229. 1960.
22. JIRŮ, D. TOMKOVA, V. YARA, and Y. WANKOVA.—Z. anorg. allg. Chem., Vol. 303: 121. 1960.
23. KRYLOV, O.V.—Kinetika i Kataliz, Vol. 3: 502. 1962.
24. KURIN, N.P. and M.S. ZAKHAROVA.—In: Sbornik "Kataliz v vysshei shkole", Vol. 2. Moskva, Izd. MGU. 1962.
25. BORESKOV, G.K. Kataliz v proizvodstve sernoi kisloty (Catalysis in Sulfuric Acid Manufacture).— Moskva, Goskhimizdat. 1954.

V.A. Roiter and G.I. Golodets

THE IMPORTANCE OF CHEMICAL FACTORS IN THE SELECTION OF CATALYSTS

In spite of the numerous attempts to find a relationship between the catalytic activity of a substance and its physical or physico-chemical properties (structure, electric conductance, electron work function, magnetic susceptibility), there have been no important advances in the solution of the problem of scientific prediction of catalytic activity on the above basis.

Catalysis is a chemical phenomenon and the problem of catalyst selection should be solved, in the first place, on the basis of correlations of the chemical properties of the catalysts, the chemical properties of the reacting substances, and the chemical nature of the reactions.

Although the chemical differences between various substances are based on the same peculiarities of their chemical structure that determine the above physical properties, the physical properties reflect only partially the various features of the chemical structure and their consideration may result in the elucidation of only separate details of the catalytic processes.

In the present state of chemical theory, it is not possible to correlate (in the form of quantitative laws) all known chemical interactions between substances, even in the case of conventional, non-catalytic processes. Even today, in spite of thorough penetrations into the secrets of molecular structure, of an understanding of the factors causing chemical interactions, and of the principles determining the degree of stability of chemical compounds, chemistry is still affected strongly by laws and rules derived in an inductive way by systematization of factual data and their rational classification. We have not mentioned the role of these empirical and semiempirical correlations for the creation and examination of the most important chemical theories.

It would appear that the development of the more complicated catalytic processes should follow the same path. At the same time, little attention has been given to the problems of the systematization and classification of catalytic reactions and catalysts. The tremendous amount of factual data on catalytic reactions has not been adequately classified, and has not been described in detail. There are no adequate handbooks. There have been virtually no attempts to process the available data for the establishment of principles for the rational classification of catalytic processes.

We are convinced that the present deplorable state of the theory of prediction of catalytic action is due mainly to an underestimation of the inductive method of research. We are attempting now to improve this state of affairs, by creating a correlated system for the classification of catalysts in which each type of reaction would be related to the smallest possible number of catalysts and vice versa.*

For instance, an attempt to introduce a rational classification in catalysis was made by S.Z. Roginskii, who suggested that catalytic reactions should be classified as homolytic and heterolytic, and that catalysts should be classified as metallic or semiconductors on the one hand, and ionic on the other. Such a classification is justified to a reasonable extent, and provides some help in the selection of catalysts. However, it is too general and ambigous: under different conditions many reactions may be either homolytic or heterolytic (see, for instance, the possible schemes for dehydrogenation on different catalysts, Figure 1). On the other hand, most semiconducting catalysts have an ionic lattice and the formation of a sufficient amount of dipole surface compounds may be expected even on the surface of metals. Hence, it would be inaccurate to exlude the possible influence of such substances on heterolytic processes.

FIGURE 1. Possible dehydrogenation schemes:

On the catalyst K_1 — by a homolytic mechanism; on the catalyst K_2 — by a heterolytic mechanism.

In any approach to a more detailed classification based on the analysis of many empirical data, the first problem is where to begin, on what to base the first step: on the classification of catalytic reactions attempted by A.A. Balandin /1/), or on the classification of catalysts.

We started with the classification of catalysts, since in this case the classification may be based on a reliable foundation for a rational classification, namely, on the periodic table. In fact, by relating the available data on catalytic reactions to the elements (in the periodic table) forming the catalysts for these reactions, it was possible (even by a superficial correlation of the data) to note some peculiarities in the catalytic properties of each element, to trace the "catalytic profile" of the element, and of the group (family) in the periodic table to which it belongs. For instance, nickel, which is a well-known catalyst for the hydrogenation of unsaturated and aromatic compounds is not a suitable catalyst for the selective dealkylation of these compounds. Suitable dealkylation catalysts, such as molybdenum oxide, are those that have no typical dehydrogenation properties. Nickel is not a suitable catalyst for the selective hydrogenation of oxygen-carbon bonds in unsaturated compounds; this, as well as the partial hydrogenation of one of two conjugated double bonds (or of triple to double bonds), is usually done with zinc.

* The difficulties involved in the solution of the above problem may be judged by the fact that about ten thousand papers describing several thousands "reaction-catalyst" systems have been published within the last 25 years alone.

The work on the data correlation has just started, and it is too early to come to any definite conclusions. We are, however, convinced that the periodic table may serve as the basis for the classification of catalysts, and within the next year we intend to publish a monograph-databook on the "Catalytic Properties of Substances".

The correlation between reactions and catalysts established in the above way could probably, in many cases, be explained on the basis of the existing concepts on the mechanism of catalytic processes. New concepts are created in other cases.

This is our idea of the approach to the creation of a theory of catalysis that could at any stage of its development (from empirical correlations to a quantitative theory) offer direct assistance to the practical selection of catalysts.

The use of thermodynamic methods probably offers the greatest promise for the development of the quantitative aspects of the theory of catalyst selection.

It is accepted that kinetic problems cannot be solved by thermodynamic methods, since thermodynamic equations include no terms for time. Under certain conditions, however, there exists a relationship between the thermodynamic and kinetic characteristics. As an example we may cite the Brönsted-Polanyi rule that is applied to reactions involving the participation of ions or radicals. A catalyst, with its unsaturated surface valency, may be regarded as a polyradical, and rules of the above type may be applied to heterogeneous catalysis.

There are several known examples of the determination of the thermodynamic criteria of a catalyst with the maximum specific activity (A. A. Balandin /2/, M. I. Temkin /3/, S. Makishima et al. /4/). Correlation of these examples leads to the following rule: if the catalytic process passes through several stages, the most favorable path would be that in which the energy effects of the stages are equal.

Let us examine, for example, the following process:

$$AB + CD \rightarrow AC + BD + Q.$$

For a non-catalytic process involving the participation of free radicals or ions, the relationship between the energy of activation ε and Q is usually described by the equation

$$\varepsilon = A - \gamma Q.$$

Since, as we mentioned above, a catalyst usually has (to a greater or lesser extent) a radical or ionic nature, the above relationship may be valid also in the case of catalytic reactions (even if the participating molecules are saturated).

Let us assume that the reaction proceeds in two stages: 1) the formation of some intermediate compound with the catalyst; 2) its subsequent transformation into the reaction product. In agreement with the multiplet theory, we assume that such an intermediate compound is represented by the model seen on the following page.

In this case the course of the reaction may be represented by the scheme in Figure 2, where $(ABCDK)^*$ is the active complex (transitional state).

Since

$$\varepsilon_1 = A_1 - \gamma q; \quad \varepsilon_2 = A_2 - \gamma(Q - q),$$

61

and the general course of the reaction is determined by the larger value of the qualities ε_1 and ε_2, the optimum conditions would be obtained at $\varepsilon_1 = \varepsilon_2$ since in this case the activation energy for the process would be at minimum. Hence:

$$A_1 - \gamma q = A_2 - \gamma (Q - q). \tag{1}$$

A. A. Balandin and his collaborators have shown in many instances that the following equation corresponds to the optimum conditions:

$$q_{opt} = \frac{1}{2} Q. \tag{2}$$

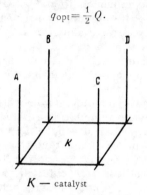

K — catalyst

Equation (2) is derived from (1) by assuming that $A_1 = A_2$. In general this is not self-evident. The works of Balandin and his school are not consistent in this respect: in most papers it is assumed that $A \approx 0$, in others it is assumed that $A = 11.5$ kcal /5/; in some cases it is assumed that for different reactions A has substantially different values /6/.

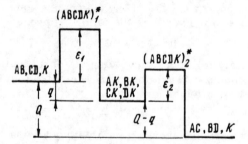

FIGURE 2. Energy diagram for a doublet reaction corresponding to the two-stage scheme.

The physical meaning of the constant A has not been investigated in detail. However, an analysis of the Brönsted equation indicates that the value of A is determined mainly by the entropy change ΔS in the formation of the active complex from the starting substances and the reaction products. In this way, the condition $A_1 = A_2$ may indicate that the active complexes $(ABCDK)_1^*$ and $(ABCDK)_2^*$ have either the same or similar compositions and structures, and that the assumed intermediate compound model also has the same composition and structure (at least for values of q close to the optimum). This corresponds to the concepts of the multiplet theory, according to which the multiplet complex (which, apparently, may be regarded as a transitional form) is represented as follows

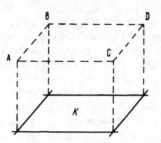

and differs from the model not in its composition or structure but in the presence of partial bonds between the A, B, C, and D atoms and in the weakening of the bond between these atoms and the catalyst (i. e., the differences are mostly energetic).

The fact that the active complexes of the first and second stages have similar structures, and an analysis of the energy scheme, lead to the self-evident conclusion that at $q < Q/2$ the process involves a single stage passing through a single transitional state with an activation energy ε_1, i. e., an intermediate chemical compound is not formed at all (Figure 3, a). At $q > Q/2$ (Figure 3, b) it could be concluded that the process involves two chemical stages, the first of which (the formation of the intermediate compound) is a rapid equilibrium stage, while the second — with an activation energy ε — is the limiting [rate-determining] stage. However, a more thorough analysis leads to the conclusion that even in this case it is more probable that the process involves a single stage. If we take into account the principle of partial equilibria, we may base the above conclusion on the extremely low probability of formation of the intermediate chemical compound when the course of reaction is reversed (a noticeably endothermic reaction with a simultaneous decrease in entropy corresponds to a substantial increase in free energy).

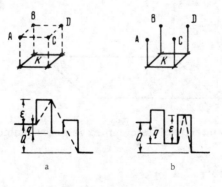

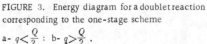

FIGURE 3. Energy diagram for a doublet reaction corresponding to the one-stage scheme

a- $q < \dfrac{Q}{2}$; b- $q > \dfrac{Q}{2}$.

Thus, the process scheme shown in Figure 2 does not represent the true course of the reaction. The plotting of such schemes may be regarded only as an auxiliary approach that makes it possible to use known thermodynamic data (bond energies) for the calculation of the required energetic parameters, as in the calculation of the heat of reaction by Hess' law, in which we divide the chemical process into arbitrary stages which do not correspond to the true mechanism.

The above analysis does not introduce any substantial change in the recommendations of the multiplet theory with respect to the selection of catalysts, but (in our opinion) introduces more clarity into such concepts of the multiplet theory as "the multiplet complex", "the active complex", "the energy barrier of a reaction", and reveals the relationship between the activation energy, the heat of formation of the multiplet complex, etc.

Let us recall, however, that the multiplet scheme of the intermediate compound model was used by us only as an example for the illustration of the scheme in Figure 2. In fact, the same considerations and conclusions may be repeated for catalytic processes of any type whose mechanism is not covered by the concepts of the multiplet theory. It is only necessary that the composition and structure of the assumed chemical complex of the reactants and the catalyst (independently of whether it actually exists in the catalytic process or not) could serve as a model of the composition and structure of the transitional state. Equation (2) must be satisfied under these conditions; hence, the equation is not specific for the multiplet mechanism.

For example, let us assume that the reaction discussed here may occur through the formation of a chemical bond between the catalyst and the atoms of only one of the molecules (AB), while the other molecule (CD) may be only adsorbed (physically), or may even leave the reaction volume ("impact" mechanism). Such a case does not correspond to the multiplet mechanism. The structure of the active complex would be:

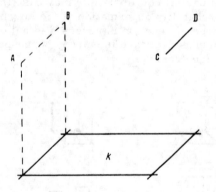

If we assume that the intermediate complex is represented by the following model:

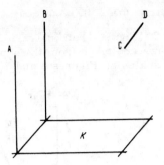

we obtain the following expression for q

$$q = q_{AK} + q_{BK} - q_{AB},$$

and all the conclusions remain the same as in the case of the multiplet complex. Such processes are very numerous. They include, for instance, most processes involving oxidation by molecular oxygen, in which the activation of the oxygen is the rate-determining stage.

In addition to the known heat of dissociation of O_2 molecules, the calculation of q in such a case requires also a knowledge of the $O-K$ bond energy or the heat of formation q of the surface oxide (the heat of chemisorption of O_2), which is determined directly by experiment.

However, many recent works (B. Trapnell et al. /7/, M. Roberts /8/, G. Schuit, L. van Reijen, and W. Sachtler /9/, G. Bond /10/, K. Tanaka and K. Tamaru /11/) as well as a comparison made by A. A. Balandin et al. /12/ indicate that a parallelism exists between the heats of formation of surface and bulk oxides; this makes it possible to assume with a fair degree of accuracy that $q = q_{OK}$ (where q_{OK} is the heat of the reaction $K + ^1/_2 O_2 = KO$, and K and KO are the bulk compounds). In this case the following equation would be valid for the optimum catalyst for a reaction of the above type:

$$(q_{OK})_{opt} = \frac{1}{2} Q.$$

In fact, such a relationship between q_{OK} and the heat of reaction has been observed, in particular, on the basis of the large amount of data collected by S. Makishima et al. /4/.

From the point of view of the above concepts, we carried out an analysis of the most reliable data (from the literature) on the oxidation of hydrogen on oxides and metals, the oxidation of carbon monoxide on oxides, the oxidation of metals on oxides and metals, the oxidation of ammonia on oxides and metals, and the conversion of carbon monoxide on oxides. A comparison of the specific rates of these reactions with the heats of formation of the corresponding models of intermediate compounds and the heats of the reactions revealed a fairly satisfactory correlation between these parameters: when $\log W$ (where W is the specific catalytic activity) was plotted as a function of q_{OK} the points formed the so-called "vulcano-shaped" curves whose maxima corresponded (on the abscissa) to $Q/2$ for each given reaction.

Since the results of the above analysis have been published by us /13/, we shall confine ourselves to a single example — a graphical illustration of the reaction:

$$H_2 + \tfrac{1}{2}O_2 = H_2O + 58 \ \text{kcal/mole} ,$$

on various oxides at 150° (Figure 4) and on various metals at 180° (Figure 5); the data on the activities were taken from the paper of G. K. Boreskov et al. /14/, and the W scales on Figures 4 and 5 are not identical. *

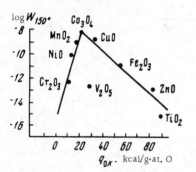

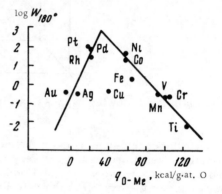

FIGURE 4. Relationship between the catalytic activity of oxides in the oxidation of hydrogen at 150°C and the heat q_{OK} of the reaction $K + \tfrac{1}{2}O_2 \rightarrow KO$.

FIGURE 5. Relationship between the catalytic activity of metals in the oxidation of hydrogen at 180°C and the heats of formation (q_{O-Me}) of oxides.

We found that equation (2) is valid also for the synthesis of methane from carbon monoxide and hydrogen on metals, for the dehydrogenation of formic acid on metals, for the synthesis of ammonia on metals, for the conversion of parahydrogen on metals, and the exchange of hydrogen for deuterium on metals and oxides.

All these facts prove the fairly general validity of the approximate laws that were formulated at first in the form of the principle of energetic correspondence (of the multiplet theory) and may be applied not only to the multiplet mechanism but also to many others.

Since equation (2) is satisfied only in cases in which the calculation of q is based on a compound with the catalyst whose composition and structure are similar to those of the active complex, the experimentally observed correlation between log W and q proves the correctness of our selection of the intermediate-state model.

For instance, the model for the synthesis of NH_3 from N_2 and H_2 may be either $2NK$, $3H_2$ or $6HK$, N_2. In the first case the points for the various metals on the log $W-q$ graph lie fairly accurately on a "volcano-shaped" curve (with a maximum close to $Q/2$, which corresponds to iron, see Figure 6). No such correlation is observed for the second assumption (Figure 7). This confirms the validity of the existing ideas on the determining effect of nitrogen-catalyst (metal) interaction in the synthesis of ammonia.

The use of the following model

---

* The possible causes of the deviation of the data for V_2O_5 and Cu are discussed below.

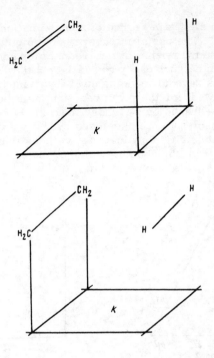

and

in the case of the hydrogenation of ethylene on metals leads to results that
are in contradiction to the principle of energetic correspondence. That
principle is satisfied only by using the model

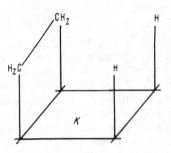

which is the one used in multiplet theory.

The discrepancy between the above model and the actual composition and
structure of the active complex could probably be used to explain the sharp
deviation of the data for V_2O_5 catalysts in the oxidation of hydrogen (see
Figure 4). It has been shown /15/ that the limiting stage in the above
reaction is the activation of the H_2 (rather than of the O_2). A similar
explanation is probably valid also for Cu catalysts (see Figure 5).

Thus, the principle of energetic correspondence, which was established
for the first time by the multiplet theory of catalysis and makes it
possible to use thermodynamic parameters in the selection of catalysts,

may be extended (with a certain degree of approximation) also to other types of catalytic reactions. The use of the above principle necessitates a knowledge (even in general terms) of the composition and structure of the active complex. When no such data are available, they may be collected by trial and error with several models, until a variant is found for which the values of q calculated (for the given reaction) as a function of loq W would lie on a volcano-shaped curve whose maximum corresponds to a value of $Q/2$ on the abscissa. We developed recently a more direct method /16/ which makes it possible to evaluate the composition and structure of the active complexes from the absolute value of the entropy calculated (approximately) on the basis of kinetic data.

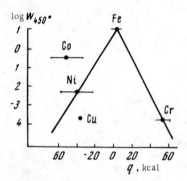

FIGURE 6. Relationship between the catalytic activities of metals in the synthesis of ammonia at 450°C and the heats of
formation of nitrides (the values of q are
calculated for two NK bonds and 3H$_2$).

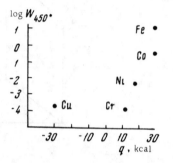

FIGURE 7. Comparison of the catalytic
activities of metals in the synthesis of
ammonia at 450°C with the heats of
formation of the corresponding hydrides
(the values of q are calculated for 6 HK
bonds and N$_2$).

The conclusions on the validity of active complex models for the hydrogenation of ethylene on metals /17/ obtained with the aid of the above method are in agreement with the above conclusions on the validity of the principle of energetic correspondence when analogous models of the intermediate compounds are used in the calculations.

We should emphasize, however, that in the present state of the theory, the principle of energetic correspondence should be regarded only as a semiempirical law, and calculations based on it are satisfactory only as an approximate guide for the selection of catalysts. In the future, however, it could probably serve as a reliable basis for the selection of catalysts. In addition, it should be recalled that even the semiquantitative, general considerations that served as a basis for the derivation of this principle referred only to elementary processes. The extension of this principle to complex multistage processes (which include most chemical reactions) requires further analysis. It is not sufficiently clear to what extent the principle of energetic correspondence could be used to explain the modification of catalysts by additives, by changes in the conditions of formation, etc. Thus, although the use of thermodynamic methods in the theory of [catalyst] selection is very promising for the future, such methods can be used at present only as one of the auxiliary means, whose most important role is to facilitate the understanding of the empirical relations obtained by systematization and correlation of the large amount of available experimental data.

For this reason, we believe that at present it is necessary to concentrate our main efforts on the systematization and classification of the available factual data, in order to prepare a basis for the creation of a sufficiently general and practical theory of catalysis.

BIBLIOGRAPHY

1. BALANDIN, A.A. — ZhFKh, Vol. 5: 679. 1934.
2. BALANDIN, A.A. — Uspekhi Khimii, Vol. 33: 549. 1964.
3. TEMKIN, M.I. — ZhFKh, Vol. 31: 3. 1957.
4. MAKISHIMA, S., J. JONEDA, and J. SAITO. Actes du 2-me Congrès International de Catalyse, Vol. 1: 617. Paris, Technip. 1961.
5. BALANDIN, A.A. Actes du 2-me Congrès International de Catalyse, Vol. 1: 1135. Paris, Technip. 1961.
6. KIPERMAN, S.L. and A.A. BALANDIN. — In: Sbornik "Kinetika i kataliz", p. 159. Moskva, Izd. AN SSSR. 1960.
7. BRENNAN, D., D.O. HAYWARD, and B.M.W. TRAPNELL. — Proc. Roy. Soc., A 256(1284): 81. 1960.
8. ROBERTS, M.W. — Nature, 188(4755): 1020. 1960.
9. SCHUIT, G., L. van REIJEN, and W. SACHTLER. Actes du 2-me Congrès International de Catalyse, Vol. 1: 893. Paris, Technip. 1961.
10. BOND, G.C. Catalysis by Metals, p. 471. — New York-London, Academic Press. 1962.
11. TANAKA, K. and K. TAMARU. — J. Catalysis, Vol. 2: 366. 1963.
12. TOLSTOPYATOVA, A.A., V.A. NAUMOV, and A.A. BALANDIN. — IAN SSSR, OKhN, p. 423. 1963.
13. GOLODETS, G.I. and V.A. ROITER. — Ukrainskii Khimicheskii Zhurnal, Vol. 29: 667. 1963.
14. POPOVSKII, V.V. and G.K. BORESKOV. — Problemy Kinetiki i Kataliza, Vol. 10: 67. 1960; BORESKOV, G.K. ZhFKh, Vol. 31: 937. 1957; BORESKOV, G.K., M.G. SLIN'KO, A.G. FILIPPOVA, and R.N. GUR'YANOVA. DAN SSSR, Vol. 94: 713. 1954.
15. ROITER, V.A. and V.A. YUZA. — Kinetika i Kataliz, Vol. 3: 343. 1962.
16. GOLODETS, G.I. and V.A. ROITER. — Kinetika i Kataliz, Vol. 4: 177. 1963.
17. GOLODETS, G.I. — Kinetika i Kataliz, Vol. 4: 561. 1963.

F. F. Vol'kenshtein

THE ELECTRONIC FACTOR IN CATALYSIS AND THE PROBLEM OF CATALYST SELECTION

1. THE PROBLEMS OF [CATALYST] SELECTION IN ELECTRONIC THEORY

The main problem in catalysis research is the selection of the most active catalyst for each given reaction.

In this paper the problem of catalyst selection is discussed on the basis of the electronic theory of catalysis, i.e., from the point of view of the role of the so-called "electronic factor" in catalysis. We shall confine ourselves to catalysts belonging to the class of semiconductors.

Ultimately, the problem involved is to gain knowledge on the means of controlling the activity and selectivity of catalysts, i.e., how to change the reaction rate to the required extent, and how to change the direction of the reaction to the required side. This problem may be considered from two points of view, either for the p r e p a r a t i o n of catalysts having prescribed properties, or for c h a n g i n g of the properties of a catalyst in the required direction, by the action of various external factors on the catalyst.

From the standpoint of the electronic theory, the activity of a catalyst is characterized by the reactivities of the molecules participating in the reaction, which are determined by the probability of existence of the respective molecules in a radical* (or ion-radical) state. Let us recall that according to the electronic theory /1/ each chemisorbed particle may exist either in the above state (characterized by the presence of non-saturated valences) or in a valency-saturated state; and that during its lifetime on the surface such a particle undergoes many transitions between these two states.

What determines the reactivity of a chemisorbed particle? To answer this question, let us examine Figure 1a, which shows the band scheme of a semiconductor serving as catalyst. The region of positive x is occupied by the semiconductor while the region of negative x is occupied by the gaseous phase. The surface $x = 0$ serves as the adsorption surface. The figure refers to a case in which the surface charge is negative (this is assumed only for the sake of definiteness): the energy bands shown in the figure as a shaded area are bent on the top. The A level represents the local surface level of the chemisorbed particle, while the FF level represents the Fermi level.

The reactivity of a chemisorbed particle of the type discussed here is determined by the position of the Fermi (FF) level with respect to the A

---

* [The reference to "radicals" throughout the book is probably to "free radicals".]

70

level, i.e., by the distance between v and ε_s (where v is the distance from the A level, and ε_s is the distance from the Fermi level to the conduction zone [band] at the surface plane; the difference $v - \varepsilon_s$ may be either positive or negative, depending on whether the Fermi level lies above (as in the figure) or beneath the A level.

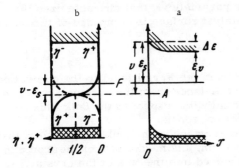

FIGURE 1.

a- band scheme of a semiconductor (A — local surface level of a chemisorbed particle; FF — Fermi level); b — dependence of the reactivity on the position of the Fermi level for the case of acceptor (dashed line η^-) and donor (continuous line η^+) particles.

This leads to the conclusion that the catalytic activity of a surface with respect to a given reaction is determined, on the one hand, by the position (in the energy spectrum) of the local levels of all particles participating in the reaction (or, in other words, by the energy spectrum of the surface), and, on the other hand, by the position of the Fermi level in the same energy spectrum. These two factors are completely independent.

The first of them belongs to the class of structure-independent factors. Indeed, the position of the local surface levels of chemisorbed particles is determined by the nature of these particles and by the nature of the lattice. On the other hand, the second of these factors is structure-sensitive. Indeed, the position of the Fermi level depends on the state of the system as a whole, and may be shifted as a result of various external influences on the system.

From the standpoint of the electronic theory, the problem of catalyst selection is reduced to a problem of the control of these two factors. The preparation of catalysts involves the control of the first factor, while changing the properties of a catalyst involves the control of the second factor. The first or the second aspect of catalyst selection would lead us to the first or the second of these factors. We shall discuss both of them, and the approaches to each of them.

2. THE ROLE OF THE FERMI LEVEL

The position of the Fermi level determines unequivocally the activity of a catalyst with respect to a given reaction only in cases in which the energy spectrum of the surface is prescribed and remains unchanged. When two catalysts of different natures are compared, the Fermi level ceases to be a characteristic of the [catalytic] activity.

This has been noted in many instances, but apparently should be stressed again, since numerous errors have been made by attributing to the Fermi level a role which it does not play in practice. For instance, various catalysts have been compared on the basis of the electron work function. A correspondence has been sought between the electron work function and the catalytic activity. Such a correspondence has no meaning. The absence of such a correspondence does not contradict the electronic theory (as some authors believe) but is rather derived from it.

The Fermi level is a governing factor in catalysis only in cases in which the local levels of the chemisorbed particles participating in the reaction remain constant.

As is evident from Figure 1a, the parameter ε_s that characterizes the position of the Fermi level on the catalyst surface is composed of two terms

$$\varepsilon_s = \varepsilon_v + \Delta\varepsilon, \tag{1}$$

the first of which (ε_v) is the distance from the Fermi level to the conduction zone within the crystal (at a sufficient distance from the surface), while the second term ($\Delta\varepsilon$) is the surface potential with respect to the bulk (this characterizes the degree of bending of the zones.

The first of these terms relates the surface to the bulk. It is known that this terms comprises, in an indirect form, the mechanism of the promoting and poisoning effect of additives introduced into the bulk of the crystal. It is used to describe the well-known correlation between the catalytic activity and electrical conductance.

The second term in (1) depends on the "history" of the surface. It describes (in an indirect form) the mechanism of mutual influence of the adsorbates (i. e., the effect of adsorption of one gas on the adsorption capacity of the surface with respect to another gas). It is used to establish the well-known correlation between catalytic activity and the [electron] work function.

A shifting of the Fermi level on the surface of a catalyst may be accomplished through the effect of various external factors on the first or the second terms in (1), or on both terms simultaneously. A shift of the Fermi level results in changes in the reactivities of all molecules participating in the reaction, and thus in the catalytic activity of the surface.

Figure 1b is a schematic presentation of the reactivity as a function of the Fermi level for chemisorbed molecules of a certain particular type. The two curves correspond to two cases: when the discussed particles are acceptors (dotted line) and when they act as donors (continuous line). The reactivities are denoted by η^- and η^+ respectively.

If the Fermi (FF) level coincides with the A level, we obtain (as is evident from Figure 1 b):

$$\eta^- = \eta^+ = \tfrac{1}{2}.$$

When the Fermi level shifts upward or downward, the reactivity (η^- or η^+) rapidly reaches a value of 0 or 1. Intermediate values (between 0 and 1) are obtained only within a narrow energy range, of the order of kT (i. e., at $|v - \varepsilon_s| \leqslant kT$).

Special emphasis should be placed upon the above statement, since it has some interesting consequences. They will be discussed in connection with the following example.

Let us assume that the reaction involves the participation of particles of two types: acceptors and donors. Let us assume that the corresponding energy levels (denoted by A and D respectively) lie in the energy spectrum rather far from each other (as compared with kT), in the manner shown in Figure 2 a. In such a case the surface would remain weakly active, independently of the position of the Fermi level.

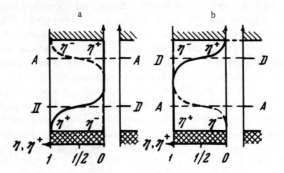

FIGURE 2. Reactivities of acceptor (dotted line η^-) and donor (continuous line η^+) particles as a function of the position of the Fermi level:

a- in the case of a weakly active surface; b- in the case of a strongly active surface.

In fact, for any position of the Fermi level on Figure 2 a, the reactivity of both types of particles (or at least of those belonging to one of the types) would be nearly zero. This may be seen directly from Figure 2 a, in which the dotted and continuous lines depict the reactivities of the acceptor and donor particles participating in the reaction as a function of the position of the Fermi level.

It is evident that in such a case the displacement of the Fermi level within the whole width of the forbidden zone between the bands would not provide for any noticeable catalytic activity. Of the two factors determining the catalytic activity (the energy spectrum of the surface and the position of the Fermi level), the second factor has (in the above case) little influence and does not control the catalytic activity.

In the above case, an increase in the catalytic activity may be achieved only by transition to another (of a different type) catalyst with a different energy spectrum. Let us assume that the A and D levels lie as shown in Figure 2 b, while the Fermi level lies between the A and D levels. In this case the surface would be characterized by a considerable catalytic activity, since particles of the two types would have simultaneously the maximum (close to unity) reactivity.

We presented the above example in order to show that in some cases the energy spectrum of the surface may affect the catalytic activity to a greater extent than the Fermi level, and also to reduce to a certain extent the importance of the Fermi level, which has assumed recently (with the help of the electronic theory) the role of the most popular factor in the theory of catalysis.

3. THE CONCEPT OF "ELECTRONIC TRANSITIONS" IN THE THEORIES OF CHEMISORPTION AND CATALYSIS

In addition to the concept of the Fermi level, there exists another concept that is widely used among scientists working in the field of catalysis (both in the USSR and abroad), and which warrants special attention. This is the concept of electronic transitions. There exists a widely accepted (but completely erroneous) belief that electronic transitions are the main stage in the mechanism of catalytic processes.

Let us emphasize at the beginning (as we have done in many instances) that the above concept has no definite meaning. It is usually accepted in its literal sense: it describes the transfer of an electron from the chemisorbed particle to the catalyst or vice versa. The above concept has a meaning only in so far as the chemisorbed particle and the catalyst are treated as two independent systems. Actually, the chemisorbed particle and the catalyst lattice form a single quantum-mechanical system, which is discussed as a whole. How can we deal with "electron transfer" (from where to where?) if the electron remains within the system?

In fact, as we showed in the first papers on the electronic theory /2/, in the formation of a "weak" chemisorbed bond the electron from an atom may be captured to a greater or lesser extent within the catalyst lattice. Is it possible in such a case to speak about electron "transfer" by the catalyst, if the electron remains bound to the atom or captured in its vicinity?

The concept of "electron transition" in quantum mechanics lacks this direct geometric meaning that is attributed to it. This concept could, however, be used in an energetic sense, to describe the electron transfer from one energy level to another, i.e., from one state to another state that (in general terms) differs from the initial electron distribution in space (of a wave function nature). Indeed, as a result of such energy transition an electron that lies initially within the region of the chemisorbed particle could be diffused within the bulk of the catalyst, or vice versa.

Let us, however, mention that the energetic transitions in chemisorption and catalysis are not always (and not necessarily) accompanied by such a spatial redistribution of the electron cloud.

For instance, the energetic transition of an electron from the conduction band to the local acceptor level (Figure 1 a) means that a free electron from the catalyst is confined within certain boundaries, but does not necessarily mean that the electron has been transferred from the catalyst to the chemisorbed particle. An electron from the catalyst, although "bound" to the chemisorbed particle, may still remain within the catalyst.

Thus, we see that the concept of "electronic transition" does not have the simple geometric meaning that is usually attributed to it. This is an example of the use of classical terminology for the description of quantum-mechanical effects.

The electronic theory has no need for such classical, quasidescriptive terminology. Such terminology should ultimately be removed from the theory (as in its time the concept of orbits was removed from the theory of the atom), since at best this terminology lacks a properly unambigous and clear physical meaning, while in the worst case it leads to an incorrect understanding of the actual processes.

At the same time it is necessary to reexamine the concept of acceptor and donor reactions as reactions which are accompanied, respectively, by the transfer of an electron from the catalyst to the reacting particle or from the reacting particle to the catalyst. In the electronic theory, reactions are also divided into these two groups, but according to a different criterion, namely, the nature of the dependence of the reaction rate on the position of the Fermi level /1/. Reactions that are accelerated by an upward shift of the Fermi level (see Figure 1), i. e., that are accelerated by electrons, are known as "acceptor" reactions, while reactions that are accelerated when the Fermi level moves downward (i. e., that are accelerated by holes) are known as "donor" reactions. When using the above definitions, there is no need to use the concept of "electronic transitions".

4. EXPERIMENTAL INVESTIGATIONS OF THE FERMI LEVEL

The appearance (fifteen years ago) of the Fermi level in the theory of catalysis as a factor controlling catalytic activity led, naturally, to a search for experimental methods for the determination of its position on the crystalline surface. The scientists working in the field of catalysis measured at first the electric conductivity and the work function. Today every laboratory in the field of catalysis that wants to follow the modern trends deems it necessary to carry out such measurements.

Unfortunately, the above two methods (determination of the electric conductivity and the work function) at present exhaust, as a rule, the approaches by which the so-called "electronic factor" reaches the catalysis laboratory.

We shall discuss below the above two (already "classical") methods, from the point of view of what is expected of them and what they can really contribute.

It is usually assumed that electric conductivity measurements provide information on the position of the Fermi level on the catalyst surface, since a knowledge of the initial electric conductivity of the sample makes it possible to determine unequivocally the first term in equation (1) p. 72. This, however, is complicated by the fact that the second term in (1) is a function of the first term. If both these terms change in the same direction (as is usually the case), the direction of displacement of the Fermi level on the surface could, indeed, be judged from the changes in electrical conductivity; however, the relationship between the electrical conductivity and the position of the Fermi level on the surface is greatly complicated if the two terms change in different directions (this may also happen in certain cases).

Thus, data on the position of the Fermi level on the surface obtained from electrical conductivity measurements cannot always be regarded as reliable.

The measurement of the thermoelectronic work function is usually regarded as a direct measurement of the position of the Fermi level on the surface. By definition, the thermoelectronic work function φ_T is described by the following expression:

$$\varphi_T = \varepsilon_s + \chi + \mu. \tag{2}$$

The meaning of the various symbols used can be seen in Figure 3. Here χ is a parameter determined by the nature of the lattice, and μ is the so-called "dipole component" of the work function, i. e., the potential jump associated with the polarization of the adsorbed molecules. (On Figure 3, the Fermi level is denoted by FF; the figure depicts the adsorption of acceptor molecules on an n-type semiconductor, e. g., O_2 on ZnO).

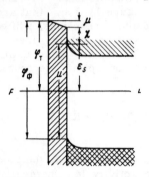

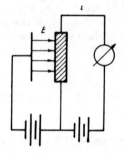

FIGURE 3. Band structure of a semiconductor:

φ_T — thermoelectronic work function; φ_ϕ — photoelectric work function; μ — potential jump associated with the dipole moment of the chemisorbed particles.

FIGURE 4. Setup for the measurement of field effects:

The investigated sample is shaded; E — external field potential; i — current used to determine the surface conductance.

According to equation (2), a change in the work function $\Delta\varphi_T$ is made up of two terms

$$\Delta\varphi_T = \Delta\varepsilon_s + \Delta\mu. \qquad (3)$$

Thus, by measuring the change in the work function $\Delta\varphi_T$ we may evaluate the displacement of the Fermi level $\Delta\varepsilon_s$ if we neglect the simultaneous change in the dipole term $\Delta\mu$. This is usually done without justification (in each particular case) for this neglect.

Let us note, however, that each of the two terms in (3) may be determined separately if the measurements of the thermoelectronic work function φ_T. are accompanied by measurements of the photoelectric work function φ_ϕ. In fact, by definition we have:

$$\varphi_\phi = U + \chi + \mu, \qquad (4)$$

where U is the forbidden zone width between the bands (see Figure 3) and hence:

$$\Delta\varphi_\phi = \Delta\mu. \qquad (5)$$

The conduction of such combined measurements would undoubtedly be of interest.

Indeed, a direct method for the determination of the Fermi level on the surface of a crystal, which moreover makes it possible to displace this level within a wide range, is widely used in semiconductor studies, but unfortunately has not found as yet an application in catalysis laboratories. This is the so-called field effect method; it involves the measurement of surface conductivity under the influence of a transverse external field (see Figure 4; the current i is measured as a function of the field potential E).

This method is undoubtedly the most promising approach to the study of the role of electronic factors in chemisorption and catalysis, although it has not been used, as yet, for this purpose.

Measurements by the field effect method opened the road to the experimental observation of a new effect, that was predicted (theoretically) as early as 1955 /3/, namely, that the chemisorption capacity and catalytic activity of a semiconductor surface should change when the potential of the transverse external field E is changed (see Figure 4). The causes of this predicted effect (which may be termed "electroadsorptive" or "electrocatalytic") are evident: the external field E creates in the semiconductor an inductive charge, which changes the surface potential (band bending), and as a result changes the surface conductivity and displaces the Fermi level on the surface. A new theoretical analysis of the above effect has recently been made (in connection with the field effect method)/4/.

In its time the electronic theory predicted the existence of a relationship between the catalytic activity on the one hand, and the electrical conductivity, the work function, the change in the sign of the photoadsorption effect (with a suitable treatment of the sample) and many other effects on the other hand. The "electroadsorptive" and "electrocatalytic" effects are additional theoretical predictions that for nine years have been waiting for experimental checking.

5. PROCESSES WITH A DISTURBED ELECTRONIC EQUILIBRIUM

Although the Fermi level is the main working parameter of the electronic theory, there are conditions under which it cannot be used in the theory. This occurs in all cases in which the electronic equilibrium in the semiconductor is disturbed. In such cases even the concept of the Fermi level loses its meaning.

One example of such a disturbed equilibrium is a catalyst under irradiation /5/. Another example is the chemisorption process itself. A theoretical analysis of this process was made recently by this author together with O. Peshev /6/. It is known that at the beginning of the chemisorption process the electronic equilibrium on the surface is disturbed. The equilibrium is gradually restored during the adsorption. In some cases the equilibrium is completely restored only upon the establishment of an adsorption equilibrium.

We shall present in brief the results of our analysis. In the first place, because the experimentators who study chemisorption and catalysis on semiconductors deal, as a rule, with the chemisorption kinetics and much more rarely with chemisorption equilibria. In the second place, because the problems of chemisorption kinetics have not been adequately investigated as yet from the point of view of the electronic theory. And in the third place, because our analysis is a further example of how to establish the electronic theory without using the concept of the Fermi level. (A certain "discrediting" of the Fermi level is, probably, one of the main points of this paper).

The nature of the kinetics depends on the relationship between three "lifetimes":

$$\tau, \ \tau_n, \ \tau_c.$$

Here τ is the lifetime of a particle in the adsorbed state; τ_n and τ_c are the lifetimes of the adsorbed particle in a neutral and a charged state, respectively. Depending on the nature of the semiconductor (concentration of carriers, nature of the energy spectrum) we may have either

$$\tau_n, \ \tau_c \ll \tau, \tag{6a}$$

or

$$\tau \ll \tau_n, \ \tau_c. \tag{6b}$$

In the first case (6a), the kinetics of chemisorption of the neutral and charged forms are shown in Figure 5 a by a dotted and a continuous curve respectively (the surface concentrations of neutral and charged particles are denoted by N_n and N_c respectively). In this case the electronic equilibrium on the surface is restored already at $t \approx \tau_c$ and continues to exist throughout the adsorption. This means that the relative surface concentrations of the neutral and the charged forms reach an equilibrium at $t \approx \tau_c$, and the subsequent increase in the amounts of these forms occurs in such a way that their ratio remains constant.

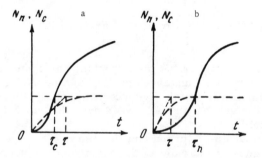

FIGURE 5. Kinetic curves for the chemisorption of neutral (dotted line) and charged (continuous line) species:

The left-hand section refers to a case in which an electronic equilibrium is maintained $(\tau_n, \tau_c \ll \tau)$; the right-hand section depicts a case in which the electronic equilibrium has been disturbed $(\tau \ll \tau_n, \tau_c)$.

In the second case (6b), the chemisorption kinetics for the neutral and charged forms are again shown by a dotted and a continuous curve respectively, on Figure 5 b. In this case an electronic equilibrium on the surface is established only with the establishment of an adsorption equilibrium. At $t \approx \tau$ the neutral species saturate the surface and further adsorption occurs only through an increase in the amount of the charged species. Figures 5a and b were plotted by assuming that at equilibrium (i. e., at $t=\infty$) the amount of the charged species is greater than that of the neutral species. In the case discussed (6 b) the activation energy for the chemisorption E includes the Fermi level as a term:*

$$E = E + \varepsilon_s = E + \varepsilon_v + \Delta \varepsilon. \tag{7}$$

This is an important result. The Fermi level again takes its place in theory. This is the same Fermi level that governs the semiconductor (although the electronic equilibrium on the surface is known to be disturbed by the course of the adsorption), if we only assume that the electronic processes occurring on the surface have little distorting effect on the state in the bulk, i. e., if we assume that the electron and hole currents flowing to or from the surface (as a result of its charging during the adsorption) are fairly small.

Thus, it becomes possible to control the activation energy by suitable treatment of the sample. According to (7), the introduction of an admixture into the bulk of the semiconductor should cause a change in E as a result of the change in ε_v; the adsorption of a foreign gas should have the same effect, due to the change in $\Delta \varepsilon$. Equation (7) shows also that an unambiguous relationship should exist between the activation energy E on the one hand, and the electric conductivity and the work function on the other. In fact, by prescribing a value to the electric conductivity we obtain a certain definite value of ε_v, while the work function is determined by $\Delta \varepsilon$ with an accuracy of the order of the dipole term. The experimental examination of these relations would be of interest.

6. THE ENERGY SPECTRUM OF THE SURFACE

At the beginning of this paper we mentioned that from the point of view of the electronic theory the catalytic activity of a surface is determined by two factors: the nature of its energy spectrum, and, for a given energy spectrum, by the position of the Fermi level in it.

Until now, we have considered the second of these factors. The reason for this was not its predominant role, but only the fact that it is controlled more easily and there is more to tell about it. Let us consider now the first of these two factors.

The problem of catalyst selection has two aspects — physical and chemical. The physical aspect is fully covered by the second factor: it characterizes the state of the system as a whole. The chemical aspect of the problem, on the other hand, is concentrated only within the first factor. Indeed, the positions of the energy levels of the particles which are chemisorbed on the surface or participate in the reaction are determined mainly by the chemical nature of the particles and the surface.

---

* Equation (7) refers to cases in which the adsorbed particles are acceptors. In the case of donor particles ε_s should be replaced by $u - \varepsilon_s$.

Let us mention, however, that the positions of these levels depend also on the nature of the adsorption centers, which may be of different kinds even for the same molecules adsorbed on the same (from the standpoint of its chemical nature) surface; this is the so-called "non-homogeneous" surface. Either regular atoms (ions) from the crystal lattice, or structural surface microdefects, having a "historical" or thermal origin, may serve as such centers. Thus, molecules of the same type that are chemisorbed on a non-homogeneous surface introduce into the energy spectrum local levels that are not of a single type but, in general terms, a whole system of levels of various types.

The arrangement (in the energy spectrum) of the local surface levels of all particles, chemisorbed or participating in the reaction with respect to one another and with respect to the energy bands predetermines the catalytic properties of the surface, as well as to what extent these properties could control the displacement of the Fermi level.

At present it is virtually impossible to make an accurate computation of the energy spectrum of a surface (of a real surface with the particles chemisorbed on it). This could not be expected from the theory, whose only contribution in this respect is a qualitative and only approximate conception of the relative arrangement of the local levels of some chemisorbed molecules, based on a knowledge of their ionization potentials and electronic affinity energies. However, we should not forget (as some authors do) that the values of these parameters for chemisorbed molecules may differ from the same values for these molecules in the free state.

In this respect, we observe on the surface the same behavior as in the bulk of the semiconductor. The positions of the local bulk levels, determined by admixtures or structural defects of various particular natures, is not as a rule calculated on the basis of theory (which in most cases is not a rewarding task), but is determined by some experimental method. This may be accomplished by analyzing the temperature dependence of the conductivity (this is the common, "classical" method), or on the basis of optical measurements (by using the absorption or luminescence spectra). Such methods have been used to establish the energy spectra of many semiconductors, alkali halide crystals, crystalline phosphors, etc.

Almost no data exist on the energy spectra of surfaces (there are a few data on the surface levels on germanium only). The above-mentioned field effect method is the one that could be used for such determinations. In principle, the above method could be used in the research on catalysis (this has not been done as yet): for the determination of the position (in the energy spectrum) of the local levels of molecules chemisorbed on the surface of a semiconductor serving as the catalyst.

Let us mention, incidentally, that the above method combined with direct adsorption measurements may be used also for the solution of another problem: the direct experimental separation of the neutral and charged forms in chemisorption (the concept of the existence and the changes in the relative concentrations of these forms under the influence of various factors is a very characteristic concept of the electronic theory).

The search for theoretical approaches and experimental methods for the determination of the energy spectra of surfaces and for the control of these spectra is at present the main problem of the electronic theory of catalysis. It is connected with the problem of catalyst selection. When the above problem is solved, the electronic factor may be considered in the problem of [catalyst] selection, and could occupy its proper place in it.

BIBLIOGRAPHY

1. VOL'KENSHTEIN, F. F. Elektronnaya teoriya kataliza na poluprovodnikakh (The Electronic Theory of Catalysis on Semiconductors). — Moskva, Fizmatgiz. 1960.
2. VOL'KENSHTEIN, F. F. — ZhFKh, Vol. 21: 1317. 1947.
3. VOL'KENSHTEIN, F. F. — Problemy Kinetiki i Kataliza, Vol. 8: 203. 1955; VOL'KENSHTEIN, F. F. and V. B. SANDOMIRSKII. DAN SSSR, Vol. 118: 380. 1958.
4. BARU, V. G. and F. F. VOL'KENSHTEIN. — DAN SSSR, Vol. 167: 1314. 1966.
5. VOL'KENSHTEIN, F. F. and I. V. KARPENKO. — Kinetika i Kataliz, Vol. 3: 72. 1962; BARU, V. G. and F. F. VOL'KENSHTEIN. IAN SSSR, seriya khimicheskaya, p. 1935. 1964.
6. VOL'KENSHTEIN, F. F. and O. PESHEV. — Kinetika i Kataliz, Vol. 6: 95. 1965.

O. V. Krylov

RULES GOVERNING THE SELECTION OF NON-METALLIC CATALYSTS

At present, the most widely used approach to the solution of the problem of catalyst selection involves a comparison of the catalytic activity of the solid in a given reaction with some other property of the same solid. A correlation between the catalytic activity and some other property of the solid is possible even if the other property (e. g., melting point, color, etc.) does not determine directly the catalytic activity, but depends, like the activity, on some other, third property.

The development of a theory of catalyst selection requires, however, the determination of those properties that determine directly the catalytic activity. For non-metallic solids, which are the subject of this paper, the electronic theory of catalysis on semiconductors /1, 2/ assumes that the activity is determined by the position of the Fermi level on the crystal surface; this position may be determined by measuring the electron work function and the magnitude and sign of the electric conductivity. Hence, a correlation should exist between the catalytic activity on the one hand, and the electric conductivity and electron work function on the other. According to the multiplet theory of catalysis /3/, the catalytic activity is associated, in particular with the lattice parameter; the crystalline field theory /4/ related the activity to the number of d-electrons in the cation; the theory of acid-base catalysis /5—7/ relates the activity to the proton-donor and proton-acceptor properties of the surface.

On the basis of the experimental work on the dehydrogenation of alcohols and the decomposition of hydrazine, the present author and S. Z. Roginskii /8/ advanced a hypothesis according to which many oxidation-reduction reactions take place on catalysts-semiconductors within the region of intrinsic conductivity. For the intrinsic conductivity, the Fermi level in a semiconductor ε_s should lie in the middle of the forbidden zone of the semiconductor (assuming that the valency band and the conduction band have the same statistical weights), i. e., $\varepsilon_s = \frac{1}{2} \Delta U$, where ΔU is the forbidden zone width. If the Fermi level really determines the catalytic activity of the semiconductor, we could expect that, all other conditions being equal, the catalytic activity would decrease with increasing ΔU. In fact, such a relation has been observed by this author and E. A. Fokina for the above-mentioned reactions.

In turn, the forbidden zone width ΔU is related functionally to other properties of the solid. It increases as the bonds in the semiconductor become more ionic. The extent to which a bond is ionic is determined, most often, by the difference Δx between the electronegativities of the metal and non-metal ions in the binary state. In the case of a semiconductor with the sphalerite structure we have /11/:

$$\Delta U = \Delta U_0 + c\Delta x^b, \qquad (1)$$

where c and b are constants depending on the mean principal quantum number n, and ΔU_0 is the forbidden zone width for the corresponding monoatomic semiconductor with a principal quantum number n.

There exists /12/ a relationship between ΔU and the dielectric constant ε:

$$\Delta U \varepsilon^2 = \text{const.} \qquad (2)$$

ΔU tends to increase with decreasing lattice parameter.

All this makes it possible to correlate the catalytic activity with Δx, ε, the lattice parameter, etc.

By using data from the literature, this author made an attempt to correlate the catalytic activity (c. a.) of various binary (and in some cases even more complex) solids in about 300 reactions of different types to the following properties of the solids: type of conductivity, forbidden zone width, electron work function, difference between electronegativities, the value of $1/\varepsilon^2$, the number of d-electrons in the cation, the polarizing power of the cation (the ratio of the square of the charge to the radius), and the distance between the atoms of the metal and the non-metal $l_{\text{Me} - \text{x}}$. Such a correlation was made possible only by the use of the most recent advances in the methods of research on catalysts and adsorbents. Nevertheless, these procedural advances are not used even now in most investigations: the specific surface is not measured, the catalysis is studied under static or flow conditions without taking the macrokinetic factors into account, the investigations are often made within a very narrow range of temperatures, pressures, etc., the c. a. is characterized by the yield of reaction products rather than by the reaction rate or rate constant referred to one square meter of surface.

Hence, in order to correlate the various data, we used the method of statistical averaging, by attributing different statistical weights to the different data /13/. The reliability of the data increases when the number of investigations of a particular process is increased, even if the above procedural conditions (measurements of the surface, the conditions, etc.) are not satisfied in each experiment. In the case of the most thoroughly investigated reactions (alcohol dehydrogenation and dehydration, oxidation of CO) the properties of the solid were correlated to its c. a. by the correlation analysis method /14/.

The results of our correlation calculations for the dehydrogenation of isopropanol are shown in the table. The values of the c. a. were taken from /13/, while the values for the various solid-body properties were taken from handbooks.

In the table, η is a correlation factor determined from the equation:

$$\eta = \sqrt{\frac{n \sum_{x} \frac{\left(\sum_{y} n_{xy} y\right)^2}{n_x} - \left(\sum_{x} \sum_{y} n_{xy} y\right)^2}{n \sum_{y} n_y y^2 - \left(\sum_{y} n_y y\right)^2}}, \qquad (3)$$

where y is the magnitude of the c. a. on a logarithmic scale; x is the property of the solid; and n is the number of experimental points. The value of η determines the closeness of the relationship between y and x. The closeness of the linear relationship between y and x is determined by the correlation coefficient

$$r = \frac{n \sum_x \sum_y n_{xy} xy - (\sum_x n_x x)(\sum_y n_y y)}{\sqrt{[n \sum_x n_x x^2 - (\sum_x n_x x)^2][n \sum_y n_y y^2 - (\sum_y n_y y)^2]}} . \qquad (4)$$

Correlation coefficients for the relationship between the catalytic activity of binary compounds in the dehydrogenation of isopropanol and different properties of the solid

Properties of the solid	η	r	b	σ	Evaluation of the presence (+) or absence (-) of correlation
Distance l_{Me-X} · · · · · · · · · · · · ·	0.55	0.40	0.27	0.92	+
Forbidden zone width ΔU · · · · · · · ·	0.58	-0.48	-0.24	0.91	+
Difference between electronegativities, Δx ·	0.64	-0.51	-0.70	0.86	+
Work function φ · · · · · · · · · · · · ·	0.55	0.40	0.20	0.68	+
$1/\varepsilon^2$ (ε is the dielectric constant) · · ·	0.44	-0.08	-0.17	0.86	-

The values of r and η lie between zero and unity, but $\eta \geqslant r$ always. An unambiguous relationship exists when the values of r and η are close to unity, and no relationship exists when the values are close to zero.

In the table, b is the coefficient of linear regression, or the slope of the straight line as determined by the method of least squares, while σ is the mean square deviation from the regression line. The last column in the table indicates the presence or absence of correlation between y and x. This is evaluated by using the formula:

$$|r| > t\sigma_r, \qquad (5)$$

where $|r|$ is the absolute value of the correlation coefficient, t is the standard deviation for a normally distributed fixed value at a level of significance of 5%, as found in tables /14/; $\sigma_r \approx \frac{1-r^2}{\sqrt{n}}$ is the dispersion of the empirical correlation coefficient.

The data in the table show that the c. a. in the dehydrogenation of alcohols increases with increasing l and φ decreases with increasing ΔU and Δx, and is independent* of $1/\varepsilon^2$.

An analogous calculation for the reaction of dehydration showed that c.a. is correlated (decreases) with Δx only and is not related to $l, \Delta U, \varphi$, and $1/\varepsilon^2$.

* The existence and nature of correlation between the c. a. and the various properties of a solid are evaluated on the basis of the magnitude and sign of r, taking into account the tabulated values of η.

The only subjective factor in our calculations was the attribution of different statistical weights to the experimental data. A change in the scale of statistical weights from 4:1 to 2:1 or to 10:1 causes, naturally, a change in the numerical values of the coefficients η, r, and b, but the conclusion concerning the presence or absence of correlation remains unchanged.

Let us analyze the above results in more detail. Data on the correlation of the c.a. to the forbidden zone width are shown in Figure 1. The question arises as to the cause of the scatter of points on the figure: whether this is due to the inaccuracy of the experimental data or to the complicated dependence of the c.a. on ΔU. In order to answer this question, it is necessary to eliminate other factors that may affect the above relationship. As is evident from Figure 2 (which was plotted on the basis of the experimental data of the present author and E. A. Fokina /10/) a better-defined dependence of the c.a. on ΔU, with a smaller dispersion of the data, is obtained for the dehydrogenation of isopropanol on semiconductors of a single structural type (sphalerite). If we eliminate also the effect of the lattice parameter and analyze the dependence of the c.a. on ΔU within the same isoelectronic series (Ge → CuBr) in which all substances have approximately the same lattice parameter, we obtain a nearly functional relationship (see Figure 3) /9/.

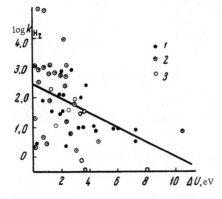

FIGURE 1. Correlation between the catalytic activity of semiconductors (in the dehydrogenation of isopropanol) and the forbidden zone width /13/:

1- most reliable data; 2- moderately reliable; 3- least reliable. $\log k_{H_2}$ — logarithm of the rate constant of the alcohol dehydrogenation reaction.

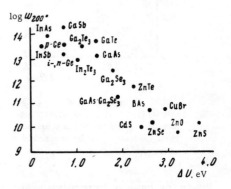

FIGURE 2. Dependence of the catalytic activity of semiconductors with the sphalerite and wurtzite structure on the forbidden zone width (for the dehydrogenation of isopropanol)

$\log w_{200°}$ — logarithm of the initial reaction rate at 200°C.

A detailed correlation of the c.a. with ΔU for other reactions was made by us in an extensive review /15/. We shall describe below the results of this correlation.

A decrease in the c.a. with increasing forbidden zone width occurs in the chemisorption of O_2, the exchange of H_2 for D_2, the exchange of hydrogen from C_2H_4 with D_2O, the homomolecular exchange of O_2, the exchange of O_2 from oxide surfaces, the recombination of H-atoms, the recombination of O-atoms, the hydrogenation of ethylene, the hydrogenation of CO to CH_4, the hydrogenation of nitrobenzene to aniline, the dehydrogenation of cyclohexane, the dehydrogenation of ethanol, isopropanol, and n-butanol, the dehydrogenation of HCOOH, the decomposition of hydrazine, KN_3, GeH_4, AsH_3, SbH_3, H_2O_2, N_2O, $KMnO_4$, $KClO_3$, HgO, nitroparaffins (CH_3NO_2, $C_2H_5NO_2$, $C_3H_7NO_2$), and hydroperoxides, the oxidation of CO, hydrogen, and CH_4, the exhaustive oxidation of n-pentane, isopentane, 2-pentene, 1-pentyne, 2-methylbutane, 2,3-dimethylbutane, n-hexane, cyclohexane, benzene, toluene, and naphthalene, and the dehydrochlorination of alkyl chlorides. As an example, Figure 4 shows the dependence of the c. a. on ΔU for the homomolecular exchange of O_2 according to the data of /16/, while Figure 5 shows the same dependence for the oxidation of CO, derived from the results of a statistical averaging of a large number of data.

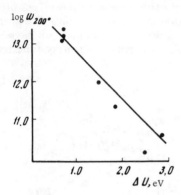

FIGURE 3. Dependence of the catalytic activity (in the dehydrogenation of iso-propanol) of semiconductors belonging to the isoelectronic series of germanium on the forbidden zone width.

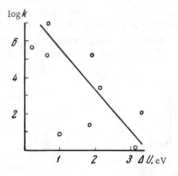

FIGURE 4. Correlation between the catalytic activity of semiconductors (in the homomolecular exchange of O_2) and the forbidden zone width:

log k — rate constant of the reaction.

In the case of heterolytic (acid-base) reactions, the data on the rules governing catalyst selection are less reliable as a rule. If such data are actually, available (as in the case of the dehydration of alcohols), our analysis shows that no correlation exists between the c. a. and ΔU.

In no case did we find a reversed correlation, i. e., an increase in c. a. with increasing ΔU.

Thus, the increase in c. a. with decreasing forbidden zone width ΔU is a common feature of many reactions with a homolytic mechanism (oxidation, hydrogenation, dehydrogenation, decomposition of hydrides, unstable oxygen-containing compounds, etc.). The scattering of points caused by other factors (lattice type, electronic structure, impurities) may in some cases distort the above relationship, but the change in c. a. as a function of ΔU is, as a rule, greater than the changes in activity caused by other factors.

The above relationship may be explained on the basis of the electronic theory of catalysis on semiconductors /1, 2/: 1) by the occurrence of the catalytic process within the range of intrinsic conductance; 2) by the fact that the product of the electron and hole concentrations (in the semiconductor) is a term in the kinetic equation; or 3) by assuming that a correlation exists between ΔU and some other, third property of the solid. In the last case, this does not necessarily mean that a relationship exists between the c. a. and the position of the Fermi level in the semiconductor.

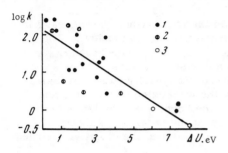

FIGURE 5. Correlation between the catalytic activity of oxides (in the oxidation of CO) and the forbidden zone width:

1- most reliable data; 2- moderately reliable; 3- least reliable.

An analysis of the experimental data shows that the catalytic process occurs most frequently within the range of impurity conductance or in the range of transition from impurity to intrinsic conductance /10/. The catalytic process may occur within the range of intrinsic conductance only in the case of high-temperature reactions, e. g., in the exhaustive oxidation of hydrocarbons.

The second of the above explanations of the relationship between the c. a. and ΔU may, apparently, be applied to the catalytic decomposition of hydrazine, which was studied by us /17/. In this case the overall reaction rate constant is a product of partial constants, some of which are proportional to the electron concentration n_- and others to the hole concentration n_+. If the overall constant comprises the product:

$$n_+n_- = n_i^2 = n_{0i}^2 e^{-\Delta U/RT}$$

(where n_i is the concentration of current carriers within the range of intrinsic conductance at a temperature T), the reaction rate would increase with decreasing ΔU even within the range of impurity conductance; this was indeed observed in reality. It has also been found /17/ that the reaction rate does not change in the transition from an n-type to a p-type semiconductor.

Let us analyze now the third possibility — that a correlation exists between ΔU and some other property of the solid.

The table shows that the c.a. increases with increasing distance between the electropositive and electronegative atoms l_{Me-X}. On the other hand, a correlation exists between l and ΔU. The correlation coefficient $r_{l|\Delta U}$, calculated by us for semiconductors that catalyze the dehydrogenation of isopropanol, has a value of -0.18. A calculation of the partial correlation coefficient between the c. a. and l, excluding the relation with ΔU, by means of the equation:

$$r_{c.a.l | \Delta U} = \frac{r_{c.a.| l} - r_{c.a.| \Delta U} r_{l | \Delta U}}{\sqrt{(1 - r_{c.a.|\Delta U}^2)(1 - r_{l | \Delta U}^2)}},$$

yields a value of 0.36. Thus, it is evident that by accounting for the relationship between l and ΔU (and, vice versa, of ΔU and l) we change only slightly the correlation coefficient of the c. a. with l (or of the c. a. with ΔU). Thus, in the dehydration of alcohols the increase in c. a. with increasing l and decreasing ΔU represent two statistically independent processes.

An analogous calculation shows that, on the other hand, the increase in c. a. with decreasing ΔU and Δx are not statistically independent. The partial correlation coefficients $r_{c.a.\,\Delta U|\Delta x}$ and $r_{c.a.\,\Delta x|\Delta U}$ are smaller than $r_{c.a.|\Delta U}$ $r_{c.a.|\Delta x}$ (by a factor of $1.5-2$), but they do not assume values of zero.

Thus, in many cases the increase in catalytic activity with decreasing forbidden zone width may be explained by the weakening of the ionic and the strengthening of the covalent nature of the bond, i. e., by the decrease in the effective charge of the surface atoms of the catalyst. A theoretical derivation of such a relationship between the c. a. and the effective charge was reported by E. L. Nagaev /18/.

For a further check of the above conclusion, it is necessary to make a direct correlation of the c. a. and the effective charges. Although experimental methods for their determination have already been developed, the available data are very scanty. For this reason, it is necessary to use the less satisfactory concept of electronegativity. A most thorough criticism of the concept of electronegativity was published recently in the Soviet literature by Ya. K. Syrkin /19/. This criticism is justified in many respects. However, Syrkin used incorrect values of ΔU in order to prove his assumption that no parallelism exists between Δx and ΔU in semiconductors. If the correct values are taken, we obtain a relationship of the same type as that described by equation (1) above.

However, ΔU and Δx are not interchangeable. For instance, in the dehydrogenation of alcohols both semiconductors (with a low Δx) and solid bases (with large values of Δx) serve as active catalysts. On the other hand, in the dehydration of alcohols the c. a. decreases with increasing Δx (this is explained readily by the relationship between the dehydration and the acidity of the catalyst), but there is no correlation between the c. a. and ΔU.

The data in the table show that a change in the trend towards an increase in the c. a. with increasing work function φ occurs in the dehydrogenation of isopropanol. This explains the fact that n-type semiconductors are more active than p-type semiconductors. The statistical-average c. a. of p-type semiconductors (in the units used earlier by this author /13/) is 2.11, while that of n-type semiconductors is 1.81.

According to data from the literature (see /15/), p-type semiconductors are more active (as compared with n-type) in the dehydrogenation of ethanol and isopropanol, the dehydrogenation of HCOOH, the recombination of O atoms, the homomolecular exchange of O_2, the oxidation of O_2 from the surface of oxides, the decomposition of N_2H_4, N_2O, and HgO, the oxidation of CO and NH_3, and the exhaustive oxidation of hydrocarbons. On the other hand, n-type semiconductors are more active (than p-type) in H_2-D_2 exchange, the hydrogenation of ethylene and propylene, the dehydrogenation of butane, and the decomposition of H_2O_2 and ozone. This shows that it is difficult to predict (on the basis of the type of reaction involved) which type of semiconductor would accelerate a reaction. Moreover, we must bear in mind the fact that the above relationships are only statistical averages — they are observed only on the analysis of very large amounts of data. No predictions concerning the catalytic activity should be made on the basis of data on the type of conductivity if the data relate only to a small number of catalysts. This is apparently due to the fact that the various stages of a process may be accelerated both by electrons and by holes, and the rate-determining stage of a reaction may change in the transition from one catalyst to another.

The correlation coefficients for the c.a. with φ are lower than for the c.a. with ΔU. Thus, the electron work function and the conductivity type are less convenient to use as criteria for the selection of catalysts (as compared with ΔU and Δx). However, when the catalyst is modified by the introduction of the oxide of a metal having a different valence into the starting oxide, the change in conductivity should be taken into account since it may have a practical effect on the selection of the catalyst.

The fact that no correlation exists between the c.a. and $1/\varepsilon^2$ in the dehydrogenation of alcohols is apparently caused by the low degree of reliability of our knowledge of the value of ε. A correlation between the c.a. and $1/\varepsilon^2$, such as that shown by equations (1) and (2), has been observed for the oxidation of CO.

In some cases, such as the dehydrogenation of alcohols (see the table), a correlation exists between the c.a. and the lattice parameter; no such correlation has been observed in other cases (dehydration of isopropanol, $H_2 - D_2$ exchange, oxidation of CO, decomposition of N_2O). An analysis of the respective kinetic data shows that in cases in which a correlation exists between the c.a. and l, the pre-exponent k_0 in the Arrhenius equation has a reduced value. This may be attributed to the formation of two- or multiple-point complexes in the adsorption.

It should be noted that in none of the reactions discussed by us (on non-metallic catalysts) were we able to observe such anomalously high values of k_0, which could not be obtained on the basis of the Eyring theory of absolute rates. The compensation effect of the parallel changes in log k_0 and E is often observed at low temperatures or upon the introduction of modifying additives to the main catalyst substance. This has been attributed by the author /10/ to the fact that the catalytic process occurs near the transition point of the semiconductor (from impurity to intrinsic conductance) or, in more general terms, to the presence of two or several active centers.

On the other hand, a different behavior is more often encountered in high-temperature catalytic reactions — E changes while k_0 remains constant (within the limits of $1-3$ orders of magnitude). As an example, let us cite the experiments on the decomposition of NO on oxides at $750 - 1050°$ /20/. In these experiments E ranged from 16 to 60 kcal/mole, while log k_0 changed between 7.9 and 10.1. Similar data were obtained also for the decomposition of NH_3 on nitrides /21/, of $KClO_4$ on oxides /22/, etc.

In addition to the forbidden zone width, another important factor affecting the activity of catalysts of the oxidation-reduction type is the number of d-eletrons in the atoms or ions of the metal comprised in the catalyst. The clearest concepts on the type of relationship between the catalytic activity and the number of d-electrons have been based on the crystalline field theory /4/. The two-peak pattern describing the catalytic activity of oxides of elements belonging to the fourth period in $H_2 - D_2$ exchange reactions is one of the main experimental facts serving as the basis for the application of the crystalline field theory to catalysis /23/. Minima in the catalytic activity have been observed on the d^0 (e.g., for V_2O_5), d^5 (Fe_2O_3), and d^{10} (Cu_2O, ZnO) systems; and maxima on the d^3 (MnO_2) and d^7 (CoO) systems. It was found that the two-peak pattern describing the c.a. in the series of elements belonging to the fourth period is observed not only for $H_2 - D_2$ exchange but also for the recombination of O and H atoms, the homomolecular exchange of O_2, the exchange of oxygen with oxides,

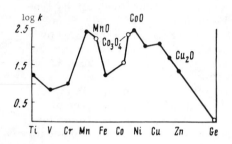

FIGURE 6. Changes in the catalytic activity of oxides of metals belonging to the fourth period, in the oxidation of CO.

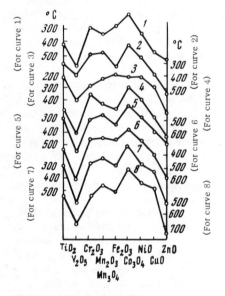

FIGURE 7. Changes in the catalytic activity of oxides of metals belonging to the fourth period, in the exhaustive oxidation of:

1- n-pentane; 2- pentene-2; 3- pentyne-1; 4- 2-methylbutane; 5- 2,3-dimethylbutane; 6- n-hexane; 7- cyclohexane; 8- benzene. The temperatures corresponding to the start of the reaction are plotted on the ordinates.

the dehydrogenation of ethanol and isopropanol, the decomposition of H_2O_2, N_2O, O_3, $KMnO_4$, $KClO_3$, $KClO_4$, and cycloparaffins, the oxidation of hydrogen, CO, and NH_3, the synthesis of HNO_3 from $NO + O_2 + H_2O$, the exhaustive oxidation of paraffins, cycloparaffins, and aromatic hydrocarbons, and the hydrolysis of HCN. As illustrative examples, we show on Figure 6 data /13/ on the oxidation of CO, and on Figure 7 — on the exhaustive oxidation of hydrocarbons: n-pentane, pentene, pentyne-1,2-methylbutane, 2,3-dimethylbutane, n-hexane, cyclohexane, benzene. It is evident that minima are obtained for the d^0, d^5, and d^{10} systems, although the minimum on d^5 (Fe_2O_3) is, as a rule, less pronounced than on d^0 and d^{10}.

The d^0, d^5, and d^{10} systems behave as the non-transition metals. To explain this fact, the crystalline field theory assumes that no energy stabilization or destabilization takes place (in weak-field approximation) during changes in coordination round the ions in the d^0, d^5, and d^{10} systems and round the ions of the non-transition metals. On other ions of the transition metals, an increase in the coordination number usually causes additional stabilization of the crystalline field energy (d-electron transfer to a lower energy level), while a decrease causes destabilization.

It is not known, a priori, whether an increase or a decrease in the coordination number occurs in the rate-determining stage of the catalysis. If a decrease occurs, the minimum endothermic effect would occur in the

90

d^0, d^5, and d^{10} systems (as in the non-transition metals), and these systems would have the greatest catalytic activity.

This author and Yu. E. Sinyak /24/ studied the polymerization of ethylene oxide on the oxides and hydroxides of various metals, and showed that the d^0, d^5, and d^{10} oxide systems, as well as oxides of the non-transition metals, are the most active catalysts for the above reaction. Figure 8 shows the pattern of catalytic activity (in the above reaction) for hydroxides of the elements belonging to the fourth period. The maximum activity was observed for hydroxides containing Ca^{2+}, Fe^{3+}, and Zn^{2+} ions. In the above case, an increase in the stabilization energy of the crystalline field did not favor the catalytic activity. Inclusion of monomer molecules (which are coordinated round the surface ions of the metal) in the growing polymer chain:

$$
\begin{array}{ccc}
\text{CH}_2-\text{CH}_2-\text{O}-\ldots & & \text{CH}_2-\text{CH}_2-\text{O}-\text{CH}_2-\text{CH}_2-\text{O}-\ldots \\
| & & | \\
\text{O} \quad \text{H}_2\text{C} & \rightarrow & \text{O} \\
| \quad \overset{\displaystyle\wedge}{} & & | \\
\text{Me}:\text{O}-\text{CH}_2 & & \text{Me}
\end{array}
$$

or, in other words, a decrease in the coordination number, takes place during the rate-determining stage of the catalytic process (chain growth). A very strong bond between the ligand — monomer molecule and the metal ion, which causes a decrease in the c.a., is formed in the $d^1 - d^4$ and $d^6 - d^9$ systems.

A decrease in the coordination number usually occurs in desorption, too. In this respect, it would be of interest to check the rules governing the selection of catalysts for reactions for which it is known that desorption is the rate-determining stage. On the basis of data from the literature, an "anti-Dowdenian" relationship, similar to the one shown in Figure 8 (i.e., with maximal c.a. for d^0, d^5, and d^{10}), has been observed by us for oxides of elements belonging to the fourth period, in the hydration of ethylene, the synthesis of acetone from acetaldehyde, the bromination of benzene, the dehydration of formic acid, and the interaction of toluyl diisocyanates with polyxydropropylene-triol. All these reactions, as well as the polymerization of ethylene oxide, are heterolytic. An indication that such a relationship may exist in homolytic reactions is found in the case of the dehydrogenation of HCOOH on oxides and the decomposition of

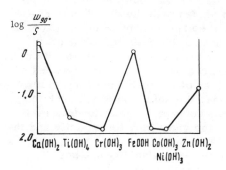

FIGURE 8. Changes in the specific catalytic activity $\log \dfrac{w_{90^\circ}}{s}$ (w_{90° is the reaction rate at 90°C and s is the surface area of the catalyst) of hydroxides of metals belonging to the fourth period in the polymerization of ethylene oxide.

NH_3 on nitrides. Since the data on the selection of catalysts for heterolytic reactions are much less reliable than for homolytic reactions, it is difficult to state at present to what extent the above conclusions are common to both types of reactions. It is very important at this stage to collect spectroscopic data indicating the type of $d-d$ transitions in adsorption and catalysis.

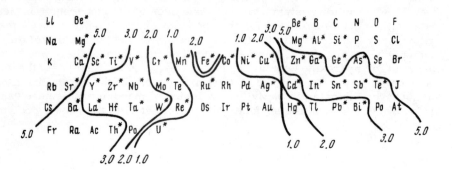

FIGURE 9. Dependence of the forbidden zone widths ΔU (eV) of oxides on the position of the metal in Mendeleev's periodic table; oxides used in the experiments are marked by an asterisk.

The concept of forbidden zone width in transition-metal oxides is not very clear. When we use the latest available values from the literature, the series of oxides of elements in the fourth period show minima for the d^3 — MnO_2 system (0.19 — 1.25 eV, according to different sources) and the d^7 system — CoO (0.68 eV), and maxima for the d^0 — TiO_2 (3.05 eV), d^5 — Fe_2O_3 (2.2 eV), and d^{10} — ZnO (3.3 eV) systems. Such a relationship may be explained by assuming that in these cases the forbidden zone covers the distance between the $2p$-band of oxygen and the lower $3d$-level of the metal. This level is lowered, which causes an increase in ΔU in the stabilization of the crystalline field in oxides with the $d^1 - d^4$ and $d^6 - d^9$ cation configurations. If this is true, the dependences of the c.a. on the number of d-electrons and on ΔU are not statistically independent.

Figure 9 shows the changes in ΔU for the most stable oxides within the whole periodic table. The curves limit regions that comprise oxides of metals having the above-mentioned values of the forbidden zone width.

In the analysis of acid-base reactions, the selection of catalysts may be based, at first approximation, on the concept of the difference in electronegativities Δx; the larger Δx, the greater is the basicity and the lower is the acidity of the solid oxide catalyst.

A relationship between the c.a. and the Lewis acidity has been established with reliability for a series of acid-type reactions.

According to Lewis, metal atoms that are able to attach to themselves electron pairs from the reacting basic substance serve as active centers. This ability increases with increasing polarizing action of the cation, which is determined by the ratio of the square of the charge to the radius e^2/r. In fact, in the above-mentioned polymerization of ethylene oxide, the c.a. increases with increasing e^2/r.

The surface oxygen ion serves as the active center in reactions catalyzed by solid basic oxides. In some cases an increase in the excess charge on this ion leads to the creation of a catalytic activity (for homolytic reactions) in solid bases.

BIBLIOGRAPHY

1. VOL'KENSHTEIN, F.F. Elektronnaya teoriya kataliza na poluprovodnikakh (The Electronic Theory of Catalysis on Semiconductors). — Moskva, Fizmatizdat. 1960.

2. HAUFFE, K. Reactions in Solids and on Their Surfaces. [Russian translation. 1962.]

3. BALANDIN, A.A. Mul'tipletnaya teoriya kataliza (The Multiplet Theory of Catalysis). Part 1. — Moskva, MGU. 1963.

4. DOWDEN, D.A. and D. WELLS. Actes 2-me Congrès International de Catalyse, Vol.2: 1499. Paris, Technip. 1961.

5. IOFFE, I.I. and S.Z. ROGINSKII. — ZhFKh, Vol.31: 612. 1957.

6. TOPCHIEVA, K.V. — Problemy Kinetiki i Kataliza, Vol.10: 247. 1960.

7. OBLAD, A.G., T.H. MILLIKEN, and G.A. MILLS. — Adv. Catalysis, Vol.3: 199. 1951.

8. KRYLOV, O.V. and S.Z. ROGINSKII. — DAN SSSR, Vol.118: 526. 1958.

9. KRYLOV, O.V. and E.A. FOKINA. — ZhFKh, Vol.35: 851. 1961.

10. KRYLOV, O.V. and E.A. FOKINA. — Kinetika i Kataliz, Vol.5: 284. 1963.

11. PEARSON, W.B. — ZhFKhO im. D.I. Mendeleeva, Vol.5: 493. 1961.

12. IOFFE, A.F. Fizika poluprovodnikov (The Physics of Semiconductors). — Moskva, Izd. AN SSSR. 1956.

13. KRYLOV, O.V. — Kinetika i Kataliz, Vol.3: 502. 1962.

14. DUNIN-BARKOVSKII, I.V. and N.V. SMIRNOV. Teoriya veroyatnostei i matematicheskaya statistika v tekhnike (The Theory of Probability and Mathematical Statistics in Technology). — Moskva, Gostekhizdat. 1955.

15. KRYLOV, O.V. Kataliz nemetallami. Zakonomernosti podbora katalizatorov (Catalysis by Nonmetals. Rules Governing the Selection of Catalysts). — Moskva, Izd. "Khimiya". 1966.

16. DZISYAK, A.P., G.K. BORESKOV, and L.A. KASATKINA. — Kinetika i Kataliz, Vol.3: 81. 1962.

17. KRYLOW, O.W., J.N. RUFOW, E.A. FOKINA, and W.M. FROLOW. Kataliza i Kinetyka Chemiczna, p.100. Warszawa. 1960.

18. NAGAEV, E.L. — ZhFKh, Vol.35: 327. 1961.

19. SYRKIN, Ya.K. — Uspekhi Khimii, Vol.31: 397. 1962.

20. FRAZER, J.M. and F. DANIELS. — J. Phys. Chem., Vol.62: 215. 1958.

21. LOTZ, C.B. and F. SEBBA. — Trans. Faraday Soc., Vol.53: 1246. 1957.

22. SOLYMOSI, F. and N. KRIX. — Acta chim. Hung., Vol.37: 241. 1962.

23. STEIN, K.C., J.J. FEENAN, G.P. THOMPSON, J.F. SHULTZ, L.J.E. HOFER, and R.B. ANDERSON. — Ind. Eng. Chem., Vol.52: 671. 1960.

24. KRYLOV, O.V. and Yu.E. SINYAK. — Neftekhimiya, Vol.2: 668. 1962.

B. V. Erofeev, E. F. Ivan'kevich, and N. V. Nikiforova

CATALYSIS AND THE LIGAND FIELD THEORY

In this paper we want to show, on the basis of a few examples, how the ligand field theory often improves the understanding of the well-known but insufficiently explained experimental facts that characterize the action of some types of catalysts. We shall use only those assumptions and conclusions of the ligand field theory that have already shown their usefulness in the analysis of other problems of the chemistry of transition metals.

The field of heterogeneous catalysis is extensive and varied from the point of view of both the types of catalysts used and the types of reactions occurring on them. The catalysts include metals, semiconductors, binary compounds, predominantly or partially ionic crystals, and complex compounds. Catalysts on carriers are an important type.

At present, the description of the chemical bonds in metals, ionic and molecular crystals, and complex compounds is still based on different models. We would be right to assume that the different types of chemical bonds in solids are exhibited also in heterogeneous catalysis processes. This situation is reflected in the existing theories of catalysis. The multiplet theory /1/ accepts in the first place the concept of valence-chemical bonds, while the electronic theory of catalysis on semiconductors /2/ accepts the idea of adsorption-chemical bonds formed through the participation of conductivity electrons and of holes. These concepts on the nature of the chemical bond leading to the formation of activated transition complexes on the catalyst surface are not, of course, the only (or even the most important) characteristics of the respective theories. For instance, the multiplet theory is based primarily on the stereochemistry of the catalytic process — the spatial relations and the principle of structural correspondence between the arrangement of atoms in the reacting molecules and the symmetry of atoms on the catalyst surface.

Other theories of catalysis (e.g., the theory of catalytically active groups /3/) discuss those features of catalytic phenomena that do not require an accurate answer to the problem of the nature of the chemical bond. However, even in this case (as in the case of any other theory of catalysis) it is, ultimately, impossible not to use the concept of a reaction between the substrate and the catalyst.

In recent years, the theory of the chemical bond has achieved new and important advances. Advances have been made in the ligand field theory, resulting from theoretical and semiempirical generalizations of the theory of molecular orbitals on the one hand and of the crystalline field theory on the other hand /4 — 7/. At present, the theory of chemical valence bonds is regarded only as a particular case of the theory of molecular orbitals /8/. The same is true also with respect to the crystalline field theory /8/. In this respect, the theory of chemical valence bonds and the crystalline field theory are parts of the ligand field theory. The latter theory is, in the first place, the theory of the chemical bond in compounds of the transition metals, i.e., of metals whose properties are determined to a great extent by the d-electrons. It is well known that these metals are of great importance in heterogeneous catalysis.

Thus, it is natural to apply the ligand field theory to the analysis of the mechanism of catalysis. This has already been done to a certain extent with respect to homogeneous catalytic reactions, by researchers such as F. Basolo, R.G. Pearson, Taube, etc. /9, 10/. It should be noted that in some cases the analysis of heterogeneous catalytic reactions from the standpoint of the ligand field theory could possibly lead to a noticeable lessening of the differences between the concepts of heterogeneous and homogeneous catalysis. In this respect, a characteristic reaction is the catalytic polymerization of ethylene on Ziegler catalysts consisting of $TiCl_3$ and trialkylaluminum. This reaction has been discussed from the standpoint of the ligand field theory in a recent paper by P. Cosse /11/; we cannot, however, deal with this paper or with the paper of D. Dowden and D. Wells /12/, which is apparently the first paper in which the problems of heterogeneous catalysis are discussed from the standpoint of the ligand field theory. In /11/ and /12/ the ligand field theory is used to discuss the nature of the intermediate transition complexes formed between the catalyst and the substrate.

However, the ligand field theory leads to a better understanding of other problems important for heterogeneous catalysis, including the role of carriers in the catalytic activity of the metals carried on them. This problem is the main subject of our paper.

The important role of carriers as factors that increase the activity and selectivity of catalysts is well known. One of the most important carriers — γ-alumina — became of especially great importance after the preparation (by N.D. Zelinskii /13/) of the Ni/Al_2O_3 catalyst, which is particularly suitable for the hydrogenation of aromatic rings and the dehydrogenation of alicyclic compounds. Subsequently, γ-Al_2O_3 assumed exceptional importance as a carrier for commercial dehydrocyclization catalysts. However, we do not know even now the reason for the exceptional importance of γ-Al_2O_3 as a carrier for the above catalysts (for example, see /14/).

The existing theories of catalysis regard the carriers mostly as inert supports, which should have a large specific surface and good mechanical and thermal stabilities. On this basis, however, we cannot understand the specific action of the carriers. It may be explained by assuming that a certain reaction takes place between the atoms or ions of the metal (on the carrier) and the crystal lattice of the carrier, and this interaction leads to the incorporation of metal ions into the surface layer of the crystal lattice of the carrier.

We shall discuss oxide carriers of the Al_2O_3, SiO_2, MgO, and other types. The arrangement of the metal in these oxides corresponds, in most cases, to a coordination of its atoms with six or four oxygen atoms, yielding frequently an octahedral or tetrahedral symmetry.

Some oxide systems may contain at the same time two types of coordinated ions and, correspondingly, two types of symmetry; this has been observed in spinel structures, which may be assumed to include γ-Al_2O_3. In spinel structures, the oxygen ions form a face-centered lattice with octahedral and tetrahedral vacancies. In $MgAl_2O_4$ spinel all octahedral vacancies are occupied by Al atoms, while the tetrahedral sites are occupied by Mg atoms; in γ-Al_2O_3 the aluminum atoms occupy all the octahedral and some of the tetrahedral positions. The structure of spinel lattices is shown in Figure 1.

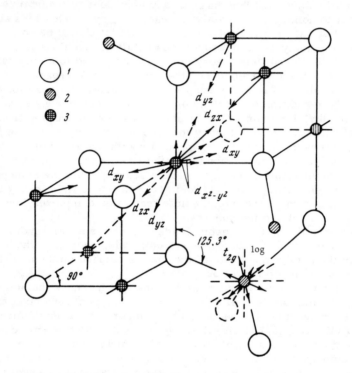

FIGURE 1. Octahedral and tetrahedral positions of the atoms in spinel structures:

The arrows show the orientation of the a-orbit. 1- oxygen atoms; 2- tetrahedral positions of the atoms; 3- octahedral positions of the atoms.

The introduction of a transition metal atom or ion (in the preparation of catalysts we deal with ions) into the carrier lattice is accompanied by the splitting of five d-electron orbitals. In octahedral and tetrahedral ligand fields those five orbitals are split into two groups: three t_{2g} orbitals and two t_e orbitals, as shown in Figure 2. In a lower-symmetry ligand field, the splitting is more complicated.

The distance between two groups of orbitals (denoted by $10Dq$) is an important characteristic that determines the ligand-field stabilization of an ion in the lattice. This stabilization depends, however, also on the distribution of d-electrons in the orbitals, which is determined in the first place by the Khund [sic] law and, in the second place, by the ligand field strength. In the case of an octahedral field we have an unequivocal distribution for the following numbers of d-electrons: 1, 2, 3, 8, 9, and 10. In the case of 4, 5, 6, and 7 d-electrons the distributions are different for weak and strong ligand fields. In the case of a tetrahedral field two different distributions exist for 3, 4, 5, and 6 d-electrons. Thus, the energy of stabilization of an ion in a lattice depends on the ligand field strength (which, however, is related to the valence of the metal ion). The energy of ligand-field stabilization in the case of a strong field equals $-4nDq$ for a number of electrons $n \leqslant 6$ and $-24Dq + 6(n-6)Dq$ for $n > 6$.

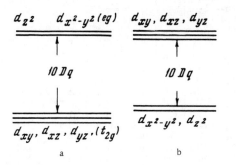

FIGURE 2. Splitting of the d-orbitals in octahedral (a) and tetrahedral (b) fields.

In a weak octahedral ligand field the energy of stabilization is equal to Dq multiplied by 4 for the d^1 and d^6 configurations, by 6 for the d^2, d^4, d^7, and d^9 configurations, and by 12 for d^3 and d^8. In a weak tetrahedral field Dq is multiplied by 4 for d^4 and d^9, by 6 for d^1, d^3, d^6, and d^8, and by 12 for d^2 and d^7. The values of $10Dq$, which are required for the calculation of the energy of stabilization in the case of an octahedral field, are determined from the absorption spectra of the ions in compounds with an octahedral coordination. For a tetrahedral configuration, experimental values of $10Dq$ are not available for most ions, but the value of Dq in a tetrahedral field is approximately equal to 4/9 of the Dq for the octahedral field. The values of the stabilization energies have been calculated by D. McClure /15/ and L. Orgel /16/ for the ions in the first transition series of the periodic table. The calculations for octahedral and tetrahedral fields were made by assuming a weak ligand field, except in the cases of Co^{2+}, Ni^{2+}, V^{3+}, and Cr^{3+} ions. A strong field was assumed to exist in the cases of Co^{2+} and V^{3+} for an octahedral field, and of Ni^{2+} and Cr^{3+} for a tetrahedral field. The results are shown in the table.

A comparison between the ligand-field stabilizations in octahedral and tetrahedral fields indicates, in the first place, that the stabilization in an octahedral field is much stronger than in a tetrahedral field. The difference is especially pronounced in the cases of the normal valence states Cr^{3+} and Ni^{2+}. This explains why γ-Al_2O_3 is particularly suitable for chromium and nickel catalysts; it is due to the fact that γ-Al_2O_3 has the spinel structure with octahedral positions that are occupied by chromium and nickel ions in the surface layer of Cr/Al_2O_3 and Ni/Al_2O_3 catalysts. At the same time, silica gel (which has no octahedral sites that could be occupied by metal ions) did not find such an extensive use as a carrier for chromium and nickel catalysts. A rather large difference between the stabilization energies in octahedral and tetrahedral fields exists also in the cases of V^{2+} and Mn^{3+}, i.e., for valence states (of the above metals) that are not used or are used only rarely for the preparation of catalysts. In the cases of Ti^{4+}, Mn^{2+}, Fe^{3+}, and Zn^{2+} the stabilization energies in ligand fields of any symmetry are equal to zero. For this reason there are only few uses for methods for the preparation of catalysts based on the above metals on carriers.

Energies of the ligand-field stabilization of ions of the first transition series, according to D. Mac Lure /15/ and L. Orgel /16/

No. of electrons	Ion	Fundamental state of the ion			Dq, cm^{-1}		Stabilization energy, kcal/mole		Excess of E_{oct} over E_{tetr}, kcal/mole
		free	in octa-hedral field	in tetra-hedral field	in octa-hedral field	in tetra-hedral field	in octa-hedral field (E_{oct})	in tetra-hedral field (E_{tetr})	
0	Ti^{4+}	^1s	$^1A_{1g}$	$^1A_{1g}$	0	0	0	0	0
1	Ti^{3+}	^2d	$^2T_{2g}$	^3E_g	2030	900	20.9	14.0	6.9
2	V^{3+}	^3f	$^3T_{1g}$	$^3A_{2g}$	1800	840	38.3	25.5	12.8 *
3	V^{2+}	^4f	$^4A_{2g}$	$^4T_{1g}$	1180	520	40.2	8.7	31.5
	Cr^{3+}	^4f	$^4A_{2g}$	$^4T_{1g}$	1770	780	53.7	16.0	37.7 *
4	Cr^{2+}	^5d	^5E_g	$^5T_{2g}$	1400	620	24.0	7.0	17.0
	Mn^{3+}	^5d	^5E_g	$^5T_{2g}$	2100	930	32.4	9.6	22.8
5	Mn^{2+}	^6s	$^6A_{1g}$	$^6A_{1g}$	750	330	0	0	0
	Fe^{3+}	^6s	$^6A_{1g}$	$^6A_{1g}$	1400	620	0	0	0
6	Fe^{2+}	^5d	$^5T_{2g}$	^5E_g	1000	440	11.9	7.9	4.0 *
	Co^{3+}	^5d	$^1A_{1g}$	^5E_g	—	780	45	26	19
7	Co^{2+}	^4f	$^4T_{1g}$	$^4A_{2g}$	1000	440	22.2	14.8	7.4 *
8	Ni^{2+}	^3f	$^3A_{2g}$	$^3T_{1g}$	860	380	29.2	8.6	20.6 *
9	Cu^{2+}	^2d	^2E_g	$^2T_{2g}$	1300	580	21.6	6.4	15.2 *
10	Zn^{2+}	^1s	$^1A_{1g}$	$^1A_{1g}$	0	0	0	0	0

* The values marked by an asterisk are taken from Orgel /16/, the remaining values are from McClure /15/.

The data in the table show that, for instance, chromium catalysts for dehydrocyclization may be prepared not only on γ-alumina but also on other refractory oxide systems that contain cationic sites with an octahedral symmetry. In this respect, it would be of interest to study the use (as carrier for chromium oxide dehydrocyclization catalysts) of spinel $MgAl_2O_4$, in view of the similarity between its crystalline structure and that of γ-Al_2O_3 (in γ-Al_2O_3 we have a = 7.9 Å, while in $MgAl_2O_4$ a = 8.05 — 8.10 Å /17/).

We carried out such an investigation. The results of some experiments are presented in Figure 3, which shows that from the standpoint of product yields the dehydrocyclization of n-hexane on chromium oxide catalysts carried on $MgAl_2O_4$ proceeds in the same way as on chromium catalysts carried on γ-alumina.

The investigation of the catalytic activity of chromium oxide catalysts carried on $MgAl_2O_4$ is of interest, in particular in view of the fact that the results of a spectroscopic study of the states of Cr in spinel have been published recently. R. Stahl-Brada and W. Low /18/ studied the EPR spectrum of Cr^{3+} in natural $MgAl_2O_4$ crystals and showed that the Cr^{3+} ions in the spinel occupy the octahedral vacancies subjected to trigonal deformation along the (111) direction of the unit cell.

A. Ford and O. Hill /19/ studied the optical spectrum of Cr^{3+} in $MgAl_2O_4$ and found that it resembles the spectrum of Cr^{3+} in α-Al_2O_3 (ruby), the only difference being that the spectrum of Cr^{3+} in spinel did not exhibit the anisotropy exhibited by the spectrum of Cr^{3+} in α-Al_2O_3. The absence of anisotropy in the spectrum of Cr^{3+} in spinel is caused by the fact that the trigonal deformations associated with the sites of Cr^{3+} ions in the spinel lattice are oriented along all four (111) diagonals in the cubic unit cell. As a result, the cubic cell of the spinel increases in size but maintains its cubic structure and isotropy.

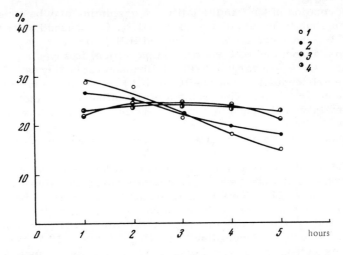

FIGURE 3. Dehydrocyclization of n-hexane on chromium catalyst carried on spinel and on γ-alumina:

11—13 g (23 ml) of the catalyst containing 13.7% Cr_2O_3; n-hexane supply rate equal to 0.1 g/min. The figures on the ordinate indicate the concentration (in the catalyst) of benzene (1, 2) and unsaturated hydrocarbons (3,4) in percent; 1, 3- catalyst on spinel; 2, 4- catalyst on γ-alumina.

Since the crystalline structure of γ-Al_2O_3 is analogous to that of spinel, it can be expected that the Cr^{3+} ions in the γ-Al_2O_3 will remain within a cubic field. On the other hand the Cr^{3+} introduced into the lattice of α-Al_2O_3 (ruby) lies within a trigonal symmetry field.

These results should be related to literature data concerning the fact that α-alumina is not a suitable carrier for chromium oxide catalysts for dehydrocyclization.

Thus, according to R. Archibald and B. Greensfelder [14], the preparation of highly active dehydrocyclization catalysts requires the use of γ-Al_2O_3. H. Taylor [20], in his introductory lecture at the First International Congress on Catalysis, spoke of this as follows: "We can write skillfully the mechanisms whereby a paraffinic hydrocarbon can be transformed to an aromatic hydrocarbon, but we are as yet unable to say why the chromium and molybdenum oxides must be spread upon γ-alumina rather than α-alumina for successful cyclization."

In view of the above data, this question may be answered as follows: in γ-alumina and spinel the chromium ions that penetrate into the surface layer of the catalyst lie within a cubic ligand field, although a trigonal field is superimposed uniformly on the cubic field (along the cube diagonals). In α-Al_2O_3 the chromium ions that enter the lattice lie within a strong trigonal field, which is exhibited by the anisotropy of the spectrum of a ruby as found by A. Ford and O. Hill [21]. Thus, when used as carriers,

γ-Al_2O_3 and α-Al_2O_3 differ with respect to the deviation in the symmetry of Cr^{3+} from an octahedral symmetry when it is introduced into the rhombohedral lattice of α-Al_2O_3.

The deformation of Cr^{3+} in the lattice of α-alumina may be considered from a somewhat different point of view. B.N. Grechushnikov and P.P. Feofilov /22/, and more recently Ford and Hill /21/ found that oscillation of the ε_u type (associated with the α-alumina lattice) is superimposed on the ^4E band of Cr^{3+}. According to C. Ballhausen /23/, this is a direct proof of the existence of a Jahn-Teller effect leading to a deformation of the ^4E state of Cr^{3+} ions. The problem of the influence of deformation of transition metal ions (caused by the Jahn-Teller effect) will be discussed again below.

Molybdenum carried on γ-Al_2O_3 is another important dehydrocyclization catalyst.

From the standpoint of its spectrum characteristics, trivalent Mo^{3+}, with a coordination number six, is completely analogous to the octahedral complex Cr^{3+} ions /24/. This is in agreement with the fact that these two ions have the same electron configurations. According to H. Hartmann and H. Schmidt /24/ the value of $10Dq$ for hydrated Mo^{3+} ions is $16,000$ cm^{-1}, while the value for Cr^{3+} (according to L. Orgel /16/) is $17,700$ cm^{-1}. Thus, it could be expected that the similar catalytic properties of molybdenum oxide and chromium oxide catalysts are due to the similarity in the electronic structures of Mo^{3+} and Cr^{3+}. In particular, this should explain also the similar behavior of γ-alumina as a carrier for these two catalysts. Unfortunately, no spectroscopic data are available as yet on the state of Mo introduced into spinels.

A comparison of the states of Cr^{3+} ions in spinel and corundum (α-Al_2O_3) lattices indicates that the catalytic activity of the chromium depends on the symmetry of the electronic configuration of the catalytically active ion or atom /25/.

Let us examine the above problem, using the case of chromium oxide dehydrocyclization catalysts as an example. On the basis of experimental investigations of chromium catalysts, it may be assumed that in dehydrocyclization at least part of the chromium on the surface of the chromium oxide catalyst is in a reduced state. Chromium catalysts are activated only after prolonged treatment in hydrogen or hydrocarbon atmospheres. Although the reaction: $Cr_2O_3 + 3H_2 \rightleftharpoons 2Cr + 3H_2O$ is characterized (at the temperatures of dehydrocyclization on crystalline chromium oxide) by low values of the equilibrium constant $K = p_{H_2O}/p_{H_2}$ of the order of $10^{-11} - 10^{-12}$ /26/, the same constant should have a much higher value in the case of the active chromium oxide used as catalyst. This corresponds to the large thermal effect accompanying the transformation of amorphous chromium oxide into the crystalline form. According to L. Wöhler and M. Rabinowitsch /27/, the heat of transformation of amorphous Cr_2O_3 to the crystalline state is $1200 - 1650$ cal/mole. Since this heat is associated with a decrease in the specific surface, and assuming that the surface molecules of chromium oxide in the active catalyst account for $1/100$ of the total number of molecules, we find that the heat of transformation is more than $120,000$ cal/mole, which yields for the constant a value greater than unity.

A.A. Balandin and I.D. Rozhdestvenskaya /28/ concluded on the basis of their experiments that the surface layer of the chromium oxide is reduced in hydrogen or hydrocarbon vapor atmospheres. This result is very important since it makes it possible to assume that the formation of the transition complex starts from the neutral state of the chromium atom $Cr3d^54s$. Although the above results have been obtained for chromium oxide catalysts without a carrier, they could naturally be applied to catalysts on carriers since the catalytic activity in a reaction should be due to active centers of the same type. As an example of such a reaction let us examine the simpler process of cyclohexane dehydrogenation.

In a spinel lattice, the octahedral positions occupied by chromium atoms could be regarded as lying over the (111) face occupied by oxygen atoms at a height $\left(\dfrac{\sqrt{3}}{2} - \dfrac{\sqrt{3}}{3}\right)\dfrac{a}{2} = 0.145\,a = 1.2\,\text{Å}$ over the centers of the triangles whose vertices and positions at the middle of its sides are occupied by oxygen atoms. In this case the distance to the nearest oxygen atoms is $2.0\,\text{Å}$. The reduction of the surface layer of the catalyst involves the occupation of the above positions by chromium atoms. The superposition of a flat six-atom ring of carbon atoms leads to the creation of pseudooctahedral symmetry and the formation of a transition complex in which a benzene ring lies over the chromium atoms, while the hydrogen atoms are drawn towards the adjacent atoms of the catalyst. The arrangement of the benzene ring formed in this case corresponds to the arrangement of the benzene ring in dibenzenechromium and other diaryl-chromium compounds.

The chemical bond formed in the above case between the chromium atom and the benzene ring may be compared to the bond between the benzene ring and the chromium atom in a dibenzenechromium molecule. The structure of this compound has been discussed by R. Berry /29/. According to Berry, the superposition of two benzene rings on a chromium atom leads to the creation of a pseudooctahedral symmetry that causes splitting of the d-orbitals. Two benzene rings occupy sites on the opposite triangular faces of the octahedron, and as a result the exact overall symmetry is D_{6h}, but with respect to the chromium atom it may be regarded as octahedral. Figure 4 shows these relationships in a dibenzenechromium molecule.

The chemical bond formed between the chromium atom and the benzene rings does not have the characteristics of chemical valence bonds. The formation of dibenzenechromium molecules requires the simultaneous interaction of all d-electrons of the chromium atom with all π-electrons of the benzene ring. No chemical valence bonds exists in dibenzenechromium and other analogous compounds.

However, the formation of a compound is possible only if a certain type of electron configuration symmetry exists in the metal atom. The discussion of the formation of dibenzenechromium from a chromium atom and benzene is based on an assumption of the existence of an initial octahedral symmetry. In reality, the overall symmetry of the transition complex is of a lower degree, even in the case of dibenzenechromium. The symmetry is even lower in the case of a chromium atom lying over the (111) plane of a spinel lattice. In the above case, the existing state is comparable to that existing in the case of benzenetricarbonylchromium. Here the D_{3d} symmetry is exactly the same as in the case of the surface transition complex assumed by us. However, the results of spectroscopic studies (see R. Berry /29/) show that the splitting of the levels and the type of bonds formed in benzene-tricarbonylchromium are the same as in dibenzenechromium. This makes it possible to apply the scheme of Berry to the formation of a transition complex on the catalyst surface.

According to the theory developed here, the catalytic activity of chromium in reactions involving six-atom rings requires conditions that lead to a certain type of symmetry in the intermediate complex. If this is correct, then other metal ions characterized by a stability in an octahedral ligand field should be suitable catalysts for the hydrogenation of aromatic rings, dehydrogenation of cyclohexane and its derivatives, and for dehydrocyclization reactions, i.e., reactions that will be designated below as reactions with six-atom rings. Finally, it may be found that catalytic activity is affected by other factors, too.

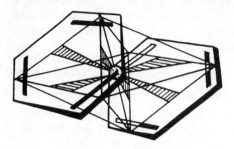

FIGURE 4. The structure of dibenzenechromium according to Berry /29/:

The shaded bands indicate the orientation of the t_{2g} orbital.

By reexamining the table (see p. 98) showing the stabilization energies of ions in an octahedral field, we find that in such a field the following ions have a zero stabilization energy: Ti^{4+}, Mn^{2+}, Fe^{3+}, and Zn^{2+}, i.e., metals that are known to be unsuitable as catalysts for reactions involving six-atom rings. The energy of stabilization of Fe^{2+} is not equal to zero, but is still so low (11 kcal/mole) that iron (like zinc) should not be considered as a catalyst for reactions involving six-atom rings.

Certain other metals should also be excluded from the list of possible catalysts, on the basis of the unstability of their ions with respect to the Jahn-Teller effect. The different d-electron configurations of transition metal ions are affected to different extents by the Jahn-Teller effect. This is exhibited, in particular, as deviations from the octahedral symmetry. According to Ch. Jörgensen /30/, the following electron configurations are stable with respect to the Jahn-Teller effect in an octahedral field:

$$d^3\;{}^4A_2 t_{2g}^3;$$
$$d^5\;{}^6A_1 t_{2g}^3 e_g^2 \text{ (spin-free)}$$
$$d^6\;{}^1A_1 t_{2g}^6 \text{ (spin-paired)}$$
$$d^8\;{}^3A_2 t_{2g}^6 e_g^2 \text{ (spin-free)}$$
$$d^{10}\;{}^1A_1 t_{2g}^6 e_g^4.$$

According to the above, catalysts containing V^{3+}, Ti^{4+}, Ti^{3+}, Cr^{2+}, Mn^{3+}, Co^{2+}, Ni^{3+}, and Cu^{2+} ions could not serve as catalysts for reactions involving six-atom rings. Since V^{2+}, Cr^{3+}, Co^{3+}, and Ni^{2+} ions are stable with respect to the Jahn-Teller effect, these metals may be considered as catalysts for six-atom rings. Thus, among the metals in the first transition group, only vanadium, chromium, cobalt, and nickel may be considered as catalysts for reactions with six-atom rings. The remaining metals cannot serve as active catalysts for such reactions. However, since the Jahn-Teller effect may be exhibited to different extents, depending on the type of ligand used, some of the "excluded" metals may serve as weakly-active catalysts for such reactions, under the conditions of relative stabilization of the octahedral configuration.

In this respect, copper is of great interest. It is known to have octahedral complexes, which however are often distorted to a great or lesser extent. According to P. Emmet and N. Skau /31/, V. Ipatiev and B. Corson /32/, and others, pure metallic copper has a negligible catalytic activity in the hydrogenation of benzene. It should be noted that the above authors investigated the behavior of copper without carriers.

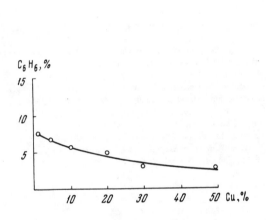

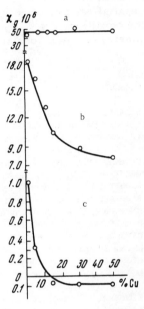

FIGURE 5. Dehydrogenation of cyclohexane on copper carried on magnesium oxide:

at 350°C; cyclohexane supply rate 0.066 g/min. The abscissa shows the copper concentration in the catalyst, and the yield of benzene is plotted on the ordinate.

FIGURE 6. Magnetic susceptibility (χ_g) of copper in copper catalysts carried on magnesium oxide:

a- non-reduced catalyst (copper formate on magnesium oxide); b- reduced catalysts; c- reduced and reoxidized catalysts.

In connection with this, we carried out a series of investigations on the determination of the catalytic activity of copper carried on γ-Al_2O_3 and MgO, on which we could expect stabilization of the copper ions in the octahedral field of the oxygen atoms of the carrier and, hence, the appearance of catalytic activity in the copper. We found indeed (see Figure 5) that copper carried on MgO and γ-Al_2O_3 causes the dehydrogenation of cyclohexane, and that the specific [catalytic] activity of the copper increases with decreasing copper concentration on the carrier. The above result may be interpreted as an increase in the relative fraction of copper atoms stabilized in the octahedral sites of the surface layer of the carrier as a result of the decrease in the amount of copper. An increase in the number of isolated and stabilized copper atoms or ions is indicated also by the appearance of paramagnetism in catalysts on carriers with a low copper concentration, and by the increase in paramagnetism with decreasing concentration. The respective data are shown in Figure 6.

The results reported in this paper show that the predictions concerning the catalytic activity of metals belonging to the first transition group and based on the ligand field theory, with respect to reactions involving six-atom rings, agree with the predictions of the multiplet theory. This agreement indicates that the conditions of structural correspondence and the spatial relations set up by the multiplet theory are inherently related to the conditions set up by the ligand field theory with respect to the symmetry of metal ions and atoms in a catalyst.

BIBLIOGRAPHY

1. BALANDIN, A. A. Mul'tipletnaya teoriya kataliza (The Multiplet Theory of Catalysis). Part 1, p. 8. — Moskva, Izd. MGU. 1963.
2. VOL'KENSHTEIN, F. F. Elektronnaya teoriya kataliza na poluprovodnikakh (The Electronic Theory of Catalysis on Semiconductors), p. 26. — Moskva, Goskhimizdat. 1960.
3. KOBOZEV, N. I. — Uspekhi Khimii, Vol. 25: 545. 1956.
4. GRIFFITH, J. S. and L. E. ORGEL. — Quart. Rev., Vol. 9: 381. 1957.
5. GRIFFITH, J. S. Theory of Transition-Metal Ions. London. 1960.
6. BALLHAUSEN, C. Introduction to Ligand Field Theory. [Russian translation. 1964.]
7. JÖRGENSEN, Ch. K. Orbitals in Atoms and Molecules. New York-London. 1962.
8. BALLHAUSEN, C. Introduction to Ligand Field Theory. [Russian translation. 1964.]
9. BASOLO, F. and R. G. PEARSON. Mechanisms of Inorganic Reactions. New York. 1958.
10. Modern Chemistry of the Coordination Compounds. [Russian translation. 1963.]
11. COSSE, P. — J. Catalysis, Vol. 3: 80. 1964.
12. DOWDEN, D. A. and D. WELLS. Actes du 2-me Congrès International de Catalyse, p. 1499. Paris, Technip. 1961.
13. ZELINSKY, N. D. and W. I. KOMAREWSKY. — Ber., Vol. 58: 1298. 1925.
14. ARCHIBALD, R. C. and B. S. GREENSFELDER. — Ind. End. Chem., Vol. 37: 356. 1945.
15. McCLURE, D. S. — J. Phys. Chem. Solids, Vol. 3: 311. 1957.
16. DUNITZ, I. D. and L. E. ORGEL. — J. Phys. Chem. Solids, Vol. 3: 318. 1957.
17. LANDOLT−BORNSTEIN. Zahlenwerte von Funktionen, Vol. 1, Part 3, p. 105. — Springer-Verlag. Berlin.
18. STAHL- BRADA, R. and W. LOW. — Phys. Rev., Vol. 116: 561. 1959.
19. FORD, A. A. and O. F. HILL. — Spectrochim. Acta, Vol. 16: 1318. 1960.
20. TAYLOR, H. S. — Adv. Catalysis, Vol. 9: 6. 1957.
21. FORD, A. A. and O. F. HILL. — Spectrochim. Acta, Vol. 16: 493. 1960.
22. GRECHUSHNIKOV, B. N. and P. P. FEOFILOV. — ZhETF, Vol. 29: 384. 1955.
23. BALLHAUSEN, C. Introduction to Ligand Field Theory. [Russian translation. 1964.]
24. HARTMANN, H. and H. J. SCHMIDT. — Z. phys. Chem. (N. F.), Vol. 11: 234. 1957.
25. ORGEL, L. E. An Introduction to Transition-Metal Chemistry, p. 114. London-New York. 1960.
26. Gmelins Handbuch der anorganischen Chemie, Syst. Numm. 52. 8. Auflage, p. 44. Leipzig. 1962.
27. WÖHLER, L. and M. RABINOWITSCH. — Koll. Z., Vol. 38: 111. 1926.
28. BALANDIN, A. A. and I. D. ROZHDESTVENSKAYA. — ZhFKh, Vol. 34: 1336. 1960.
29. BERRY, R. S. — J. Chem. Phys., Vol. 35: 29. 1961.
30. JÖRGENSEN, Ch. K. Orbitals in Atoms and Molecules, p. 44. New York-London. 1962.
31. EMMET, P. H. and N. J. SKAU. — J. Am. Chem. Soc., Vol. 65: 1059. 1943.
32. IPATIEV, V. N. and B. B. CORSON. — J. Phys. Chem., Vol. 45: 431. 1941.
33. BOND, G. C. Catalysis of Metals, p. 38. London-New York. 1962.

A. L. Klyachko-Gurvich and A. M. Rubinshtein

DEPENDENCE OF THE SPECIFIC SURFACE ON THE COMPOSITION OF BINARY OXIDE SYSTEMS

The problem of texture control is of great importance for the development of the fundamental principles of the synthesis of catalysts with predetermined properties. Special promoters are often added to the catalyst in order to increase its specific surface; however, it is still not known how the surface area changes with changes in the chemical composition. In this paper we have made an attempt to correlate the existing data on this problem for binary oxide systems.

In the first place, we must clarify what determines the specific surface of a pure oxide. It is well known that the specific surface depends on the method and conditions of preparation of the oxide. When the oxide is prepared by a series of consecutive stages, the conditions in each stage affect to a greater or lesser extent the surface area of the final product. The fact that the specific surface depends on the nature of the oxide itself is taken into account much less frequently. Different oxides prepared under identical conditions have different specific surfaces. Thus, when prepared by ignition of the respective hydroxides at temperatures not exceeding $400 - 500°$, silica gel has a specific surface of $300 - 500$ m^2/g, Al_2O_3 $150 - 300$, MgO $50 - 100$, NiO $20 - 40$, Cr_2O_3 and Fe_2O_3 $15 - 30$, while ZnO is rarely obtained with a surface area greater than $3 - 5$ m^2/g.

Thus, when prepared under standard conditions each oxide has a specific surface area (for the given oxides). It is still not clear how the oxide properties affect the specific surface. We know that the specific surface is inversely proportional to the density. However, the density cannot be the main factor determining the specific surface, since the densities of the different oxides differ by a factor of $5 - 6$ (at maximum) while the specific surfaces differ by a factor of tens or even hundreds. Moreover, for each oxide it is possible to obtain samples of different surface areas, while the density remains virtually constant.

Concerning the influence of other oxide properties on the surface area, we can only make assumptions, since their importance has not been elucidated. When different hydroxides are precipitated under the same conditions, these conditions would not be identical for all of them since each has a specific pH range of precipitation and a specific solubility. After calcination at relatively low temperatures, the oxides formed often retain some bound water whose amount differs in different oxides calcinated under the same conditions. According to the Tammann law, rapid sintering of the oxides occurs at different temperatures. The magnitude of the surface area is probably associated with the structure and energy of the crystal lattice, the surface energy and the surface tension of the oxide and the hydroxide particles.

The surface properties of solids have been studied to very little extent /1/. Surface energy determinations and calculations have been made mainly with respect to alkali halides. In the case of oxides, such data are available only for Mg, Ca, and Si oxides. No method exists for the experimental determination of the surface tension in solids. At the same time, it has been shown that the surface tension changes as a result of physical adsorption of gases. Hence, the surface tension should be affected by changes in the chemical or crystallographic composition of the oxide.

All the above statements on the effect of various factors on the surface area of pure oxides are also true for binary oxide mixtures. In order to establish (in a distinct form) the effect of the composition of a binary oxide system on the surface area, it is necessary to exclude to the maximum possible extent the effect of all other factors. All catalysts must be prepared under strictly standard conditions. Moreover, the investigation must be carried out on a sufficiently large number of samples of different compositions. A failure to fulfill the above conditions could lead to random results that are difficult to explain.

Many researchers have noted that when two oxides are prepared together their surface area is greater than that of the pure oxides. However, the rules governing this phenomenon have not been established as yet.

According to the supersaturation theory of S.Z. Roginskii /2/, in the case of a mixture of two oxides the possibility of increasing the supersaturation (and hence the degree of dispersion) is greater than in the case of pure oxides. The above theory relates the degree of dispersion of a catalyst to the properties of its phases, but the effect of phase composition on the degree of dispersion has not been analyzed in detail.

W. Milligan et al. /3/ have shown in their many published papers that in the simultaneous preparation of two oxides, at certain concentrations the oxides prevent the crystallization of each other and form catalysts that are amorphous when examined by X-ray diffraction. According to Milligan, this effect (which is called by him "mutual protection against crystallization") is due to adsorption of one of the oxides on the surface of the other oxide. Such "mutual protection" should be accompanied by an increase in the specific surface. Milligan's explanation of the causes for the increase in the specific surface is accepted by many authors. However, the fact that the maximum in specific surface coincides with the region in which a protection against crystallization exists has been checked with one system only. The theory of "mutual protection" does not take into account the natures of the interacting oxides and makes no attempt to predict the oxides and concentrations for which an increase in the surface area may be expected. At the same time, the available data show that different oxides behave differently with respect to one another.

We believe that an answer to the above problems should be sought on the basis of the changes in the phase composition of the catalysts. When the chemical composition of a system is changed, solid-solution or chemical-compound phases could be formed in it under certain conditions and at certain concentrations. Each such phase differs from the starting pure oxides in its physicochemical and crystallographic properties. As the pure oxide phase formed under certain conditions has a characteristic specific surface, the phase formed in the interaction of two oxides should also have a specific surface that is a function of its properties. The appearance or disappearance of a phase from the system should affect the changes in the specific surface of a catalyst, which depends on the surfaces of the separate phases.

Such a correspondence between the changes in the specific surface and in the phase composition has been observed by us in several binary oxide systems. The $Al_2O_3 - Cr_2O_3$ system (Figure 1) is characterized by limited mutual solubility /4/. When small amounts of Cr_2O_3 are added to γ-Al_2O_3, the specific surface increases until the solubility limit has been reached. The saturated solid solution has the maximum specific surface. A further increase in the Cr_2O_3 concentration causes the formation of a second phase — α-Cr_2O_3, and the specific surface decreases since the new phase has a much smaller specific surface. On the other hand, the surface area of α-Cr_2O_3 remains almost unchanged upon the dissolution in it of up to 10% of Al_2O_3, and an increase in the surface area is observed only upon the appearance of the γ-Al_2O_3 phase (containing dissolved Cr_2O_3) in the system.

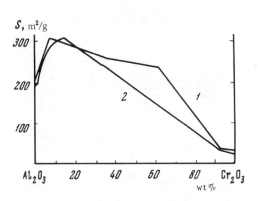

FIGURE 1. Dependence of the specific surface (S) on the composition and calcination temperature for the $Al_2O_3-Cr_2O_3$ system:

1- 450°C; 2- 600°C.

The existence of a connection between the changes in the specific surface and the formation of solid-solution phases has been confirmed by another fact. Each catalyst in which the concentrations of components are intermediate between the concentrations of the two saturated solid solutions contains two phases. Changes in the chemical composition within this heterogeneous region cause only changes in the ratio of the amounts of the two phases whose compositions are constant. If we assume that each of these phases has a characteristic specific surface, the total specific surface should change linearly within the heterogeneous region. Such a linear change in the surface is, indeed, observed in the case of $Al_2O_3 - Cr_2O_3$ catalysts (calcined at 600°) in the range between 33 and 93 wt % of Cr_2O_3.

In catalysts that have been calcined at 450°, a linear change in the surface area starts at a Cr_2O_3 concentration of 60 wt %, which agrees with the appearance of the α-Cr_2O_3 phase at this concentration.

The $Fe_2O_3 - Al_2O_3$ and $NiO - Cr_2O_3$ systems (Figures 2 and 3) show a similar behavior. By using these systems as examples, we may trace the changes in specific surface as a function of the calcination temperature. When the calcination temperature in the $NiO - Cr_2O_3$ system is increased from 400 to 800° there occurs a marked decrease in the surface area of all catalysts, although the general dependence of the surface area on the composition remains unchanged. The same behavior is observed in the case of $Fe_2O_3 - Al_2O_3$ catalysts /5/ when the calcination temperature is increased from 400 to 750°. After calcination at $900 - 1000°$ /5, 6/ an increase in the Fe_2O_3 concentration causes a rapid decrease in the surface area due to the γ-Al_2O_3 — α-Al_2O_3 phase transformation, which is catalyzed by the ferric oxide.

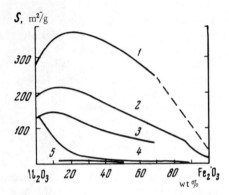 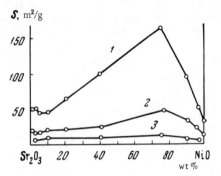

FIGURE 2. Dependence of the specific surface on the composition and the calcination temperature for the Al_2O_3—Fe_2O_3 system:

1- 400°C; 2- 600°C; 3- 750°C; 4- 950°C; 5- 1000°C.

FIGURE 3. Dependence of the specific surface on the composition and the calcination temperature for the Cr_2O_3—NiO system:

1- 400°C; 2- 600°C; 3- 800°C.

The belief that changes in the phase composition should affect the changes in specific surface has been advanced in several papers, although not in a very clear form. It could be assumed that the relationship between the surface area and the phase composition of a system is a general law for binary oxide systems. Such an assumption is in agreement with the continuity principle used in physicochemical analysis. It should, however, be remembered that in the case of mixed catalysts we usually deal with non-equilibrium systems, and that different phases may have similar surface areas. These facts may tend to obscure the dependence of the specific surface on the phase composition.

At present we have no means of predicting the surface area of a pure oxide or of a binary oxide compound. We may, however, make an attempt to answer a simpler question: should an increase in the specific surface occur upon the dissolution of an oxide in another oxide? The answer to this problem is quite important, since the formation of solid solutions is very frequent in the case of mixed oxide catalysts.

Milligan /7/ used the crystallochemical properties of the components and their ability to form solid solutions in order to explain the changes in surface area caused by changes in the composition in the In_2O_3 — BeO system. The Be^{2+} ions have a smaller radius (0.34 Å), are readily dissolved in the In_2O_3 lattice, and do not distort its structure even at considerable concentrations. The dissolution of BeO has little effect on the properties of the In_2O_3 phase and the specific surface ramains unchanged. On the other hand, when even a small amount of In^{3+} ions (r = 0.92 Å) is added to BeO, the crystal lattice is distorted and the surface area increases.

The analytical method of Milligan may be extended also to other cases involving the formation of solid solutions.

It may be assumed that when the introduction of a foreign ion causes a decrease in the crystal lattice energy, the phase becomes less stable, the growth of its crystals is hindered and slowed-down, and its specific surface increases. The theory of supersaturation also predicts that the degree of dispersion increases with decreasing stability of a phase. In order to check the validity of the above assumption, we have examined the direction of the changes in lattice energy in the formation of solid solutions with oxides for which there are literature data on the changes in the surface area.

L. Pauling /8/ gives the following equations for the crystal lattice energy of a ionic crystal:

$$U_0 = \frac{NAe^2z^2}{R_0}\left(1 - \frac{1}{n}\right),$$

where R_0 is the minimum distance between the anion and cation, N is the Avogadro number, e is the charge of the electron, z is a parameter depending on the ionic valence, A is the Madelung's constant, depending on the type of crystal lattice, and n is the Born coefficient, associated with the structure of the electronic shell of the ion.

In the formation of solid solutions of the substitution type, the type of the crystal lattice remains unchanged and all values in the nominator remain constant. The direction of the change in the lattice energy depends only on R_0 and n.

The above comparison suffers from several limitations. The equation is valid for ionic crystals but is not strictly correct for many oxides. A metal ion may change its radius upon entering the lattice of the oxide of another metal. Certain oxides do not together form solid solutions of the substitution type. In spite of these limitations, the above assumption on the existence of a relationship between the changes in the surface area and the changes in the crystal lattice energy is valid for many systems. The data in the table show that of the 24 cases (of solid-solution formation) examined, our assumption is wrong in four cases only, while two cases are doubtful. The cases in which no correspondence exists between the changes in surface area and the changes in lattice energy refer to the dissolution of oxides in lattices of a different valence and ion coordination. It is possible that this is accompanied by a change in R_0. In some cases the agreement is astonishing. For instance, the surface area of Cr_2O_3 is not increased upon the dissolution of NiO but increases upon the dissolution of MgO (which has similar properties), as should be expected on the basis of data on the changes in the lattice energy.

Thus, we have made an attempt to find a new approach to the solution of the problem concerning the dependence of the texture of a catalyst on its chemical composition. This attempt was based on the following assumptions:

1) a change in the surface area upon the formation of a solid solution between two oxides is associated with a change in the crystal lattice energy;

2) each phase formed in the binary oxide system has (for the given conditions of preparation) a characteristic surface area, and the changes in the phase composition are reflected in the changes in the specific surface.

Both these assumptions require further examination and more accurate definition.

Relationship between the changes in the specific surface and the crystal lattice energy in the formation of a solid solution of two oxides

Main oxide	Dissolved oxide	Change in the lattice energy upon dissolution*	Change in the surface area upon dissolution**	Correspondence between the changes in energy and surface area
SiO$_2$	Al$_2$O$_3$	−0.092	+	Yes
CuO	Al$_2$O$_3$	−0.043	+	"
Al$_2$O$_3$	Cr$_2$O$_3$	−0.027	+	"
	Fe$_2$O$_3$	−0.019	+	"
	ZrO$_2$	−0.043	+	"
	NiO	−0.025	+	"
Cr$_2$O$_3$	Al$_2$O$_3$	+0.027	−	"
	NiO	+0.002	−	"
	MgO	−0.010	+	"
	CuO	+0.070	−	"
	SnO$_2$	+0.013	+	No
Fe$_2$O$_3$	Al$_2$O$_3$	+0.019	(?)	(?)
	Cr$_2$O$_3$	−0.008	+	Yes
	CdO	−0.050	+	"
NiO	Al$_2$O$_3$	+0.025	+	No
	Cr$_2$O$_3$	−0.002	+	Yes
MgO	NiO	+0.012	−	"
In$_2$O$_3$	BeO	+0.100	−	"
BeO	In$_2$O$_3$	−0.100	+	"
CeO$_2$	La$_2$O$_3$	−0.050	+	"
La$_2$O$_3$	CeO$_2$	+0.050	(?)	(?)
CdO	Fe$_2$O$_3$	+0.050	+	No
ZnO	Cr$_2$O$_3$	−0.070	+	Yes
SnO$_2$	Cr$_2$O$_3$	−0.013	−	No

* Negative values indicate a decrease in the lattice energy.

** The sign + indicates a rapid increase in the surface area upon the introduction of small amounts of the second oxide, the sign - indicates that no such increase occurs, and the sign(?) indicates that the change in surface area is doubtful.

BIBLIOGRAPHY

1. YATES, D.J.C.—Adv. Cat., Vol. 12: 265. 1960.
2. ROGINSKII, S. Z.—ZhFKh, Vol. 15: 697. 1941; ZhPKh, Vol. 17: 3. 1944.
3. MILLIGAN, W.O., et al.—J. Am. Chem. Soc., Vol. 63: 149. 1941; J. Phys. Chem., Vol. 50: 465. 1946; Vol. 51: 521. 1947; Vol. 52: 230, 942. 1948; Vol. 55: 497. 1951; Vol. 57: 883. 1953.
4. RUBINSHTEIN, A.M., A.L. KLYACHKO—GURVICH, and V.M. AKIMOV.—IAN SSSR, OKhN, p. 780. 1961.
5. EL'TEKOV, Yu.A., K.I. SLOVETSKAYA, and A.M. RUBINSHTEIN.—In: Sbornik "Kinetika i kataliz", p. 169. Moskva, Izd. AN SSSR. 1960.
6. ALKHAZOV, T.G. and M.S. BELENSKII.—Izv. VUZov, Nefti i Gaz, No. 11: 83. 1959; No. 3: 69. 1962.
7. MILLIGAN, W.O. and C.R. ADAMS.—J. Phys. Chem., Vol. 57: 885. 1953.
8. PAULING, L. Priroda khimicheskoi svyazi (The Nature of the Chemical Bond), p. 326.—Moskva, Goskhimizdat. 1947.

V. B. Kazanskii and Yu. I. Pecherskaya

DEPENDENCE OF THE ACTIVITY OF CHROMIUM OXIDE CATALYSTS FOR THE POLYMERIZATION OF ETHYLENE ON THE NATURE OF THE CARRIER

The selection of a carrier is of great importance in the preparation of catalysts for laboratory use and for the chemical industry. The carrier determines many of the valuable properties of a catalyst, e.g., its specific surface and mechanical strength; it prevents sintering of the catalyst at high temperatures; and facilitates the transfer of the heat released during the reaction. All these factors are determined by the strictly physical and mechanical properties of the carrier. On the other hand it is known that in some cases the carrier should not be regarded as a completely inert (from the standpoint of catalytic activity) support; it often affects strongly the activity and selectivity of the catalyst. These properties of the support have been studied to a much lesser extent. In this paper we report the results obtained in EPR (electron paramagnetic resonance) studies of the structure of chromium oxide catalysts for the polymerization of ethylene on various carriers, and of their catalytic activity.

It is known from the literature that chromium oxide carried on silica gel aluminosilicates, zirconium silicates, alumina, and other supports is an active catalyst for the polymerization of ethylene. In a previous paper, the present authors together with G.K. Boreskov (a member-correspondent of the USSR Academy of Sciences) showed that in the case of chromium catalysts supported on aluminosilicate the active centers for the polymerization are Cr^{5+} ions stabilized on the surface of the carrier and yielding characteristic narrow bands in the EPR spectra /1/. The same conclusion was reached independently by K.V. Topchieva et al. /2/, and by A.E. Semenova, M.P. Votinov, B.I. Sazhin et al. /3/. It would be of interest to determine whether the above conclusion is valid also for catalysts on other carriers, and to elucidate the effect of the carrier on the specific activity of the catalyst.

The characteristics of the substances used by us as carriers are listed in Table 1. The catalysts were prepared by saturating the carrier with an aqueous solution of chromic acid, followed by drying in air and subsequent firing in vacuo for 7 hours at 400°. Their activity was determined on the basis of the yield of polyethylene in grams per gram of catalyst. The reaction was carried out in an autoclave under an ethylene pressure of 35 atmospheres at 125°, using heptane as a solvent. The experimental determinations of the catalytic activity were carried out by the staff of the Catalysis Institute of the SO USSR Academy of Sciences. The samples used in the measurements of the catalytic activity and for the tracing of the

EPR spectra were prepared simultaneously in glass ampuls in vacuo, at 400°. The EPR spectra were traced at room temperature using the EPR-2 radiospectrometer. The experimental method is described in more detail in /1, 4/.

TABLE 1. Characteristics of the carriers

Carrier	Method of preparation*	Surface area (measured by the BET method), m^2/g
Silica gel	Addition of H_2SO_4 to Na_2SiO_3	320
97% SiO_2 — 3% Al_2O_3	Commercial aluminosilicate	360
90% SiO_2 — 10% Al_2O_3 80% SiO_2 — 20% Al_2O_3 50% SiO_2 — 50% Al_2O_3 25% SiO_2 — 75% Al_2O_3	Precipitation with NaOH (pH 8) from a solution of $Al(NO_3)_3$ and Na_2SiO_3	380 270 350 370
γ-Al_2O_3	Precipitation from $Al(NO_3)_3$ at pH 7	230
13% ZrO_2 — 87% SiO_2	Coprecipitation with NH_3 from a solution of zirconium nitrate and silicon ethylate	400
ZrO_2	Precipitation from zirconium nitrate	100
α-Cr_2O_3	Ignition of chromium oxide gel in air at 500°C	90
Activated carbon	—	600

* After precipitation from the solution all substances were ignited in air at 500°C.

The typical EPR spectrum of one of the samples (aluminosilicate containing 97% SiO_2, 3% Al_2O_3, 2.5% Cr) is shown in Figure 1. The spectrum consists of a very weak wide band of Cr^{3+} ions, on whose background we observe a strong narrow band of Cr^{5+}. By integration of this band was determined the amount of Cr^{5+} ions in the catalyst and from this the specific catalytic activity per milligram of Cr^{5+} ions. Since we showed previously /4/ that in supported chromium oxide catalysts all Cr^{5+} ions are on the surface of the carrier, the above magnitude has exactly defined physical meaning.

The results of the study of the total activity of the above catalysts, their Cr^{5+} content, and their specific catalytic activity are presented in Table 2, which shows that a satisfactory qualitative agreement exists between the amount of Cr^{5+} ions and the total activity of the catalyst. In fact, the most active catalysts are those which use silica gel and aluminosilicates with a low

Al concentration as the supports, and which have the highest Cr^{5+} contents. The catalysts on α-Cr_2O_3 and on carbon, which contain no Cr^{5+}, showed no activity. The catalysts with a low Cr^{5+} content (e.g., on ZrO_2) occupied an intermediate position. At the same time, the specific activity varies strongly in the transition from one support to another (for instance, it changes by a factor of nearly 30 in the transition from silica gel to alumina).

TABLE 2. Dependence of the activity of chromium oxide catalysts (2.5% Cr) on their Cr^{5+} content

Carrier	Yield of polymer, g/g·hr	Concentration of Cr^{5+} ions, % of the total amount of Cr	Yield of polymer (specific activity) g/mg Cr^{5+}
SiO_2	70	3.5	80.5
97% SiO_2 — 3% Al_2O_3	70	3.5	80.5
90% SiO_2 — 10% Al_2O_3	70	7	40.5
80% SiO_2 — 20% Al_2O_3	35	3.5	40.2
50% SiO_2 — 50% Al_2O_3	25	14	7.23
25% SiO_2 — 75% Al_2O_3	15	14	4.3
γ-Al_2O_3	16	14	4.6
13% ZrO_2 — 87% SiO_2	15	3.5	17.3
ZrO_2	Traces	0.04	—
α-Cr_2O_3	Nil	—	—
Activated carbon	''	—	—

In order to determine the reasons for the differences in the specific catalytic activity of catalysts on different supports, it is necessary to analyze the shapes of the EPR lines for the Cr^{5+} ions. The corresponding spectra are shown in Figure 2, which shows that the shapes of these lines change markedly in the transition from one support to another. On SiO_2, Al_2O_3/SiO_2, and zirconium silicate these lines are asymmetric, while on alumina, and on aluminosilicates with a high aluminum content the lines are symmetrical. The characteristic shape of the asymmetric lines indicates the absence of anisotropy from the g-factor in the EPR signals, i.e., it indicates that the Cr^{5+} ions associated with these lines lie within a crystalline field whose symmetry differs substantially from the cubic.

Catalysts on different supports are characterized by different deviations from the cubic in the crystalline field symmetry: the g-factor anisotropy is the maximum for a catalyst on zirconium silicate, has an intermediate value for the catalyst on silica gel and aluminosilicate, and has a minimum when alumina is used as the support. In other words, the fact that the Cr^{5+} lines in chromium catalysts on different supports have different shapes indicates that the active centers in these catalysts have different structures. This, apparently, is the cause of the differences in specific activity in the transition from one support to another.

A more detailed analysis of the EPR spectra makes it possible to make certain assumptions concerning the actual models of the structures of the active centers. Indeed, from the spectra obtained by us it is easy to determine the values of $g_\parallel$ and $g_\perp$, which according to the theory of EPR spectra are associated with the type of crystalline field symmetry and the degree of splitting of the orbital levels of the ions in this field. An analysis of the possible structural models of the active centers was made by us for catalysts supported on SiO_2 and Al_2O_3. We assumed that the Cr^{5+} ions are stabilized on the surfaces of silica gel and aluminosilicates with a low alumina content by replacing the silicon atoms in the tetrahedrons of the surface layer, in the manner depicted below:

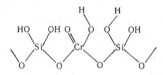

Our calculations, made on the basis of the crystalline field approximation, showed that in this case the splitting of the orbital levels would agree with the scheme shown in Figure 3 a, while $g_\perp$ and $g_\parallel$ would satisfy the following expressions:

$$g_\perp = 2 - \frac{2\lambda}{\Delta E} ; \quad g_\parallel = 2 - \frac{8\lambda}{\Delta E} ,$$

where λ is the spin-orbital interaction constant.

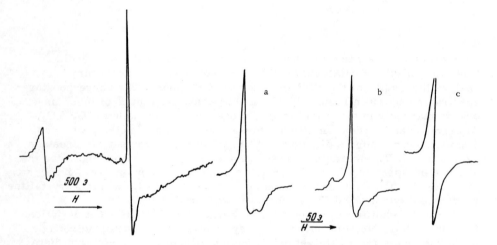

FIGURE 1. EPR spectrum of a chromium oxide catalyst (2.5% Cr) supported aluminosilicate (3% Al_2O_3); the left-hand part of the spectrum shows the signal from the glass ampul and the support.

FIGURE 2. Comparison of the shapes of the signals from Cr^{5+} ions on different supports:

a- SiO_2; b- 13% $ZrO_2 - 87\%$ SiO_2; c- Al_2O_3.

As a result, both $g_\parallel$ and $g_\perp$ should be smaller than 2; $g_\parallel$ is smaller than $g_\perp$ and the difference between $g_\perp$ and 2 is smaller by a factor of 4 the difference between $g_\parallel$ and 2. All these theoretical predictions have been confirmed experimentally (for the catalyst supported on silica gel $g_\perp = 1.98$ and $g_\parallel = 1.90$), and the structural model proposed by us for the active centers has been confirmed by the shape of the observed EPR signals.

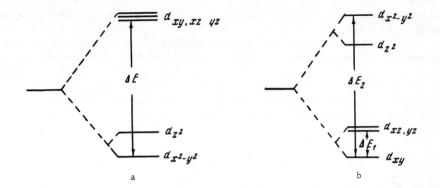

FIGURE 3. Scheme of the splitting of the orbital levels of an ion with one d-electron in the case of distorted tetrahedral (a) and tetragonal-pyramidal (b) coordinations.

In the case of catalysts supported on γ-Al_2O_3 the active centers apparently have a different structure. It is known that γ-Al_2O_3 has a densely packed cubic lattice of oxygen ions, in which some of the tetrahedral and octahedral vacancies are occupied by Al ions. Since the above substance contains a large number of unoccupied vacancies, P. Cossee and L. Van Reijen /6/ assumed that the Cr^{5+} ions may occupy these vacancies and be stabilized in the pentavalent state. They assumed also that the Cr^{5+} ions in the octahedral vacancies exist as chromyl ions ($Cr = O^{3+}$) in which one of the octahedral bonds is much shorter than the other. They assumed also that the oxygen ion lying opposite the double bond is desorbed readily, and the Cr^{5+} ions in the surface layer have a tetragonal-pyramidal coordination. This model is in qualitative agreement with the values of $g_\perp$ and $g_\parallel$ calculated from the spectra of the Cr^{5+} ions in the alumina-chromate catalyst, which were traced by us with the EPR apparatus at a working wavelength of 8 mm.

Because of the strong magnetic resonance field in the above case, the contribution of anisotropy to the shape of the line becomes substantial, and the signals have a slightly asymmetric shape, whose analysis yields readily the following values: $g_\perp \approx 1.97$ and $g_\parallel \approx 1.95$. A scheme showing the splitting of the orbital levels for the contracted tetragonal pyramid is presented in Figure 3 b. In the above case, the expressions for $g_\parallel$ and $g_\perp$ are:

$$g_\parallel = 2 - \frac{8\lambda}{\Delta E_2}; \quad g_\perp = 2 - \frac{2\lambda}{\Delta E_1}.$$

Since $\Delta E_2 > \Delta E_1$ it is evident that in this case $\Delta g = g_\parallel - g_\perp$ has a much smaller value than in the above-discussed case of tetrahedral coordination, which explains the more symmetric shape of the lines in alumina-chromium catalysts.

Thus, the changes in the specific activity and in the shape of the EPR signals in the transition from silica gel to alumina as a support should naturally be attributed to differences in the structure of the active centers in these systems. It is evident that, in principle, a similar analysis of the shape of the EPR signals and the structures of the active centers could be made also for catalysts on other supports, although the interpretation of the results would be less unambiguous because of the greater complexity of their crystalline structures.

The results obtained in this work show that the role of the support in supported catalysts is not confined solely to providing the maximum surface area for the active component; the presence of a support markedly affects the structure of the active centers and the magnitude of the specific activity. Evidently, the last consideration should be taken into account in the selection of catalysts for various chemical processes.

BIBLIOGRAPHY

1. BUKANAEVA, F.M., Yu.I. PECHERSKAYA, V.B. KAZANSKII, and V.A. DZIS'KO.—Kinetika i Kataliz, Vol.3: 358. 1962.
2. SERGEEV, G.B., O.K. SHARAEV, K.V. TOPCHIEVA, A.I. PEREL'MAN, and A.V. TOPCHIEV.— Neftekhimiya, Vol.2: 18. 1962.
3. ANTUF'EV, V.V., M.P. VOTINOV, A.G. SAVIN, B.I. SAZHIN, A.E. SEMENOVA, and M.I. LEITMAN.—Kinetika i Kataliz, Vol.3: 353. 1962.
4. KAZANSKII, V.B. and Yu.I. PECHERSKAYA.—Kinetika i Kataliz, Vol.4: 230. 1963.
5. ALEKSANDROV, I.A., V.B. KAZANSKII, and I.D. MIKHEIKIN.—Kinetika i Kataliz, Vol.6: 439. 1965.
6. VAN REIJEN, L.L., P. COSSEE, and H.J. VAN HAREN.—J. Chem. Phys., Vol.38: 572. 1963.

II. KINETIC FACTORS IN THE SELECTION OF CATALYSTS

S.L. Kiperman

ON THE KINETIC FACTORS AND THE PROBLEM OF THE OPTIMUM CATALYST

We may assume that the problem of the scientific selection of catalysts involves the determination of the characteristics that form the basis for the choice of the optimum catalyst for a given reaction and for the prediction of this catalyst.

The requirements with respect to the optimum catalyst may differ depending on the nature of the process, its mechanism, and the conditions under which it is carried out in practice. We shall discuss here the optimum catalyst only with respect to the possibility of conducting on it the required reaction at the fastest possible rate, although in general the optimum characteristics may refer also to other parameters of the process such as the slowest possible rate of side reactions, the best heat transfer conditions, etc.

Since the optimum characteristics depends on both thermodynamic and kinetic factors, which determine the nature and the rules governing the reaction, the problem of the optimum catalyst may be discussed from the standpoint of the kinetics of the process. Such an approach to the problem was made by A.A. Balandin /1, 2/ in his discussion of the energetic considerations of the multiplet theory. The problem has been discussed also by N.I. Kobozev /3/ and by Dutch scientists /4/. M.I. Temkin /5/ has shown that a relationship exists in certain cases between the kinetics of a process and the problem of the most active catalyst. In an earlier paper by Temkin and this author /6/ the problem was posed of the maximum reaction rate under the prescribed conditions, as applied to the particular case of ammonia synthesis.

Below we shall carry out a more generalized discussion of the kinetic considerations in the problem of the optimum catalyst, as well as of some conclusions as applied to various reactions. This discussion refers to the most simple cases and is only approximate, although it is necessary as a basis for the consideration of more complicated systems.

I. ANALYSIS OF THE OPTIMUM CHARACTERISTICS

In order to elucidate the optimum characteristics that yield the highest possible reaction rate (under the given conditions) it is necessary to analyze the kinetic laws governing the process, or, in the discussion of a number of catalysts, to analyze the most probable rules governing the reaction kinetics on these catalysts. If side reactions cannot be excluded under the given conditions, the kinetic rules (even assumed ones in some cases) governing these reactions should also be taken into account in order to elucidate the factors for which the side reaction rates are the lowest.

The laws governing the course of the process in the kinetic region may be determined by the nature of the intermediate surface compounds, their stability, and their formation and decomposition rates; by the adsorbability of the reaction components and the adsorption equilibrium; by the filled surface section in which the reaction occurs; by the extent of deviation from the equilibrium; and by the existence or non-existence of a rate-determining (limiting) stage. Since the above factors may change in the transition from one catalyst to another and also as a function of the history, promotion and support of the catalyst, changes in the optimum characteristics may occur as a result. The analysis of these optimum characteristics must take into account the above factors.

For each optimum catalyst under a given set of conditions there must be a certain optimum stability of the corresponding intermediate surface compounds (depending on the conditions under which the reaction is carried out), which may change sharply in the transition from one site on the catalyst surface to another. In the simplest case the reaction may be characterized by a single, simple or complex, intermediate surface compound (adsorbed molecules, their complexes, dissociation products, etc.). By assuming the formation of such a single surface compound (or, in other words, if the slow stage of the given process does not involve a reaction between different surface compounds) many reactions of different classes may be covered by the simplest two-stage scheme of Temkin /5/, that assumes the formation of a surface compound I $[K]$ in one stage and its decomposition in the other stage:

$$\text{I. } A_1 + A_2 + \ldots + [K] = X_1 + X_2 + \ldots + I\,[K];$$
$$\text{II. } I\,[K] + C_1 + C_2 + \ldots = Y_1 + Y_2 + \ldots + [K] \tag{1}$$

($[K]$ are the sites on the catalyst surface). A number of reactions described by more complex schemes may also be described with some simplification by scheme (1).

If a reaction on the non-homogeneous surface of a catalyst takes place with the formation and decomposition of a single intermediate surface compound, or with the formation of several surface compounds in such a way that a single surface compound (whose stability is not affected by the other surface compounds) is formed or decomposed in the rate-determining stage, the highest rate will be attained at surface sites that satisfy the following condition /5 — 7/:

$$\sigma_i = \frac{p}{p + b_i} = \alpha, \tag{2}$$

where σ_i is the probability of coverage of the given site (the degree of coverage of the given group of sites, whose heat of formation q differs by no more than dq from that of the surface compound); p is the volatility of the adsorbed layer forming the given surface compound; α is the Brönsted-Polanyi-Temkin /8/ ratio coefficient ("linearity ratio"); and b_i is the desorption coefficient from the given site:

$$b_i = B_0 e^{-\frac{q_i}{RT}} \tag{3}$$

(B_0 is a constant which to a first approximation is independent of the temperature and the site on the surface).

Since condition (2) is satisfied only for certain sites on a non-homogeneous surface, the problem of the optimum catalyst may, in the first place, be reduced to a discussion of the problem of determining which are the surface sites that would be the optimal under the given process conditions.

Condition (2) yields the following expression for the optimum characteristics:

$$(b_i)_{\text{opt}} = \frac{1-\alpha}{\alpha}\, p \tag{4}$$

and

$$(q_i)_{\text{opt}} = RT \ln \frac{\alpha B_0}{(1-\alpha)\,p}\,. \tag{5}$$

When one of the stages of the process is the slowest [rate-determining], the remaining stages are virtually in equilibrium with respect to this stage and the volatility of the adsorbed layer p may be expressed by means of the adsorption-chemical equilibrium condition /9/ for the fast stages:

$$p = \left(K \frac{P_j}{P'_j} \right)^{\pm 1}, \tag{6}$$

where K is the equilibrium constant of the reaction; P_j and P'_j are the products of the partial pressures of the substances that react from the gaseous or liquid phases in the fast stages and, respectively, of the substances that are formed in these reactions; the minus sign in the exponent refers to a case in which the rate-determining stage involves the formation of the intermediate surface compound.

Condition (6) is not necessary in cases in which the fast stages involve adsorption or desorption of the given substance, and p is equal to the partial pressure of that substance.

From equations (5) and (6) we obtain an expression for the optimum heat of formation of the intermediate surface compound q_{opt}:

$$q_{\text{opt}} = RT \ln \frac{\alpha}{1-\alpha} B_0 \pm RT \ln \frac{P'_j}{KP_j} \tag{7}$$

(the minus sign before the second term refers to a case in which a surface compound is formed in the slow stage).

If the value of q is expressed in terms of the bond energy of the surface compound formed $Q_{I-[K]}$ and the sum of the energies of the broken initial bonds ΣQ_{init} we obtain:

$$q = -\Sigma Q_{\text{init}} + Q_{I-[K]}, \tag{8}$$

and the optimum stability of the surface compound $Q_{I-[K]\text{opt}}$ is characterized by the equation:

$$Q_{I-[K]\text{opt}} = \Sigma Q_{\text{init}} + \Delta, \tag{9}$$

where

$$\Delta = RT \ln \frac{\alpha}{1-\alpha} B_0 \pm RT \ln \frac{P'_j}{KP_j} \tag{10}$$

119

(the minus sign again refers to a case in which the surface compound is formed in the slow stage).

Equations (7) — (10) show that the optimum characteristics of the surface sites depend not only on the rupture energy of the initial bonds but also on a number of other factors, namely: the composition and nature of the surface compounds, which determine the value of B_0; the equilibrium constants of the reaction; the temperatures that affect the values of Δ and especially of K; the partial pressures of the components; the linearity ratio coefficients, and which stage is the rate determing one.

It is evident that the values of q_{opt} and $Q_{I-[K]opt}$ may vary with changes in the conditions of the reaction and its mechanism, and in the transition from one homolog to another as a result of changes in the equilibrium constants, even if the orientation with respect to the surface is the same. The above values may change even during the course of the process, as in the case of rather sharp changes in the partial pressure ratios caused by the reaction.

If the reaction takes place without a rate-determining stage, condition (2) remains valid but the value of p cannot be expressed by means of equation (6) and it cannot be equal to the partial pressure of the corresponding component. The same condition (2) leads to the conclusion that in such a case the maximum reaction rate would be obtained when the various stages occur at the same rates. For reactions that take place in agreement with scheme (1) the probability of coverage of the i-th site on the surface (the degree of coverage of sites of the i-th type) may be expressed /5/ by the following equation:

$$c_i = \frac{(\vec{k_I})_i P_I + (\vec{k_{II}})_i P'_{II}}{(\vec{k_I})_i P_I + (\overleftarrow{k_I})_i P'_I + (\vec{k_{II}})_i P_{II} + (\overleftarrow{k_{II}})_i P'_{II}}, \qquad (11)$$

where $(\vec{k_I})_i$, $(\overleftarrow{k_I})_i$, $(\vec{k_{II}})_i$, and $(\overleftarrow{k_{II}})_i$ are the rate constants of the stages on the i-th surface sites in the forward and reverse directions; P_I, P'_I, P_{II}, and P'_{II} are the products of the partial pressures of the substances taking part in the first and second stages in the forward and reverse directions. Far from the equilibrium we have:

$$\left.\begin{aligned}(\overleftarrow{k_{II}})_i P'_{II} &\ll (\vec{k_I})_i P_I; \\ (\overleftarrow{k_I})_i P'_I &\ll (\vec{k_I})_i P_I.\end{aligned}\right\} \qquad (12)$$

The rate constants of the stages may be expressed by means of the linearity ratio (when the coefficients α have the same values at each stage) /5/:

$$\left.\begin{aligned}(\vec{k_I})_i &= G_I (K_I)_i^{\alpha}; \quad (\vec{k_{II}})_i = G_{II} (K_{II})_i^{1-\alpha}; \\ (\overleftarrow{k_I})_i &= G_I (K_I)^{-(1-\alpha)}; \quad (\overleftarrow{k_{II}})_i = G_{II} (K_{II})_i^{-\alpha}.\end{aligned}\right\} \qquad (13)$$

In the above equations G_I and G_{II} are factors whose values are independent of the temperature and the site on the surface; $(K_I)_i$ and $(K_{II})_i$ are the rate constants of the stages on the i-th sites of the surface.

From conditions (2) and (12), and expressions (11) and (13) we obtain the following expressions for the forward and reverse reactions respectively:

$$G_I (K_I)_i^{\alpha} P_I = \frac{\alpha}{1-\alpha} G_{II} (K_{II})_i^{1-\alpha} P_{II}, \qquad (14)$$

$$G_\mathrm{I}(K_\mathrm{I})_i^{-(1-\alpha)} P_\mathrm{I}' = \frac{1-\alpha}{\alpha} G_\mathrm{II}(K_\mathrm{II})_i^{-\alpha} P_\mathrm{II}'. \tag{15}$$

From the above equations, taking into account the fact that:

$$(K_\mathrm{I})_i = K_\mathrm{I}^0 e^{\frac{(Q_\mathrm{I})_i}{RT}}; \tag{16}$$

$$(K_\mathrm{II})_i = K_\mathrm{II}^0 e^{\frac{(Q_{II})_i}{RT}} \tag{17}$$

[where $(Q_\mathrm{I})_i$ and $(Q_\mathrm{II})_i$ are the heat effects of the first and second stages respectively, on the i-th sites of the surface; the preexponents K_I^0 and K_II^0 do not depend (to a first approximation) on the temperature and the site on the surface] we obtain the following expressions for the forward and reverse reactions respectively:

$$Q_{\overrightarrow{I-[K]opt}} = \alpha\left(\sum Q_\mathrm{init} + \frac{1-\alpha}{\alpha} \sum Q_\mathrm{prod}\right) + RT \ln \frac{\alpha\,(K_\mathrm{II}^0)^{1-\alpha}\, G_\mathrm{II} P_\mathrm{II}}{(1-\alpha)(K_\mathrm{I}^{0\alpha} G_\mathrm{I} P_\mathrm{I}}; \tag{18}$$

$$Q_{\overleftarrow{I-[K]opt}} = (1-\alpha\left(\sum Q_\mathrm{init} + \frac{\alpha}{1-\alpha} \sum Q_\mathrm{prod}\right) + RT \ln \frac{\alpha\,(K_\mathrm{II}^0)^{\alpha}\, G_\mathrm{I} P_\mathrm{I}'}{(1-\alpha)\,(K_\mathrm{I}^0)^{1-\alpha} G_\mathrm{II} P_\mathrm{II}'}, \tag{19}$$

where ΣQ_prod is the sum of the bond energies for the bonds formed in the reaction.

If the reaction takes place without a limiting [slowest] stage, at a small distance from the equilibrium (e.g., in the case of isotopic reactions and their analogs), the inequality (12) is no longer valid but equation (14) remains valid at a first approximation. In this case it would contain the factor γ in its right-hand term:

$$\gamma = \frac{1 - \frac{\alpha}{1-\alpha} x_\mathrm{II}}{1 - x_\mathrm{I}} \tag{20}$$

(x_I and x_II are the ratios of the partial pressures of the products of the first and second stages to the equilibrium pressure); the value of γ is close to unity and equation (18) would be valid for both the forward and reverse reactions. Far from the equilibrium, equations (18) and (19) may not be valid at the same time, i.e., sites that are optimal for the forward reaction may not be optimal for the reverse reaction, as we observed in /5/.

When $\alpha = 1/2$, $G_\mathrm{I} = G_\mathrm{II}$, $K_\mathrm{I}^0 = K_\mathrm{II}^0$, $P_\mathrm{I} = P_\mathrm{II}$, and $P_\mathrm{I}' = P_\mathrm{II}'$, equations (18) and (19) become a quantitative expression of the principle of energetic correspondence which was formulated by A.A. Balandin /2/ and was derived subsequently by M.I. Temkin /5/ for "symmetrical" reactions:

$$Q_{I-[K]opt} = {}^1\!/_2 \left(\sum Q_\mathrm{init} + \sum Q_\mathrm{prod}\right). \tag{21}$$

Hence, we can determine the conditions under which equation (21) is valid. When the second term in the right-hand part of equations (18) and (19) is small with respect to the first term and there is no limiting [slowest] stage, the Balandin equation may be approximately valid not only under the above conditions. In general, when the two stages differ fairly

121

markedly from the standpoint of their kinetic and thermodynamic characteristics, these characteristics may have a marked effect on the optimum bond strength.

Since the value of the coefficient α for different catalysts and reactions is in most cases (or often) rather close to $1/2$, condition (2) implies that σ_i is also close to $1/2$. This is most probable in the region of medium filling of the surface when (according to the definition of this region /7, 8/) within a fairly wide range of non-homogeneity the sites with the highest and lowest adsorption capacities are virtually completely occupied and vacant, respectively. Hence, it could be expected that when all other conditions are equal the reaction rate would be the highest in the region of medium filling, since in this case it is most probable that the degree of coverage of some sites would be near 50% /5 — 7/. If the optimum (under the given conditions) sites lie near the lower limit of the non-homogeneity range, the reaction could proceed at a fairly high rate after the coverage of the remaining sites, i.e., within the saturation region. If the optimum characteristics are related to sites near the upper limit of the non-homogeneity range, the reaction could proceed at a fairly high rate in the Henry region.

Thus, in a discussion of the optimum characteristics it is necessary to take into account to what extent they are influenced by the reaction kinetics and mechanism, by the thermodynamic conditions, the process parameters, and the changes in concentration during the reaction.

II. EVALUATION OF THE OPTIMUM SITES ON A SURFACE

On the basis of the above relationships, let us examine the optimum characteristics of sites on the surface of a catalyst, and their changes in several reactions.

1. **Reactions that take place according to the doublet scheme of the multiplet theory:**

$$AB + CD = AC + BD. \tag{22}$$

Such a reaction may be represented by a two-stage scheme /5/ that assumes the formation and decomposition of an intermediate surface compound (in this case — a multiplet complex). In the slow stage of formation of such a complex its stability is expressed on the basis of equations (9) and (10) by the following equation (for $\alpha = 1/2$):

$$Q_{I-[K]_{opt}} = Q_{A-B} + Q_{C-D} + RT \ln B_0 K - \Delta, \tag{23}$$

where:

$$\Delta = RT \ln (P_{AC} P_{BD}). \tag{24}$$

The value of Δ may change substantially, for instance during the process. Thus, at one atmosphere and 350° a change in the degree of conversion from 0.01 to 0.9 changes the value of Δ from 13 to 2 kcal/mole. In the absence of a limiting stage, the optimum stability is expressed by equations (18) or (21).

2. Dimerization of ethylene:

$$2C_2H_4 = C_4H_8. \tag{25}$$

The kinetics of the above reactions in the presence of nickelous oxide on carriers in a continuous-flow system corresponds to the following equation /10/:

$$\omega = kP_{C_2H_4}^{2(1-x)} \tag{26}$$

(ω is the reaction rate, $\alpha = 1/2$) and may be represented by the scheme:

$$\left.\begin{array}{l} \text{I. } 2C_2H_4 + [K] = (C_2H_4 \cdot C_2H_4)\ [K]; \\ \text{II. } (C_2H_4 \cdot C_2H_4)\ [K] = C_4H_8 + [K], \end{array}\right\} \tag{27}$$

in which the second stage (stage II) is the limiting [slowest]. Equation (7) for the above case yields:

$$q_{opt} = RT \ln B_0 - 2RT \ln P_{C_2H_4}. \tag{28}$$

In this case, the value of B_0 evaluated with the aid of statistical mechanics (by the method described in /6/) equals 10^{15} atm. The values of q_{opt} for different initial ethylene pressures $P_{C_2H_4}^0$ are shown in Table 1.

TABLE 1. Values of q_{opt} for the dimerization of ethylene

°C	$P^0{}_{C_2H_4}$, atm	Degree of conversion	q_{opt}, kcal/mole
230	0.3	0	36.8
330	0.3	0	44.0
330	0.3	0.5	45.6
330	64	0	31.3
330	64	0.7	34.0

3. Dehydrogenation of alcohol:

$$C_nH_{2n+1}OH = C_nH_{2n}O + H_2. \tag{29}$$

The kinetics of the above process in a liquid phase in stationary and gradient-free systems was studied (by using as an example the dehydrogenation of isopropyl alcohol on nickel) by N.V. Nikolaeva, I.R. Davydova, and this author /11/. It was assumed that the reaction occurs according to the following scheme:

$$\left.\begin{array}{l} \text{I. } C_nH_{2n+1}OH + [K] = C_nH_{2n}O[K] + H_2 \\ \text{II. } C_nH_{2n}O\ [K] = C_nH_{2n}O + [K], \end{array}\right\} \tag{30}$$

in which the second stage (stage II) is the slowest, which corresponds to the equation:

123

$$\omega = \vec{k} \left(\frac{c_{alc}}{c_{H_2}} \right)^{1-\alpha} - \overleftarrow{k} c_{acet} \left(\frac{c_{H_2}}{c_{alc}} \right)^{\alpha} \tag{31}$$

(the sign c denotes the concentration).

The optimum heat of adsorption may be described by the equation

$$q_{opt} = RT \ln \frac{B_0}{K} + RT \ln \frac{c_{H_2}}{c_{alc}}. \tag{32}$$

For the above reaction in the liquid phase at 83° we have $K = 2 \times 10^{-3}$ atm. /12/.

By taking into account the solubility of hydrogen in the alcohol we may assume that $c_{H_2}/c_{alc} \approx 10^{-4}$; by substituting the value of $B_0 \approx 10^{10.8}$ atm /7/ we obtain $q_{opt} = 15.6$ kcal/mole.

The above reaction in a vapor phase may also be described by scheme (30) /13/; for 327° we have $K = 3.6$ and for atmospheric pressure we obtain $q_{opt} = 26.5$ kcal/mole. In this case the value of q_{opt} changes sharply as a function of changes in the position of the equilibrium and the respective concentrations.

If the dehydration of alcohols were to take place on metals, it would be possible to evaluate the bond energy between the catalyst surface and the oxygen by representing the above reaction by a similar scheme involving the formation and decomposition of a surface compound $H_2O[K]$. This energy should be at least 90 kcal/mole (for one bond), while the maximum bond energy between oxygen and the surfaces of metals of group VIII does not exceed $65 - 70$ kcal/mole. This may be one of the reasons for the fact that no dehydration of alcohols takes place on metals.

4. Dehydrogenation of formic acid on nickel:

$$HCOOH = H_2 + CO_2. \tag{33}$$

The kinetics and the mechanism of the above reaction in a gradient-free system were studied by I.S. Nagishkina and this author /14/. Within the whole range of degrees of conversion reaction (33) is a zero-order reaction and may be described by the scheme

$$\left.\begin{array}{l} \text{I. } HCOOH + [K] = HCOO \,[K] + \frac{1}{2}H_2; \\ \text{II. } HCOO \,[K] = CO_2 + H \,[K]; \\ \text{III. } H \,[K] = \frac{1}{2}H_2 + [K], \end{array}\right\} \tag{34}$$

in which the second stage is the rate-determining. The value of q_{opt} for the formation of the surface formate in stage I may be evaluated from the equation

$$q_{opt} = RT \ln \frac{B_0}{K} - RT \ln \frac{P_{HCOOH}}{P_{H_2}^{0.5}}. \tag{35}$$

The values obtained by the above method are tabulated in Table 2.

According to the data of /15/ the heat of formation of the surface compound (nickel formate) in agreement with scheme (34) varies between 33 and 18 kcal/mole depending on the degree of coverage of the surface. Hence, in accordance with the data in Table 2, nickel is not the optimum catalyst under the above conditions; the optimum sites on its surface may lie within a lower range of the distribution and participate in the catalytic process when the reaction occurs within the saturation range, which is in agreement with the experimentally observed zero order. For the above reasons, the reaction should be faster on metals for which the heat of formation of surface formates is lower than on nickel. In this case the stability of the formate should be determined by the bond energy between the metal surface and oxygen. Since the excess free energy in the surface compounds of the metals with oxygen is small /16, 17/, we might expect a correlation between the stability of the bulk formates and the catalytic activity of the corresponding metals in reaction (33), with a certain stability being the optimal. In fact, according to the data of /15/ such a relationship does exist in the shape of a broken (analogous to the "volcano-shaped") curve on which nickel occupies a position to the right of the maximum.

TABLE 2. Values of q_{opt} for the formation of a surface formate in the dehydrogenation of formic acid

°C	P_{HCOOH}, mm Hg	Degree of conversion	q_{opt}, kcal/mole
177	230	0.5	8.1
327	0.1	0.1	15.1
327	0.1	0.9	19.0

5. Dehydrogenation of cyclohexane:

$$C_6H_{12} = C_6H_6 + 3H_2 \qquad (36)$$

was studied in a continuous-flow circulation system on nickel /18/ and on chromium oxide. The following equation is valid for the second case:

$$\omega = k P_{C_6H_{12}}, \qquad (37)$$

and the reaction may be described by a simplified scheme:

$$\left.\begin{aligned} &\text{I. } C_6H_{12} + [K] = C_6H_6\,[K] + 3H_2; \\ &\text{II. } C_6H_6\,[K] = C_6H_6 + [K], \end{aligned}\right\} \qquad (38)$$

in which the first stage is the rate-determining, assuming that the reaction takes place within the range of low degrees of filling. The above scheme corresponds to the equation:

$$q_{opt} = RT \ln B_0 - RT \ln P_{C_6H_6}. \qquad (39)$$

By substituting in the above equation the calculated value of $B_0 = 5.6 \times 10^{13}$ atm we obtain approximate values for q_{opt}, which are tabulated in Table 3.

As is evident from Table 3, the values of q_{opt} are fairly high. Since the heats of adsorption of benzene on chromium oxide should be lower than the values in Table 3 (this may be assessed from the values on nickel and copper /19/), we might expect that the reaction would proceed at low degrees of filling of the surface, which is in agreement with the observed kinetic equation.

6. Para-ortho conversion of hydrogen. According to the data of I.R. Davydova and this author /20/, the kinetics of the above reaction on nickel are described by the equation:

$$\omega = kP_{H_2}^{1-a} \qquad (40)$$

(α = 0.4 — 0.5) and by the scheme:

$$\left. \begin{array}{l} \text{I. } p\text{-}H_2 + 2\,[K] = 2H\,[K]; \\ \text{II. } 2H\,[K] = o\text{-}H_2 + 2\,[K] \end{array} \right\} \qquad (41)$$

(neither of the stages is rate-determining), which corresponds to the equation /7/:

$$q_{opt} = RT \ln 3B_0 - RT \ln P_{p\text{-}H_2} . \qquad (42)$$

The approximate values of q_{opt} obtained for $B_0 = 10^{6.6}$ atm are shown in Table 4.

TABLE 3. Optimum heats of adsorption of benzene in reaction (36)

°C	$P^\circ_{C_6H_{12}}$, mm Hg	Degree of conversion	q_{opt}, kcal/mole
377	760	0.2	43.9
477	760	0.2	50.6
477	10	0.2	56.1

TABLE 4. Optimum heats of adsorption of hydrogen q_{opt} at 300°K in the para-ortho conversion of hydrogen

Pressure, mm Hg	q_{opt}, kcal/mole
760	8.8
20	12.4
0,02	16.6

It is evident that changes in the pressure may affect sharply the value of q_{opt}. It might be expected that metals on which the heat of adsorption of hydrogen q_{H_2} is within the range of q_{opt} would be better catalysts than metals for which the values of q_{H_2} are lower for instance. Data from the literature on the reaction rates on various metals and on the corresponding values of q_{H_2} are shown in Table 5.

As is evident from Table 5, the reaction rate is the lowest on metals belonging to subgroup IB, which is usually attributed to the absence of d-electron vacancies in these metals. The heats of adsorption of hydrogen are also the lowest on these metals. This may mean that the optimum sites on these metals are the sites with the greatest adsorption capacity; hence, the reaction may take place at low degrees of filling which is in agreement with the fact that the reaction on these metals is of the first order (according to the changes in pressure). In most cases the evaluated values of q_{opt} are close to the middle of the range of variations of q_{H_2} (except for the metals belonging to subgroup IB and possibly tungsten). At the same time in most cases the reaction is of a fractional order, which could indicate that it takes place at medium degrees of filling. The reaction rate on tungsten is the highest, although it is still possible that the reaction takes place at high degrees of filling. The maximum in the reaction rate is apparently associated with the great mobility of the adsorbed layer and some other factors /26/. The problem of the optimum rate of the para-ortho conversion of hydrogen has been discussed in detail in another paper by this author /27/.

TABLE 5. Reaction rate of the para-ortho conversion of hydrogen according to the data of /21/ at 1.2 mm Hg and the rates of adsorption of hydrogen q_{H_2}

Catalyst	Reaction rate calculated for 0°C, mole·sec^{-1}·cm^{-2}	Activation energy, kcal/mole	q_{H_2}, kcal/mole
Ni	$7.7 \cdot 10^{17}$	2.6	22—4 [22]
Co	$2.2 \cdot 10^{18}$	4.5	19—9 [23]
Fe	$4.9 \cdot 10^{17}$	3.9	18—8 [23]
W	$5.7 \cdot 10^{20}$	3.7	45—4 [24]
Pt	$1.4 \cdot 10^{19}$	2.7	30—9 [25]
Pd	$1.0 \cdot 10^{18}$	3.5	30 [24]
Cu	$4.0 \cdot 10^{14}$	8.8	14—8 [25]
Ag	$7.5 \cdot 10^{14}$	7.7	—
Au	$1.1 \cdot 10^{15}$	6.1	—

7. **Synthesis of ammonia.** In an earlier paper, M.I. Temkin and this author /6/ evaluated the optimum heat of adsorption of nitrogen for the synthesis of ammonia in which the rate-determining stage is the adsorption of nitrogen; the values of q_{opt} were 38 kcal/mole at 450° and 1 atm, and q_{opt} 30.3 kcal/mole at 300 atm. These values are close to the middle of the range of heats of adsorption of nitrogen q_{N_2} on iron /9/ and tungsten /28/, which are active catalysts for the above reaction, but are rather far from the value of q_{N_2} on tantalum, for instance (140 − 90 kcal/mole /29/). It is well known that tantalum does not catalyze the synthesis of ammonia, although it readily adsorbs nitrogen.

8. **Hydrogenation of ethylene.** The kinetics of the above reaction on nickel at 50 − 100° have been studied in a gradient-free system by G.I. Kaplan and this author /30/ and correspond to the equation:

$$\omega = kP_{H_2}. \tag{43}$$

The value of q_{opt} may be expressed by means of the equation

$$q_{opt} = RT \ln B_0 - RT \ln P_{C_2H_4}, \tag{44}$$

assuming that the fast stage involves the formation of a surface compound of ethylene. By substituting the value of $B_0 \approx 10^{7.5}$ atm we obtain at 330°K and 1 atm $q_{opt} \approx 11$ kcal/mole, while at a pressure of about 1 mm Hg we obtain $q_{opt} \approx 14$ kcal/mole. The heats of adsorption of ethylene on nickel are high (40 − 58 kcal/mole /31/), and hence the most active sites could be those with the lowest adsorption capacity, which indicates the probability of occurrence of the reaction within the range of high degrees of filling. We could also expect high reaction rates on metals on which the heat of adsorption of ethylene is lower than for nickel. In fact, rhodium which is characterized by the lowest heat of adsorption of ethylene (among all metals studied in /31/) is also the most active.

9. Liquid-phase hydrogenation:

$$A + nH_2 = AH_{2n} \qquad (45)$$

(A is an unsaturated compound).

The above reactions, which were studied in detail by D. V. Sokol'skii et al., /32/ pass through a number of successive stages and may be described by the following simplified schemes:

$$\left. \begin{array}{l} \text{I. } n\,H_{2\,\text{dissolv}} = 2n\,H_{\text{ads}}; \\ \text{II. } 2n\,H_{\text{ads}} + A_{\text{dissolv}} = AH_{2n\,\text{dissolv}} \end{array} \right\} \qquad (46)$$

where

$$\left. \begin{array}{l} \text{I. } A_{\text{dissolv}} = A_{\text{ads}}; \\ \text{II. } A_{\text{ads}} + n\,H_{2\,\text{dissolv}} = AH_{2n\,\text{dissolv}}. \end{array} \right\} \qquad (47)$$

Scheme (46) corresponds to the following expressions for q_{opt}, when the first or the second stage respectively is the rate-determining:

$$q_{\text{opt}} = RT \ln B_0 K + RT \ln \frac{c_A}{c_{AH_{2n}}}; \qquad (48)$$

$$q_{\text{opt}} = RT \ln \frac{B_0}{RT} - nRT \ln c_{H_2}, \qquad (49)$$

and scheme (47) corresponds to the following equations, respectively:

$$q_{\text{opt}} = RT \ln B_0 K + RT \ln \frac{c_{H_2}}{c_{AH_{2n}}}; \qquad (50)$$

$$q_{\text{opt}} = RT \ln \frac{B_0}{RT} - RT \ln c_A \qquad (51)$$

(c_A, c_{H_2}, and $c_{AH_{2n}}$ are the corresponding concentrations).

As is evident from the above equations, changes in the reaction mechanism may cause a sharp change in the calue of q_{opt}. By using equation (48) we find that at temperatures near room temperature for $K = 10^{17}$ atm^{-1} (e.g., for the hydrogenation of the most simple olefins) and $B_0 = 10^{6.6}$ atm /7/ (for the adsorption of hydrogen on metals) when $c_A/c_{AH_{2n}}$ decreases during the process from 100 to 0.01 the value of q_{opt} will change from 35 to 30 kcal/mole as a result of the reaction alone. Under the above conditions but at $K = 10^{10}$ atm^{-1} the value of q_{opt} will change from 25.5 to 20.0 kcal/mole. In the case of such a mechanism the reaction may take place on metals belonging to group VIII within the range of medium or low degrees of filling, and it is possible to use catalysts for which the values of q are fairly high. Hence, in such a case it would be of advantage to introduce additives that increase the value of q_{H_2}.

In the case of the other mechanism (when equation (49) is valid) and by taking into account the solubility of hydrogen (7.25 $\times$ 10^{-4} moles/l in water at 30° /40/) we obtain $q_{\text{opt}} = 11$ kcal/mole; in this case the value of q_{opt}

should not change during the reaction, since the solubility of H_2 remains unchanged. In such a case, if the adsorption bond of the hydrogen is strong enough (i.e., if the values of q_{H_2} are high, as in the case of metals belonging to group VIII) the reaction will proceed within the saturation range and it would be of advantage to introduce additives that reduce the value of q_{H_2} in order to accomplish the transition to the range of medium degrees of filling. Let us mention that the values of c_{H_2} may change also as a result of the addition of electrolytes and variations in the polarizability of the medium /34/; it is also necessary to take into account possible changes in the double layer on the catalyst /32/. For instance, if c_{H_2} changes by a factor of 100, q_{opt} may assume a value of 14 instead of 11 kcal/mole. Hence, it may be of advantage to introduce additives that reduce the solubility of hydrogen, or to replace the water by another solvent for which c_{H_2} would be lower.

Similar changes in the value of q_{opt} may take place also when scheme (47) is valid, as a function of the rate-determining stage. As in the previous case, the values of q_{opt} will be greater if stage I is the slow stage. Fairly great changes in q_{opt} are also possible here as a result of changes in the equilibrium constant in the transition from one compound to another. Cases of selective hydrogenation may be interpreted in an analogous way.

Thus, in the case of liquid-phase hydrogenation processes, a noticeable change in the reaction rate under the effect of various factors may be due to changes in the optimum characteristics of the sites on which the reaction takes place preferentially. The problem of the kinetic factors and the optimum reaction rates in liquid-phase hydrogenation has been discussed by the author in detail /33/.

III. THE OPTIMUM CATALYST

The examples discussed above show the effect of changes in the kinetic conditions and the reaction mechanism on the optimum characteristics of sites on the catalyst surface. Strictly speaking, all the above discussion does not refer to the optimum catalyst as a whole. It is evident that the optimum catalyst cannot be determined qualitatively on the basis of the optimum surface sites alone. In fact, the average adsorption and energetic characteristics of a catalyst in which 90% of the surface sites are optimal may be virtually the same as, or similar to, the characteristics of a catalyst in which only 1% of the surface sites are optimal (provided that the characteristics of these sites are near the middle of the whole range of variations of the adsorption capacity). At the same time, a sharp difference will exist between the activities of these two catalysts.

It is evident that the optimum condition derived from the quantitative expression for the principle of energetic correspondence (equation (21)) must be referred to the optimum surface sites on the catalyst (or to this average characteristic) rather than to the catalyst as a whole.

Hence, the optimum catalyst will be the one whose surface comprises a sufficiently large number of sites that are optimal under the given reaction conditions. The maximum possible number of optimum sites will be characteristic of a certain homogeneous surface. Such a hypothetical catalyst that is the optimal under certain conditions may be far from optimal when the process conditions are changed or when they change during the reaction itself. Hence, a catalyst with a homogeneous surface may be less advantageous.

The range of variation of the energetic characteristics of sections on a non-homogeneous surface is fairly wide; thus, there is a great probability that after a change in the process conditions the surface will still contain a sufficiently large number of sites that are optimal under the new conditions. This leads to the conclusion that a change in the reaction conditions on a non-homogeneous surface may not cause a sharp decrease in the reaction rate (as compared with the maximum possible) if the relative number of sites that are optimal under the changed conditions still remains sufficiently high.

Thus, in order to create optimum catalysts it is necessary to develop methods for the control of their surfaces, which should possess the required range of adsorption characteristics. In this case the optimum catalyst (for the given reaction within the prescribed range of conditions) will be that catalyst whose surface comprises the maximum possible relative number of sites whose adsorption properties correspond to the optimum characteristics.

A contradiction arises here: on the one hand the number of optimum sites should be the greatest possible, i.e., it is of advantage to have the greatest possible homogeneity, while on the hand it is necessary to have a non-homogeneous surface that possesses sites which could be the optimum sites when the reaction conditions are changed. It may be assumed that it would be sufficient to work with non-homogeneous surfaces in which the heats of adsorption on various sites vary between 8 and 10 kcal/mole. In this case the values of the adsorption coefficients α at 150° will differ by a factor of $10^4 - 10^5$, i.e., the following condition will be satisfied /7, 8/:

$$(a)_{min} \; p \ll 1 \ll (a)_{max} \; p \tag{52}$$

(where p is the volatility of the adsorbed layer); the above condition sets up the range of medium degrees of filling /8/.

IV. COMPARISON OF THE ACTIVITIES OF CATALYSTS AT THE TIME OF THEIR SELECTION

Not enough attention is given in every case to the correct comparison of the activity of catalysts at the time of their selection. It is evident that in order to determine the best catalyst it is necessary to compare the reaction rates under the optimum conditions. In the contrary case, we may find that a catalyst tested under conditions that are far from the optimum shows a lower activity than that of a less satisfactory catalyst which is tested under its specific optimum conditions, and this could lead to erroneous conclusions.

The optimum reaction parameters — temperature, starting composition, and pressure — depend on the thermodynamics and kinetics of the reaction. This problem has been discussed elsewhere /6, 35 —37/ and in more detail it has been discussed in a monograph /7/. The optimum characteristics are tabulated in Table 6.

130

TABLE 6. Optimum reaction parameters

Parameter	Characteristic of the reaction	Optimum condition	Note
Temperature	Exothermic	$$K_T = \tau_{\text{opt}} = \left(\frac{\overleftarrow{E}}{\overrightarrow{E}}\right)^{\chi} \frac{\prod_j (c'_j)^{v'_j}}{\prod_j c_j^{v_j}}$$	$K_T = \tau_{\text{opt}}$ — equilibrium constant at the optimum temperature; $\overrightarrow{E}$ and $\overleftarrow{E}$ — activation energies of the forward and reverse reactions; χ — stoichiometric number of the rate-determining (slowest) stage of the reaction; c_j and c'_j — concentrations of the starting substance and the reaction product respectively; v_j and v'_j — stoichiometric coefficients.
Composition of the starting mixture	At equilibrium and near the equilibrium	$P^0_{A_1} : P^0_{A_2} : P^0_{A_3} = v_1 : v_2 : v_3$	Kinetic equation: $$\omega = \overrightarrow{k} P^{n_1}_{A_1} P^{n_2}_{A_2} P^{n_3}_{A_3} P^{n_4}_{A_4} \ldots -$$ $$- \overleftarrow{k} P^{n'_1}_{A_1} P^{n'_2}_{A_2} P^{n'_3}_{A_3} P^{n'_4}_{A_4} \ldots$$
	Far from the equilibrium	$P^0_{A_1} : P^0_{A_2} : P^0_{A_3} = n_1 : n_2 : n_3$	
	In the intermediate region	$$K\left(\frac{n_1 n_2}{n'_1 n'_2}\right)^{\chi} = \frac{(v_1 + v_2)^{v_1 + v_2}(1-y)^{v_1 + v_2}\, r^{v_1}_{\text{opt}}\left[(1 - r_{\text{opt}})\frac{v_1}{v_2} + 1\right]^{v_2}}{(v'_1)^{v'_1}(v'_2)^{v'_2}}\, p^{\Delta v}$$	y — the prescribed degree of conversion; r_{opt} — the optimum deviation from the stoichiometric composition; Σn and $\Sigma n'$ — algebraic sums of the exponents for the forward and reverse reactions; m — constant; K — equilibrium constant.
Pressure	$\Delta v > 0; \ \Sigma n > 0$	$$P_{\text{opt}} = K^{1/\Delta v}\left(\frac{\Sigma n}{\Sigma n'}\right)^{\frac{\chi}{\Delta v}} m^{\frac{1-y}{\Delta v}}\, \frac{1 - y\,\frac{v_1 + v_2}{\Delta v}}{y\,\frac{v_1 + v'_2}{\Delta v}}$$	

131

It is evident that a change in the kinetic rules may cause a sharp change in the optimum conditions, even for the same reaction. Since the transition from one catalyst to another may be accompanied by a change in the reaction mechanism and kinetics, certain conditions may be the optimum for one catalyst but far from the optimum for a different catalyst. In order to determine the optimum conditions it is necessary to study the reaction kinetics, and in the transition to another catalyst it is necessary to make a rough evaluation of the most probable rules governing the kinetics (of course, this cannot serve as a substitute for a detailed study of the reaction kinetics).

It is very important how the comparison of reaction rates is made on the different catalysts. Evidently, a comparison of the rate constants is possible only for identical reaction-kinetics equations on the catalysts to be compared, otherwise the constants will have different dimensions. The initial rates should also be compared only for reaction kinetics of the same nature. For example, if the reaction products on one of the catalysts inhibit the reaction and this is not immediately evident, the reaction rates may be similar at first and this may lead to erroneous conclusions. Incorrect results may also be obtained if the comparison is based on the temperatures required to obtain a prescribed degree of conversion (in the case of different temperature coefficients). Hence, it is most correct to compare the reaction rates in terms of the amounts of products formed per unit surface area of the catalysts under the optimum conditions for each catalyst.

It must be also borne in mind that when the catalysts to be compared have different porosities, this may lead to different degrees of internal-differential inhibition, and a comparison of the reaction rates in such a case is meaningless. This indicates that it is necessary to take into account the optimum macrokinetic factors, which have been discussed in detail by G.K. Boreskov /37 — 39/.

Thus, in the development of the scientific principles of catalyst selection, great importance should be attached to the study of the reaction kinetics and mechanism and to the analysis of the kinetic rules in order to determine the optimum reaction conditions, and also to the development of analogous methods and the predicition of the most probable kinetic rules.

BIBLIOGRAPHY

1. BALANDIN, A.A. —ZhRFKhO, ch. khimicheskay, Vol. 61: 909. 1929; ZhOKh, Vol. 16: 793. 1946.
2. BALANDIN, A.A.—Uspekhi Khimii, Vol. 33: 549. 1964; BALANDIN, A.A. Mul'tipletnaya teoriya kataliza (The Multiplet Theory of Catalysis). Part 2. Moskva, MGU. 1964.
3. KOBOZEV, N.I.—ZhFKh, Vol. 1: 189. 1930; Vol. 31: 2162. 1957.
4. SCHUIT, G.C.A., L.L. VAN REIJEN, and W.M.H. SACHTLER. Actes du 2-me Congrès International de Catalyse, Vol. 1: 893. Paris, Technip. 1961.
5. TEMKIN, M.I.—ZhFKh, Vol. 31: 3. 1957.
6. TEMKIN, M.I. and S.L. KIPERMAN.—ZhFKh, Vol. 21: 927. 1947.
7. KIPERMAN, S.L. Vvedenie v kinetiku geterogennykh kataliticheskikh reaktsii (Introduction to the Kinetics of Heterogeneous Catalytic Reactions).—Moskva, Izd. "Nauka". 1964.
8. TEMKIN, M.I.—ZhFKh, Vol. 15: 296. 1941.
9. ROMANUSHKINA, A.E., S.L. KIPERMAN, and M.I. TEMKIN.—ZhFKh, Vol. 27: 1181. 1953.
10. KIPERMAN, S.L. Proceedings of the 3rd International Congress on Catalysis, Vol. 2: 603. —Amsterdam, North-Holland Publ. Co. 1965.

11. KIPERMAN, S.L., N.V. NIKOLAEVA, and I.R. DAVYDOVA.—In: Sbornik "Kataliticheskii sintez
    monomerov". Trudy Instituta Khimicheskikh Nauk AN KazSSR, Vol. 8: 3. 1962; Kinetika
    i Kataliz, Vol. 4: 603, 723. 1963.
12. VVEDENSKII, A.A. Termodinamicheskie raschety neftekhimicheskikh protsessov (Thermodynamic
    Calculations of Petrochemical Processes).—Leningrad, Gostoptekhizdat. 1960.
13. BALANDIN, A.A. and S.L. KIPERMAN.—ZhFKh, Vol. 31: 139. 1957.
14. NAGISHKINA, I.S. and S.L. KIPERMAN.—Kinetika i Kataliz, Vol. 6: 1010. 1965.
15. FAHRENFORT, J., L.L. VAN REIJEN, and W.M.H. SACHTLER. Mechanism of Heterogeneous Catalysis.
    Proc. of Symp., Ed. J.H. de Boer, p. 23. Amsterdam-London-New York-Princeton. 1960.
16. KIPERMAN, S.L., A.A. BALANDIN, and I.R. DAVYDOVA.—IAN SSSR, OKhN, p. 1129. 1957; In:
    Sbornik "Kinetika i kataliz", p. 141. Moskva, Izd. AN SSSR. 1960.
17. KIPERMAN, S.L. and A.A. BALANDIN.—In: Sbornik "Kinetika i kataliz", p. 159. Moskva, Izd. AN
    SSSR. 1960.
18. ANDREEV, A.A. and S.L. KIPERMAN.—Kinetika i Kataliz, Vol. 6: 869. 1965; Vol. 7: 120. 1966;
    GADZHI-KASUMOV, V.S., S.L. KIPERMAN, G.V. ISAGULYANTS, and A.A. BALANDIN.
    Kinetika i Kataliz, Vol. 7: 273. 1966.
19. YUNG-FANG, Yu., J.J. CHESSIK, and A.C. ZETTLEMOYER.—J. Phys. Chem., Vol. 63: 1626. 1959.
20. KIPERMAN, S.L. and I.R. DAVYDOVA.—Kinetika i Kataliz, Vol. 2: 762. 1962.
21. ELEY, D.D. and D.R. ROSSINGTON. Chemisorption. Ed. W.E. Garner, p. 137. London. 1957.
22. EUCKEN, A. and W. HUNSMANN.—Z. phys. Chem., Vol. 44: 163. 1939.
23. KWAN, T. Catalysis. Investigation of Heterogeneous Processes.—Collection of translated papers,
    p. 314. Moskva, IL. 1956.
24. TREPNEL, B. Chemisorption. [Russian translation. 1958.]
25. BEEBE, R.A. Handbuch der Katalyse, Vol. 4: 473.—Wien. Hrsgb. G.-M. Schwab. 1943.
26. COUPER, A. and D.D. ELEY.—Proc. Roy. Soc., Vol. A 211: 536, 544. 1952.
27. KIPERMAN, S.L.—Kinetika i Kataliz, Vol. 7: 579. 1966.
28. DAVIS, R.T.—J. Am. Chem. Soc., Vol. 68: 1395. 1946.
29. BEECK, O., W.A. COLE, and A. WHEELER.—Disc. Faraday Soc., Vol. 8: 321. 1950.
30. KIPERMAN, S.L. and G.I. KAPLAN.—In: Sbornik "Kataliticheskie reaktsii v zhidkoi faze". Trudy
    Vsesoyuznoi Konferentsii, p. 7. Alma-Ata, Izd. AN KazSSR. 1963; Kinetika i Kataliz,
    Vol. 5: 888. 1964.
31. BEECK, O.—Disc. Faraday Soc., Vol. 8: 118. 1950.
32. SOKOL'SKII, D.V. Gidrirovanie v rastvorakh (Hydrogenation in Solutions).—Alma-Ata, Izd. AN
    KazSSR. 1962.
33. KIPERMAN, S.L.—In: Sbornik "Katalizatory gidrirovaniya zhirov, sakharov i furfurola". Trudy
    Vsesoyuznogo Soveshchaniya. Chimkent. 1964. Alma-Ata, Izd. AN KazSSR. 1966;
    Tezisy dokladov (Abstracts of Papers), p. 42. Chimkent. 1964.
34. GIL'DEBRAND, D.G. Rastvorimost' neelektrolitov (Solubility of Nonelectrolytes).—Moskva, GONTI.
    1938.
35. TEMKIN, M.I. and V.M. PYZHEV.—ZhFKh, Vol. 13: 851. 1939.
36. BORESKOV, G.K. and M.G. SLIN'KO.—ZhPKh, Vol. 16: 377. 1943.
37. BORESKOV, G.K. Kataliz v proizvodstve sernoi kisloty (Catalysis in Sulfuric Acid Manufacture).—
    Moskva-Leningrad, Goskhimizdat. 1954.
38. BORESKOV, G.K.—In: Sbornik "Geterogennyi kataliz v khimicheskoi promyshlennosti", p. 5. Moskva,
    Goskhimizdat. 1955.
39. BORESKOV, G.K.—In: Sbornik "Problemy kinetiki i kataliza", Vol. 6: 404. Moskva, Izd. AN SSSR,
    1949.
40. Spravochnik po rastvorimosti. T. 1. Binarnye sistemy (Handbook of Solubilities. Vol. 1. Binary
    Systems).—Moskva, Izd. AN SSSR. 1961.

V. P. Lebedev

RELATIONSHIP BETWEEN THE COMPOSITION OF THE
ACTIVE CENTER, THE PROPERTIES OF THE ACTIVE
INTERMEDIATE COMPOUND, AND THE KINETICS OF
THE HETEROGENEOUS CATALYTIC PROCESS

Since any reacting chemical system passes through some active
intermediate compound, chemical processes may be classified on the basis
of the properties, composition, and the mechanism of formation of this
intermediate compound /1/. From the above point of view, a
heterogeneous catalytic process is a chemical process
which takes place with the participation of a substance
that is not included in the stoichiometric equation for
the reaction, that is in a different phase with respect
to the reacting substances, and that enters into the
composition of the active intermediate compound (AIC)
formed on the phase boundaries. Ultimately, the properties
of the AIC determine both the kinetics /2/ and the direction of the process,
while the selectivity and the specific activity of the catalyst are determined
in most cases by changes in the properties of the AIC as a result of changes
in the chemical nature of the catalyst. Thus, the AIC occupies a central
position in heterogeneous chemical processes: on the one hand its properties
are related to the chemical nature (the possible valence states) and the
composition of the active center, while on the other hand it (the AIC)
determines the reaction kinetics and the final state of the reacting system.

I. APPROACH TO AN ELUCIDATION OF THE COMPOSITION
AND STRUCTURE OF THE AIC

The experimental determination of the composition and structure of the
AIC is made difficult by the fact that in addition to the specific set of active
centers the catalyst surface is characterized by a more general set
of adsorption centers containing the active centers. Hence, the
experimental methods (which usually are physical methods) in general
reveal the nature of the adsorption states rather than of the AIC. This
makes it necessary to use indirect methods for the estimation of the
composition of the AIC. The following logical scheme of approach is
proposed.

1) A hypothetical structure of the AIC is assumed on the basis of data on
the composition of the active centers, collected for example by using the
geometrical principle of the multiplet theory /3, 4/ or by the statistical

method of the theory of active aggregates /5, 6/ (we should mention that in spite of differences in their fundamental assumptions, the above two methods in many cases lead to the same results, e.g., in the hydrogenation of multiple carbon-to-carbon bonds). This structure must satisfy a number of conditions: physically acceptable valence relationships should be assumed for the reactions between the active centers and the reagents; the redistribution of bonds within the AIC, with the formation of molecules of the products, should be assumed to be possible; and finally, it should not be in contradiction with the principle of detailed equilibrium.

2) The correctness of the selection of the AIC structure is judged by the possibility of deriving on its basis a kinetic equation that describes the experimental data. Although the above rule is not strictly sufficient, it is at least necessary.

The above leads to a descriptive definition of the active center. Its composition should be such that it provides (from the standpoint of stoichiometry) for the formation of the AIC, the distances between the separate atoms in the active center should permit the required bond redistribution in the AIC, and the valence states of the atoms in the active center should be such that the separate components of the AIC can be formed. The last condition may be made more specific by assuming that each of the centers composing the atoms should either contain two free valencies /7, 8/ or should pass fairly easily into a divalent state on interaction with the reactant /9/. The above shows that no special statements are made with respect to the "amorphous" or "crystalline" nature of the active center.

II. OXIDATION REDUCTION PROCESS

A number of papers based on the method of the theory of aggregates have shown that the elementary stage of catalytic oxidation-reduction processes takes place on a monoatomic active center. This has been established for the oxidation of sulfur dioxide on platinum and palladium carried on silica gel and alumina gel /10/; for the oxidation of ammonia on platinum carried on silica gel /11/ and alumina gel /12/; for the oxidation of the sulfite ion /13/; for the reduction of nitrophenol and picric acid on platinum on carbon /14/; for the reduction of acetone on nickel in mixed Ni/MgO catalysts /15/; and, finally, for the decomposition of hydrogen peroxide on various adsorption catalysts /13, 14, 16 — 19/. Below we shall discuss the last process realized with the use of platinum adsorption catalysts on carbon /20/, silica gel /21/, cadmium oxide /19/, and cadmium /18/.

A determination of the order of reaction n from the experimental kinetic curves shows (Figure 1 and Table 1) that n is related to the chemical nature of the carrier: for carbon $n = 1.7$, for silica gel $n = 1.2$, for cadmium oxide $n = 0.8$, and for metallic cadmium $n = 0$, i.e., the order of the reaction varies from two to zero. It is evident that the general kinetic equation must yield for the particular cases kinetic orders of zero to second, and it must also describe the experimental data for all four cases, which from the standpoint of kinetics appear to be quite different.

Let us assume (to a certain extent on the basis of the concepts advanced by the Schpitalsky /22/ and Kobozev /23/ theory of intermediate products in homogeneous catalysis) that the active intermediate compound is $Pt\diagdown\!\!\!\diagup\begin{smallmatrix}O\\|\\O\end{smallmatrix}$

and that it is in equilibrium with the starting components:

$$2H_2O_2 + Pt \overset{K}{\rightleftharpoons} PtO_2 + 2H_2O.$$

The intramolecular rearrangement on the AIC leads to the regeneration of the active center and to the evolution of oxygen:

$$PtO_2 \overset{k_r}{\rightarrow} Pt + O_2.$$

The process rate is directly proportional to the AIC concentration:

$$-\frac{d\,[H_2O_2]}{dt} = k_r\,[PtO_2]. \tag{1}$$

The concentration of free active centers is determined by the equation:

$$[Pt] = [Pt]_0 - [PtO_2]. \tag{2}$$

From (1), (2), and the equation for the equilibrium constant

$$K = \frac{[PtO_2]}{[H_2O_2]^2\,\{[Pt]_0 - [PtO_2]\}} \tag{3}$$

we obtain the kinetic equation:

$$-\frac{d\,[H_2O_2]}{dt} = k_r K\,\frac{[H_2O_2]^2\,[Pt]_0}{1 + K\,[H_2O_2]^2}. \tag{4}$$

By using equation (4) we can obtain variations in the order of the reaction between zero and two, i.e., in the required experimental range. The order of the reaction decreases when the equilibrium characterized by the constant in (3) shifts in the direction of the formation of the AIC; it increases if the direction shifts towards the formation of the starting components. In order to check the agreement with the experimental kinetic curves and with the graphical calculation of the constants, equation (4) should be written in the following linear form:

$$\frac{1}{-\dfrac{d\,[H_2O_2]}{dt}} = \frac{1}{k_r K\,[Pt]_0}\,\frac{1}{[H_2O_2]^2} + \frac{1}{k_r\,[Pt]_0}. \tag{5}$$

Graphs for all four cases are shown on Figure 2; they show that in spite of the apparent difference between the experimental data, equation (4) clearly describes the heterogeneous decomposition of hydrogen peroxide on platinum carried on carbon, silica gel, cadmium oxide, and cadmium.

The calculated results are shown in Table 1. The main remarkable observation is the fact that the energy of recombination of the AIC on PtO_2 is constant and independent of the chemical nature of the carrier (about 30,000 cal/mole). Hence, the properties of the AIC are virtually independent of the nature of the carrier, and all differences in the experimental data are associated with changes in the value of the experimental constant /3/.

The above facts make it possible to describe as follows the effect of the carrier: the chemical nature of the carrier has a decisive effect on the adsorption equilibrium between the active centers and the starting substances, but the properties of the AIC proper are independent of the carrier, be it an insulator, semiconductor, or conductor.

TABLE 1. Kinetic parameters of the decomposition of hydrogen peroxide on platinum on various carriers /18−21/

Catalyst	α *	% Me	n	E apparent, cal/mole	k_r, mol·sec^{-1}· atom^{-1}	ΔH, cal/mole
Pt/C	0.025	—	1.7	—	0.76	31000
	0.035	—	1.7	10500	1.05	30000
	0.050	—	1.7	—	0.32	29300
Pt/SiO$_2$	0.011	—	1.2	—	2.59	30000
	0.017	—	1.2	—	2.02	30600
	0.021	—	1.2	11500	1.37	30000
	0.033	—	1.2	—	0.78	29700
Pt/CdO	—	3	0.8	—	2.77	30500
	—	6	0.8	5300	3.03	30700
	—	8	0.8	—	4.33	31200
Pt/Cd	1	1	0	—	—	30800

* Degree of filling.

At the same time, what is the reason for the variations in the activation energy between 5,000 and 11,000 cal/mole, in spite of such a large (and unchanging, even as a result of variation in the chemical nature of the carrier) energy of recombination of the AIC? This is due to the fact that the rate constant k_{exp}, determined experimentally by a formally kinetic method is in fact, in accordance with equation (4), the product of the recombination constant k_r and the equilibrium constant K:

$$k_{exp} \approx k_r K = k_0 e^{\frac{\Delta S}{R}} e^{-\frac{E_r + \Delta H}{RT}}. \tag{6}$$

Hence, the apparent energy of activation E_{app} equals:

$$E_{app} = E_r + \Delta H. \tag{7}$$

As an example let us examine the data for the Pt(6%)/CdO catalyst. The equilibrium constant K at 20° equals 5.35 cm^{-6} and at 25° it equals 2.64 cm^{-6}, which yields $\Delta \bar{H}$ = -24,000 cal/mole and indicates that the formation of the AIC is essentially an exothermic reaction. By substituting in (7) the numerical values we obtain:

$$E_{\text{app(Pt/CdO)}} = 30\ 700 - 24\ 000 = 6700 \text{ cal/mole},$$

which is in agreement with the experimental value of 5,300 cal/mole.

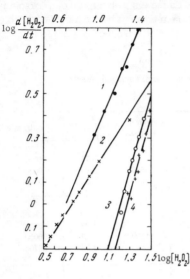
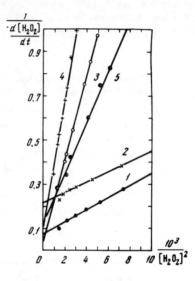

FIGURE 1. Determination of the order of reaction in the heterogeneous decomposition of hydrogen peroxide on adsorption platinum catalysts

1- Pt/SiO$_2$, n_{SiO_2} = 1.2, α = 0.033; 2- Pt(6%)/CdO, n_{CdO} = 0.8; 3- Pt/C, n_{C} = 1.7, α = 0.015; 4- Pt/C, n_{C} = 1.7, α = 0.035.

FIGURE 2. A check of the kinetic equation for the decomposition of hydrogen peroxide, based on experimental data

1 — 4 see Figure 1; 5- Pt(1%)/C.

Thus, the proposed composition of the AIC yields a kinetic equation that describes satisfactorily the experimental data, makes it possible to explain the experimentally observed laws, and provides a unified basis for the discussion of cases with quite different formal kinetics.

III. HYDROGENATION OF UNSATURATED COMPOUNDS

Both the fundamentals of the multiplet theory /3, 4, 24/ and experiments carried out by the method of the theory of aggregates /13, 14, 25—31/ lead to the conclusion that an elementary active hydrogenation center should be diatomic: doublet, diatomic aggregate, etc. (The considerations concerning the activity of more complex structures /4, 14, 24, 29, 31—34/ require a special analysis and will not be taken into account in the present paper). The following scheme for the hydrogenation process has been proposed on the above basis /35, 36/.

Dissociative adsorption of hydrogen:

$$H_2 + Me \rightarrow Me \begin{matrix} \diagup H \\ \diagdown H \end{matrix}$$

and of the molecule to be hydrogenated:

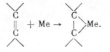

take place on the diatomic active center, each atom of which has two free valencies. The AIC is a complex of the reactants adsorbed on the diatomic center:

in which a rearrangement of the bonds leads to the formation of a saturated molecule:

If the above mechanism is valid, it may be used as a basis for the derivation of the kinetic equation for the hydrogenation of unsaturated C —C bonds. In this case it is unnecessary to derive a new equation, since the kinetics of hydrogenation processes have been studied in detail by A.A. Balandin /37/. On the basis of his concept on the existence of two types of surfaces: "hydrocarbonic" and "hydrogenic", Balandin derived the following general kinetic equation for hydrogenation processes:

$$v_h = \frac{ql}{i} zS'S \frac{b'\,[B]}{1+b'\,[B]+c'\,[C]+h'\,[H_2]} \frac{h\,[H_2]}{1+b\,[B]+c\,[C]+h\,[H_2]} = \frac{Kb'h\,[B]\,[H_2]}{M}, \quad (8)$$

where q, l, and i are kinetic constants; z is related to the equilibrium between atomic and molecular hydrogen; S' and S are the numbers of active centers on the hydrocarbonic and hydrogenic sections of the surface respectively; b' and b, c' and c, and h' and h are the adsorption coefficients for the hydrocarbonic and hydrogenic sections of the surface respectively; B denotes an unsaturated molecule and C denotes a saturated molecule;

$$K \equiv \frac{ql}{i} zS'S; \quad (9)$$

$$M \equiv 1 + (b + b')\,[B] + (c + c')\,[C] + (h + h')\,[H_2] +$$
$$+ (b'c + c'b)\,[B]\,[C] + (b'h + h'b)\,[B]\,[H_2] + (c'h + h'c)\,[C]\,[H_2] + \quad (10)$$
$$+ b'b\,[B]^2 + c'c\,[C]^2 + h'h\,[H_2].$$

Thus, the problem is to derive an equation (whose algebraic structure is analogous to that of equation (8)) on the basis of the proposed scheme of the elementary hydrogenation act. We shall use part of the notation used by Balandin. The number of diatomic centers on the surface is denoted by

139

$[Z]_0$, and the diatomic active center is denoted by Z. The rate of hydrogenation is directly proportional to the AIC concentration:

$$-\frac{d[B]}{dt} = k_r [H_2ZB]. \tag{11}$$

In addition to the AIC, several inactive intermediate compounds may be formed on the active center: H_2ZH_2, H_2ZC, BZB, CZC, CZB, CZ, H_2Z, and BZ. Hence, the number of free active centers is determined by:

$$[Z] = [Z]_0 - [H_2Z] - [BZ] - [CZ] - [H_2ZH_2] - [H_2ZB] - [H_2ZC] -$$
$$-[BZB] - [BZC] - [CZC]. \tag{12}$$

Let us assume that an adsorption equilibrium exists between the intermediate compounds and the reactants:

$$
\begin{aligned}
&H_2 + Z \underset{}{\overset{K_H}{\rightleftarrows}} H_2Z, && K_H = \frac{[H_2Z]}{[H_2][Z]}; && (a)\\[4pt]
&H_2 + H_2Z \underset{}{\overset{K_{HH}}{\rightleftarrows}} H_2ZH_2, && K_{HH} = \frac{[H_2ZH_2]}{[H_2][H_2Z]}; && (b)\\[4pt]
&B + H_2Z \underset{}{\overset{K_{BH}}{\rightleftarrows}} BZH_2, && K_{BH} = \frac{[BZH_2]}{[B][H_2Z]}; && (c)\\[4pt]
&C + H_2Z \underset{}{\overset{K_{CH}}{\rightleftarrows}} H_2ZC, && K_{CH} = \frac{[H_2ZC]}{[C][H_2Z]}; && (d)\\[4pt]
&B + Z \underset{}{\overset{K_B}{\rightleftarrows}} BZ, && K_B = \frac{[BZ]}{[B][Z]}; && (e)\\[4pt]
&H_2 + BZ \underset{}{\overset{K_{HB}}{\rightleftarrows}} H_2ZB, && K_{HB} = \frac{[H_2ZB]}{[H_2][BZ]}; && (f)\\[4pt]
&B + BZ \underset{}{\overset{K_{BB}}{\rightleftarrows}} BZB, && K_{BB} = \frac{[BZB]}{[B][BZ]}; && (g)\\[4pt]
&C + BZ \underset{}{\overset{K_{CB}}{\rightleftarrows}} BZC, && K_{CB} = \frac{[BZC]}{[C][BZ]}; && (h)\\[4pt]
&C + Z \underset{}{\overset{K_C}{\rightleftarrows}} CZ, && K_C = \frac{[CZ]}{[C][Z]}; && (i)\\[4pt]
&H_2 + CZ \underset{}{\overset{K_{HC}}{\rightleftarrows}} H_2ZC, && K_{HC} = \frac{[H_2ZC]}{[H_2][CZ]}; && (j)\\[4pt]
&B + CZ \underset{}{\overset{K_{BC}}{\rightleftarrows}} BZC, && K_{BC} = \frac{[BZC]}{[B][CZ]}; && (k)\\[4pt]
&C + CZ \underset{}{\overset{K_{CC}}{\rightleftarrows}} CZC, && K_{CC} = \frac{[CZC]}{[C][CZ]}. && (l)
\end{aligned}
\tag{13}
$$

From the equilibria (13, a, b, e, and f) we obtain:

$$[H_2ZB] = (K_H K_{BH} + K_B K_{HB})[H_2][B][Z]. \tag{14}$$

From (12) and equilibria (13, a — m) we obtain:

$$[Z] = \frac{[Z]_0}{N}, \tag{15}$$

140

where:

$$N \equiv 1 + K_H[H_2] + K_B[B] + K_C[C] + (K_HK_{BH} + K_BK_{HB})[H_2][B] +$$
$$+ (K_HK_{CH} + K_CK_{HC})[H_2][C] + (K_BK_{CB} + K_CK_{BC})[B][C] +$$
$$+ K_HK_{HH}[H_2]^2 + K_BK_{BB}[B]^2 + K_CK_{CC}[C]^2. \tag{16}$$

By inserting equations (14) and (15) into (11) we obtain a general kinetic equation for the hydrogenation process:

$$-\frac{d[B]}{dt} = \frac{k_2(K_HK_{BH} + K_BK_{HB})[H_2][B]}{N}[Z]_0. \tag{17}$$

The algebraic structures of equations (8) and (17) are quite similar, but the physical meanings of the constants are somewhat different, which is due to the fact that equation (17) has been derived by assuming that the process takes place on the diatomic centers on the catalyst, without making a distinction between "hydrogenic" and "hydrocarbonic" sites. According to equations (8) and (17), the order of reaction of catalytic hydrogenation may vary from +1 to -1 (with respect to both the hydrogen and the substance to be hydrogenated). In most cases this prediction is confirmed by the experimental results. As a rule, the exceptions may be attributed to side reactions /36/. By analogy, additional terms for the effect of the solvent and for the hydrogenation of mixtures may be introduced into equation (17).

IV. IRREVERSIBLE POISONING OF ACTIVE CENTERS IN THE COURSE OF THE PROCESS

The above discussion concerned cases in which a stationary concentration of the active centers was established on the catalyst surface during the course of the process as a result of adsorption equilibrium. A more complicated pattern is observed in cases in which during the course of the catalytic process some of the centers are blocked as a result of irreversible adsorption, and the catalyst gradually loses its activity. This phenomenon may be observed by using many different experimental methods, for instance, by successive catalytic experiments on the same batch of the catalyst.

TABLE 2. Autopoisoning of platinum black in the successive decomposition of 100% ozone on the same sample at -195.6°C. Sample weight 60 mg, surface area 9 m^2/g

Serial No. of experiment	Contact time, hours	Decomposition of the O_3, %	Mean activity of the catalyst, $mol \cdot sec^{-1} \cdot atom^{-1}$	Relative decrease in activity
1	19.0	36.5	2.87	1
2	16.0	7.4	0.69	0.24
3	16.5	4.6	0.41	0.14
4	22.0	3.5	0.24	0.08

Data on the low-temperature (-195.6°) catalytic decomposition of 100% ozone /38, 39/ are shown in Table 2. It is possible to propose in this case, too, the following method (based on the theory of active centers) that leads to the derivation of a kinetic equation which takes into account the autopoisoning of the active centers in the course of the reaction. Since the rate of formation of the AIC is directly proportional to the concentration of the reactants and the number of the active centers, in cases in which it is sufficient to take into account the changes in only one of the reactants we may write the expression for the reaction rate as follows:

$$-\frac{d[B]}{dt} = k[B][Z], \tag{18}$$

and the number of free active centers at any moment of time may be determined from the equation:

$$[Z] = [Z]_0 - \beta\{[B]_0 - [B]\}, \tag{19}$$

where β is the probability of autopoisoning during each elementary act on the active center.

By substituting equation (18) in (19) and integrating we obtain the kinetic equation:

$$\log\frac{\frac{1}{\beta}[Z]_0 - [B]_0 + [B]}{[B]} = \{[Z]_0 - \beta[B]_0\}\frac{kt}{2,3} + \log\frac{[Z]_0}{\beta[B]_0}. \tag{20}$$

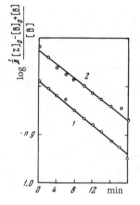

FIGURE 3. Check of the kinetic equation for the hydrogenation of benzalaniline against experimental data (taking into account the auto-poisoning) ($\frac{1}{\beta} = 30$):

1- $[Z]_0 = 2.6\cdot10^{18}$; 2- $[Z]_0 = 6.1\cdot10^{18}$.

Equation (20) was checked and showed good agreement with the experimental data for the polymerization of ethylene on oxide catalysts /40/ and for the hydrogenation of benzalaniline on platinum on silica gel /41/. In the last case an independent determination yielded a value of $\beta = 0.033$, i.e., irreversible poisoning of an active center occurred on the average in only one out of 30 elementary acts. A graphical check of equation (20) against the above experimental data is shown in Figure 3 (in this case the total number of platinum atoms on the carrier was taken as $[Z]_0$). Other, more detailed expressions should be used instead of equation (19) for more complicated cases, e.g., for the decomposition of ozone.

V. THE ACTIVITY OF AMORPHOUS AND CRYSTALLINE PHASES

The concept of a "crystalline" phase has a clear physical meaning: it is a phase in which a crystallographic order of arrangement of the particles exists at any point, in any direction of the three-dimensional space. From the standpoint of its use in catalytic problems, the concept of the "amorphous phase" is much less unambiguous. The experimental methods for the determination of the degree of dispersity are reduced, ultimately, to a determination of the adsorption accessibility of the surface atoms of the catalyst. Using such a definition, the term "amorphous phase" includes single atoms of the metal on the surface of the carrier, the monolayer of catalyst atoms on the surface of the carrier, and single (not included within the crystallographic system) atoms on the crystal surface. In connection with this, a problem posed earlier /42/ could be rewritten as follows: whether the catalytic activity is a specific function only of the surface components covered by the above definition of an "amorphous phase", or whether such an activity is a property also of surface atoms of the crystal that are part of the crystallographic system?

Previously we set only two conditions with respect to the active centers: that the required bond rearrangement should be possible, and that the atoms composing these centers should be divalent. Since both conditions are satisfied by both "amorphous" formations and the surface atoms of a crystal lattice /43, 44/ it is unnecessary to make a specific requirement concerning the "amorphous" or "crystalline" nature of the active center.

The same conclusion is reached on the basis of other facts, too; for instance, experiments show clearly a catalytic activity in adsorption catalysts known to have a fully crystallized surface /45, 46/. By applying to such a case the thermodynamic theory of non-ideal microcrystals, O.M. Poltorak /47/ showed that the concentration of the "amorphous" phase on the crystalline surface is only $10^{-3} - 10^{-4}\%$ of all surface atoms, while a direct catalytic experiment /48−50/ showed that 10−25% of the surface atoms of a crystal posses catalytic activity. Hence, a comparison of a thermodynamic analysis with experimental data leads to the conclusion that the productivity of crystalline catalysts cannot be attributed solely to the activity of the "amorphous" phase. Thus, we should assume that certain atoms from the surface lattice may serve as active centers.

BIBLIOGRAPHY

1. LEBEDEV, V.P.—In: Sbornik "Kataliz" v vysshei shkole", Part 1, p. 219. Moskva, Izd. MGU. 1962.
2. PSHEZHETSKII, S. Ya.—In: Sbornik "Geterogennyi kataliz v khimicheskoi promyshlennosti", p. 158. Moskva, GNTI. 1955.
3. BALANDIN, A.A.—ZhRKhO, Vol. 61: 909. 1929; Vol. 62: 703. 1930.
4. BALANDIN, A.A.—Z. phys. Chem., Vol. 33: 167. 1929.
5. KOBOZEV, N.I.—ZhFKh, Vol. 13:1. 1939.
6. KOBOZEV, N.I.—Uspekhi Khimii, Vol. 25: 545. 1956.
7. BALANDIN, A.A.—ZhOKh, Vol. 15: 1160. 1940.
8. SHCHEKIN, V.V.—Trudy Instituta Nefti AN SSSR, Vol. 13: 161. 1959.
9. LEBEDEV, V.P.—ZhFKh, Vol. 38: 2290. 1964.
10. SHEKHOBALOVA, V.I., N.I. KOBOZEV, and I.V. KRYLOVA.—ZhFKh, Vol. 26: 703, 1666. 1952.
11. SHEKHOBALOVA, V.I. and N.I. KOBOZEV.—ZhFKh, Vol. 37: 2131. 1963.
12. KOBOSEW, N.I., W.P. LEBEDEW, and W.I. SCHECHOBALOWA.—Chem. Techn., Vol. 10: 278. 1958.
13. KOBOZEV, N.I.—ZhFKh, Vol. 19: 71. 1945.
14. KOBOZEV, N.I. and N.A. RESHETOVSKAYA.—ZhFKh, Vol. 23: 388. 1949.
15. LEBEDEW, W.P.—Z. phys. Chem., Vol. 225: 101. 1964.
16. LOPATKIN, A.A., V.I. SHEKHOBALOVA, and V.P. LEBEDEV.—ZhFKh, Vol. 28: 2222. 1954.
17. NIKOLAEV, L.A. and N.I. KOBOZEV.—ZhFKh, Vol. 20: 145. 1946.
18. LEBEDEV, V.P. and E.A. TROSMAN.—ZhFKh, Vol. 34: 687. 1960.
19. STREL'NIKOVA, Zh.V., E.A. TROSMAN, and V.P. LEBEDEV.—ZhFKh, Vol. 35: 1327. 1961.
20. LEBEDEV, V.P.—Problemy Kinetiki i Kataliza, Vol. 10: 204. 1960.
21. STREL'NIKOVA, Zh.V. and V.P. LEBEDEV.—Vestnik MGU, No. 5: 25. 1960.
22. SCHPITALSKY, E.J.—Z. phys. Chem., Vol. 122: 17. 1926.
23. KOBOZEV, N.I.—ZhFKh, Vol. 15: 882. 1941.
24. BALANDIN, A.A. Mul'tipletnaya teoriya kataliza (The Multiplet Theory of Catalysis). Part 1.— Moskva, Izd. MGU. 1963.
25. FROST, A.V. and Yu.P. LAPIN.—Vestnik MGU, No. 1: 95: 1946.
26. BUKHAM, A.V. and D.V. SOKOL'SKII.—Izv. AN KazSSR, No. 2: 64. 1948.
27. GRYAZNOV, V.M., Yu.P. SIMANOV, L.K. USOVA, and A.V. FROST.—DAN SSSR, Vol. 65: 867. 1949.
28. SOKOL'SKII, D.V. and K.I. STENDER.—ZhFKh, Vol. 25: 369. 1951.
29. MAL'TSEV, A.N. and N.I. KOBOZEV.—ZhFKh, Vol. 29: 142, 292. 1955.
30. SOKOL'SKII, D.V. and E.I. GIL'DEBRAND.—ZhFKh, Vol. 29: 760. 1955.
31. STREL'NIKOVA, Zh.V. and V.P. LEBEDEV.—ZhFKh, Vol. 36: 1567. 1962.
32. BALANDIN, A.A.—Uspekhi Khimii, Vol. 4: 1004. 1935.
33. LEBEDEW, W.P.—Chem. Techn., Vol. 10: 267. 1958.
34. KOBOSEW, N.I., W.P. LEBEDEW, and A.N. MALZEW.—Z. phys. Chem., Vol. 217: 1666. 1961.
35. STREL'NIKOVA, Zh.V. and V.P. LEBEDEV.—Vestnik MGU, No. 1: 38. 1961.
36. SOKOL'SKII, D.V. Gidrirovanie v rastvorakh (Hydrogenation in Solutions).—Alma-Ata, Izd. AN KazSSR. 1962.
37. BALANDIN, A.A.—ZhOKh, Vol. 15: 608, 619, 770, 781. 1945; Vol. 16: 557. 1946.
38. EMEL'YANOVA, G.I., V.P. LEBEDEV, and N.I. KOBOZEV.—Vestnik MGU, No. 6: 7. 1960; No. 6: 31. 1961.
39. EMEL'YANOVA, G.I., V.P. LEBEDEV, and N.I. KOBOZEV.—In: Sbornik "Kataliticheskie reaktsii v zhidkoi faze", p. 454. Alma-Ata, Izd. AN KazSSR. 1963.
40. LANDAU, M.A.—Neftekhimiya, Vol. 4: 53. 1964.
41. LEBEDEV, V.P. and Zh.V. STREL'NIKOVA.—Nauchnye Doklady Vysshei Shkoly, No. 2: 260. 1959.
42. In: Sbornik "Kataliz v vysshei shkole", Part 1, pp. 5, 43, 64, 78, 107, 123, 189, 209.—Moskva, Izd. MGU. 1962.
43. PAULING, L. The Nature of the Chemical Bond. New York. 1960.
44. LANDAU, M.A.—IAN SSSR, OKhN, p. 582. 1962.
45. CHESALOVA, V.S. and G.K. BORESKOV.—ZhFKh, Vol. 30: 2560. 1956.
46. EMEL'YANOVA, G.I. and V.P. LEBEDEV.—ZhFKh, Vol. 38: 2293. 1964.
47. POLTORAK, O.M.—ZhFKh, Vol. 29: 1650. 1955; Vol. 32: 722. 1958.
48. SOKOL'SKII, D.V.—Problemy Kinetiki i Kataliza, Vol. 6: 157. 1949.
49. STREL'NIKOVA, Zh.V. and V.P. LEBEDEV.—ZhFKh, Vol. 37: 920. 1963.
50. GOROKHOVA, T.I., A.K. MAL'TSEV, and N.I. KOBOZEV.—ZhFKh, Vol. 39: 1206. 1965.

V.E. Vasserberg

ACCOUNTING FOR THE NON-HOMOGENEITY OF THE ACTIVE SURFACE IN THE SELECTION OF OXIDE CATALYSTS

The problem of the selection of the optimum catalyst for any technological process involves also a study of the reaction kinetics on the given catalyst. At the same time, the existing laboratory methods of kinetics studies involve, as a rule, experiments at relatively low degrees of conversion in gradient-free systems, and other similar artificial conditions that differ markedly from the conditions existing in industry. On the other hand, it is known that a catalytic reaction consists of a series of successive processes involving adsorption and desorption stages as well as the chemical reaction proper, which in many cases take place on non-homogeneous surfaces. Different sections of the surface, that differ in their adsorption and catalytic activities /1—5/, may work during the different reaction stages. The reaction kinetics also change markedly; hence, the factors associated with the non-homogeneity must be taken into account in the selection of the laboratory investigation methods.

In general, the rate of a catalytic reaction on a non-homogeneous surface should depend on three factors: 1) the number of active centers operating under the given conditions; 2) the catalytic activity of these single active centers or, more accurately, the mean activity of the working groups of active centers; and 3) the so-called mobility of the active sections. The term "mobility" refers to the ease of regeneration of an active section after a single elementary reaction act, or the ability of an active section to provide for a fairly rapid repetition of these single elementary acts.

A laboratory kinetic study should preferably make it possible to take into account all these three factors; however, it is difficult to evaluate all existing methods from this point of view, since the presently available data on the nature of surface non-homogeneity and on the elementary reaction acts are very scarce. In this paper we have made an attempt to make such an evaluation for the case of alumina-based catalysts prepared by various methods (Table 1), which have been investigated in a number of works /5—9/. The kinetics of dehydration of isopropanol on these catalysts were studied by various methods.

In the first place, the method for the study of reaction kinetics in adsorbed layers was applied to the study of the activity of separate active sections and of the nature of the non-homogeneity of the catalytic surface. It was found that the method of preparation has a marked effect both on the total activity (using the half-conversion time $\tau_{0.5}$ as a measure) and on the

145

energy of activation of the reaction in the adsorbed layer E, as well as on the nature of the surface non-homogeneity as determined by the so-called differential method /5/ (the method of progressive blocking). The results presented in Table 2 and Figure 1 show* that the surfaces of all catalysts used are markedly non-uniform. There are sections on which the alcohol molecules are adsorbed preferentially and the decomposition rate of the alcohol molecules is high, while on other sections the molecules are adsorbed to a lesser extent and the sections exhibit no catalytic activity. The data in Table 2 show also that a compensation effect (the preexponential factor increases with increasing E) is observed in the adsorbed layer under the conditions of the reaction.

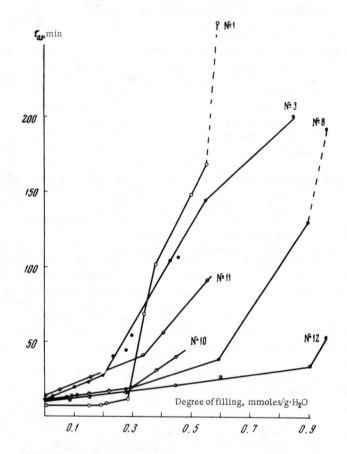

FIGURE 1. Distribution curves for the active centers on alumina catalysts prepared by different methods. The numbers on the curves correspond to the number of the catalyst; the experiments with catalyst No. 1 were carried out at 140°C, with No. 12 at 130°C, with No. 10 and 11 at 120°C, with No. 3 at 110°C, and with No. 8 at 100°C.

* In the calculation of the number of active sections we assumed that one molecule of the alcohol occupies one section, and took into account the difference between the specific areas of alcohol and water ($\omega_{eff\,H_2O}$ = 10.8 Å).

TABLE 1. Characteristics of the catalysts

Catalyst No.	Arbitrary designation	Method of preparation	Specific surface for N_2, m^2/g	Pore radius, Å	Effective elementary area (for iso-C_3H_7OH), Å^2
1	$K-$comm. Al_2O_3	Commercial active alumina, brand A-1, manufactured by the NIIUIF	130	32.5	32.6
2	$K-NH_4O_4$, 100°	Alumina precipitated from an aluminum nitrate solution by aqueous ammonia at 100°C	166	57.5	32.0
3	$K-CO_2$, 0°	Alumina precipitated from an aluminum nitrate solution by gaseous CO_2 at 0°C	220	10.0	31.7
4	$K-NH_4AT$	Another batch prepared by the same method as No. 2	195	—	—
5	$K-$aluminate + 10% ZnO	Precipitation by H_2SO_4 from a mixed sodium aluminate-nitrate solution, at the above ratio	295	22.5	42.1
6	$K-$aluminate + 5% ZnO	The same	265	—	—
7	$K-$aluminate + 2% ZnO	" "	41	Non-porous	36.0
8	$K-$aluminate + 0% ZnO	Precipitation by H_2SO_4 from Na aluminate solution ...	275	22.5	43.0
9	$K-NH_4OH$ + 10% ZnO	Precipitation by aqueous ammonia from a mixed solution of aluminum and zinc nitrates at the given ratio, at 100°C	290	33.0	52.0
10	$K-NH_4OH$ + 0.5% ZnO	The same	247	22.5	42.3
11	$K-NH_4OH$ + 0% ZnO	Precipitated by aqueous ammonia from a solution of aluminum nitrate at 100°C	173	—	—
12	$K-NH_3$(gas) + 10% ZnO	Precipitated from a mixed solution of aluminum and zinc sulfates at the given ratio by slow current of air passed in advance through concentrated aqueous ammonia at 20°C	245	—	—
13	$K-NH_3$(gas) + 5% ZnO	The same	236	—	—
14	$K-NH_3$(gas) + 3.5% ZnO	" "	270	—	—
15	$K-NH_3$(gas) + 2% ZnO	" "	304	—	—
16	$K-NH_3$(gas) + 0% ZnO	Precipitated from an aluminum sulfate solution by slow current of air saturated with ammonia at 20°C	176	—	—
17	$K-$Br, 60°	Precipitated from a Na aluminate solution by bromine water at 60°C ...	290	12.0	43.0

TABLE 2. Comparison of data collected in the study of the kinetics of dehydration of isopropanol on alumina catalysts prepared by different methods, under different reaction conditions

| No. of the catalyst | Arbitrary designation* | Energy of activation, kcal/mole | | | | Relative activity**, °C | | Mobility | | | log k_s for the reaction in the adsorbed layer | No. of active centers, 10^{10}/g |
| | | in the adsorbed layer (E_{ads}) | in the continuous-flow setup (E_{fl}) | in a chromatographic regime | | t°_{20} | t°_{100} | Flow rate of the gas, l/hr | | m | | |
				$E_{initial}$	E_{stat}			$v=10\ hr^{-1}$	$v=60\ hr^{-1}$			
1	K —comm. Al_2O_3	**17.0**	35.0	23.5	29.0	129	232	1.2	2.1	—	6.1	9.0
2	K — NH_4OH, 100°	**22.5**	30.0	18.0	24.0	114	216	1.5	4.3	0.29	9.5	8.0
3	K — CO_2, 0°	24.8	26.5	14.0	25.0	126	225	1.0	2.7	0.48	11.1	—
4	K — $NH_4 \cdot AT$	14.2	23.8	20.0	28.0	110	225	1.6	6.0	0.46	4.9	—
5	K — aluminate +10% ZnO	**24.5**	17.5	16.5	24.3	123	213	1.6	6.0	0.63	9.3	—
6	K — aluminate +5% ZnO	—	—	26.5	28.7	—	208	1.3	5.1	0.53	—	—
7	K — aluminate +2% ZnO	19.0	10.0	14.0	15.0	97	183	2.0	4.7	0.60	—	—
8	K — aluminate +0% ZnO	21.0	—	—	—	122	—	1.3	7.4	0.62	—	15.0
9	K — NH_4OH +10% ZnO	17.0	—	—	37.0	107	217	1.3	3.4	0.43	8.4	17.0
10	K — NH_4OH +0.5% ZnO	20.5	—	15.0	26.0	116	216	2.0	3.6	0.46	6.6	8.0
11	K — NH_4OH +0% ZnO	19.5	—	18.0	24.0	123	213	1.2	3.4	0.29	—	12.0
12	K — NH_3 (gas) +10% ZnO	21.4	—	—	37.0	127	215	1.4	3.0	0.41	—	—
13	K — NH_3 (gas) +5% ZnO	21.5	—	—	31.5	117	201	1.1	2.9	0.34	—	—
14	K — NH_3 (gas) +3.5% ZnO	22.0	—	—	21.5	124	218	1.1	3.8	0.58	—	—
15	K — NH_3 (gas) +2% ZnO	16.5	—	—	31.0	102	203	1.3	2.1	0.32	—	—
16	K — NH_3 (gas) +0% ZnO	—	—	—	24.5	117	223	1.6	4.0	0.51	—	—
17	K — Br, 60°	26.7	—	27.0	34.5	—	—	1.6	3.7	0.38	—	—

* For the methods of preparation refer to Table 1.

** As an arbitrary measure of the relative activity we used the temperatures at which the reaction rates are the same on all catalysts: t°_{20} is the temperature at which the half-decomposition time in adsorbed-layer reactions equals 20 min.; t°_{100} is the temperature at which the amount of propylene formed when the reaction is carried out in a chromatographic regime equals 100 arbitrary units (100 units on the chromatograph scale).

The results for the adsorbed layer, obtained by using the above method (i.e., the true energy of activation of the chemical reaction directly on the active sections, the number of such sections, the nature of their distribution, etc.) undoubtedly characterize some important parameters of the catalyst, but the above method is still inadequate for the selection of the optimum catalyst. Indeed, a comparison of the data obtained in the study of the same catalysts at first by the above method and then in a conventional continuous-flow setup at atmospheric pressure (see Table 2) show the absence of agreement in the activation energies, the temperature ranges, and the relative activities: catalysts that have the highest activities in an adsorbed layer may have a moderate activity under conventional conditions. This could possibly be attributed to the fact that sections with an especially high adsorption and catalytic activity are set free during the evacuation of the catalysts under high-vacuum and high-temperature conditions. Under the usual conditions of the reaction these sections are occupied by strongly adsorbed water and are unavailable to the alcohol molecules.

The validity of the above assumption was checked by another method, involving a study of the reaction kinetics under the so-called chromatographic regime (the method of pulsed intakes) /10/. By using this method it is possible to carry out both the reaction and the regeneration under usual conditions, and it may be regarded as a method for the study of adsorbed-layer reactions at atmospheric pressure.

It was found that dissimilarities exist in the activities of the investigated oxide catalysts, and that the catalysts can be classified into two groups. On some samples the rate of the dehydration reaction (as determined by the chromatographic method on the basis of the total amount of propylene formed) was high for the first batch of alcohol passed, but decreased gradually for subsequent batches (without regeneration) and reached a constant value after 5–8 passages. The same pattern was repeated after regeneration at 450–500° (see Figure 2). On other catalysts (data for these are not shown in Figure 2) we observed the opposite behavior: very little propylene was formed in the first passages, but the amount of propylene increased gradually and became constant again after 5–8 passages. Both phenomena were explained by assuming that the working groups of active centers changed: in the first case the water formed in the reaction poisoned the most active dehydration centers, while in the second case it poisoned the centers that were also able to polymerize the propylene formed in the reaction (polymerization of the produced olefin on the corresponding catalyst was observed by us also in the case of an adsorption

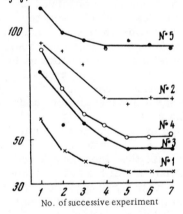

FIGURE 2. Dehydration of iso-propanol at 210°C in a pulsed chromatographic regime on alumina catalysts prepared by different methods.

The numbers on the curves correspond to the numbers of the catalysts.

149

layer in vacuo). Indeed, when the appropriate amount of water was adsorbed in advance on the catalyst working in a chromatographic regime, we found that the activity in both cases immediately reached a constant value.

By using the catalyst activities at different temperatures, we plotted the Arrhenius lines both for the highly-active fresh surface and for the stable, partially hydrated surface. The values of E (apparent) obtained were different for catalysts of different origins; different values were also obtained for the initial and steady activities of the same catalyst (see Table 2). In a number of cases these values differed from the values of E for the same catalysts that were determined previously in a monolayer and under conventional conditions; this should be taken into account in an evaluation of the possibilities of chromatographic regimes.

In addition to the changes in the activity of the catalyst as a result of the partial blocking of the surface by the water formed in the reaction, the reaction rates on separate active sections may change also as a result of the reaction itself. Thus, we have described elsewhere /6/ a case of conjugated dehydration of alcohols in an adsorbed layer, which was attributed to a reaction between the surface complexes formed in the process. A decrease in the extent of such an interaction was the factor used by us to explain /11/ the large (by a factor of 5—10) increase in the rate of dehydration of isopropanol in an adsorbed layer at extremely low degrees of coverage (of the order of 0.002—0.004 mmoles/g instead of the usual 0.06—0.10 mmoles/g). An increased rate of production of the olefin in the low-temperature dehydration of isopropanol may be observed on "isolated" sections of the alumina surface under usual conditions, too, by conducting the reaction in a current of carbon dioxide, nitrogen, or argon.

Returning to an analysis of the data collected under a chromatographic regime, we must agree that this method of kinetic studies permits us to collect valuable data on the reaction mechanism but does not, by itself alone, allow us to predict the course of the reaction under regular conditions, when the active working surface has a different nature and when the reaction has a different effect on the system.*

The methods of investigation of the reaction in an adsorbed layer make it possible to evaluate the relative activities of the different sections, but provide a seemingly static picture of the surface, that does not take into account the differences in the performance dynamics of the active centers. This may be accomplished by measuring the productivity of the catalysts — the amounts of reaction products formed during a gradual increase in the volumetric flow rate v_{vol}. As is evident from Figures 3 and 4, the differences between the investigated catalysts are relatively small at v_{vol}, and these differences are determined by the relative activity and the low number of active centers on the respective samples. The picture changes noticeably at high flow rates, and the mobility factor becomes predominant. Catalysts possessing centers with a high mobility are capable of processing larger amounts of the substance within the same time. It is of interest to mention that the highest productivity may be characteristic of catalysts that do not have the greatest number of active centers or centers that have

---

* The problem of the effect of the reaction proper on the system: catalyst — reactant was set in a general form quite a long time ago by G.K. Boreskov /12, 13/ , and was developed (although from a different point of view) in subsequent works on the electronic theory of catalysis.

the greatest activity in the individual reaction act. In these cases the mobility plays an important role in the activity of the catalyst.

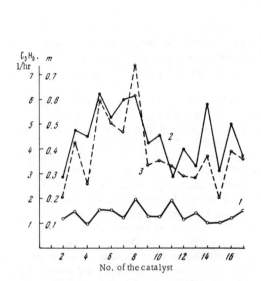

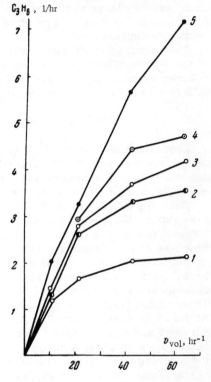

FIGURE 3. Productivity and mobility of various alumina catalysts in the dehydration of isopropanol at 285°C:

1- reaction rate at v_{vol} = 10 hr^{-1}; 2- reaction rate at v_{vol} = 60 hr^{-1}; 3- mobilities ratio m.

FIGURE 4. Dependence of the rate of dehydration of isopropanol at 285°C on v_{vol} for alumina catalysts with different porous structures:

1- catalyst No. 2, with a pore radius r = 57.5 Å; 2- catalyst No. 10, r = 22.5 Å; 3- catalyst No. 3, r = 10 Å; 4- catalyst No. 7, non-porous; 5- catalyst No. 8, r = 22.5 Å.

Curves similar to those in Figure 4 had been obtained previously by other investigators, but for catalysts for which there were no data on the number of the active centers and the activity in the elementary reaction act. Thus, the mobility factor remained hidden, and it was included in the concept of surface activity. The differences in the productivities of catalysts as a function of changes in the flow rates were usually attributed to macrokinetic factors: diffusion hindrances, difficult access to the inner surface as a result of ultramicroporosity, etc. The influence of macrokinetic factors is very great, but the experimental data show that in the cases studied by us these factors have no decisive effect on the productivity.

We made an experimental determination of the porous structure of the catalysts studied by us (on the basis of the adsorption branches of the adsorption-desorption isotherms for dichloroethane at 0°). We found that all structural curves had a sharp maximum indicating that a certain most-probable pore radius is strongly predominant, and that pores with very small or very large radii are virtually absent. The values of the predominant pore radii are shown in Table 2 with the mobility of the corresponding catalyst.

The so-called mobilities ratio m may serve as a quantitative measure of the degree of mobility. Numerically it is equal to the ratio of the reaction rates w (in this case — the rate of formation of propylene) at different flow rates divided by the ratio of these flow rates:

$$m = \frac{w_2}{w_1} : \frac{v_2}{v_1} = \frac{w_2 v_1}{w_1 v_2} .$$

From the above definition it is clear that the maximum value of m is unity; at the same time the reaction does not depend on the ease of regeneration of the centers and its rate is directly proportional to the rate of supply of the starting substance.

The values listed in the table show that in the case discussed here the pore radius of the catalyst does not govern its activity. Furthermore, the largest pore radius (54 Å) characterizes the least productive catalyst, for which we could assume a priori the strongest diffusion hindrances.

The experimental results are also shown in Table 2, and on Figures 3—6. As is evident from Table 2 and Figure 5, the values of E for the decomposition of isopropanol, calculated by different methods* and for different catalysts, lie within a fairly wide range (from 10 to 37 kcal/mole). At the same time, a correlation (strict correspondence) exists only for curves 3 and 4, corresponding to different phases in the activities of the same catalysts under a chromatographic regime. Apparently, in all cases the blocking by water causes in the first place the deactivation of centers characterized by a lower energy of activation for the dehydration reaction, but the nature of the surface inhomogeneity differs from catalyst to catalyst. For instance, in the case of catalysts No. 1—5 the differences between the values of E for the most active centers (the first to be poisoned by the water) is 7—10 kcal/mole, which is of the same order of magnitude as the heat of adsorption of water on alumina; in the case of the promoted catalysts (No. 6 and 7) the difference is only about 2 kcal/mole, which is rather close to the experimental error and indicates a less energetic non-homogeneity of the active surfaces of these catalysts. Let us mention, by the way, that a direct determination of the nature of active-center non-homogeneity on the basis of reactions in a monolayer (see Figure 1 and Table 2) was made for catalysts No. 9 and 10 (which also contain zinc as a promotor) and showed the presence of many sections characterized by a relative low and constant activity. The difference between the values calculated from curves 1 and 2 is about 18 kcal/mole for catalyst No. 1, and only 2 kcal/mole for catalyst No. 3; such differences cannot, apparently, be attributed to the effect of any single factor and are caused by differences in the nature of the non-homogeneity and mobility and, possibly, in the reaction mechanism under the conditions existing in a monolayer and in a continuous-flow setup for catalysts made by different methods.

* The value of E for catalyst No. 4 (which was kindly provided by A. A. Tolstopyatova) was calculated by the Balandin equation.

2187

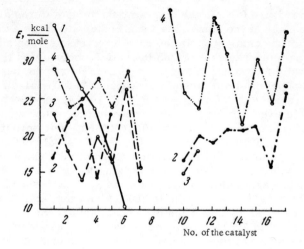

FIGURE 5. Energies of activation E calculated by different kinetic methods for the dehydration of isopropanol on alumina:

1- E(apparent) calculated (approximately) on the basis of the degree of conversion in a continuous-flow setup under usual conditions; 2- E (true) for dehydration in an adsorbed layer; 3- E(apparent) for a reaction in a chromatographic regime at a steady activity of the catalyst; 4- the same for the first passages of the alcohol.

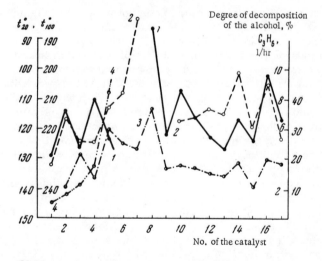

FIGURE 6. Relative activities of catalysts under different operating conditions:

1- t_{20}° for a reaction in an adsorbed layer; 2- t_{100}° in a chromatographic regime; 3- rate of formation of C_3H_6 (l/hr) in a continuous-flow setup at 285°C and at v_{vol} = 60 hr^{-1}; 4- degree of decomposition of the alcohol in a continuous-flow setup at 240°C and v_{vol} = 3.6 hr^{-1}.

A somewhat better correlation is obtained by a direct comparison of the activities of the catalysts in a chromatographic regime and in an adsorbed layer in vacuo (Figure 6). On the diagram, the temperatures at which the reaction takes place at the same rate for all catalysts serve as a measure of the activity of the catalysts. In the case of reactions in an adsorbed layer this is the temperature at which the half-decomposition time is 20 minutes (t_{20}°) while for a chromatographic regime this is the temperature at which the amount of olefin formed corresponds to 100 scale divisions in the chromatographs (t_{100}°). Catalysts No. 2, 4, 10, 14, and 16 were found to be the most active; however, their productivities at low volumetric flow rates were not only the best (see Figure 3) but their activities were below the average. This also shows that under the usual continuous-flow conditions (even at small v_{vol}) the reaction does not take place on the most active sections that can be determined by kinetic studies in a monolayer or by a chromatographic method (according to Roginskii-Yanovskii). The effect of the mobility factor is exhibited by the fact that at high flow rates the difference between the activities of the catalysts becomes much larger: it increases from 2 to 7.4 l/hr (propylene) when the reaction is carried out under the same conditions (with respect to the amount of catalyst taken, the grain size, etc.) but on different samples. At the same time, the most active are those catalysts (for instance, No. 5 or 14) that are not the best at low flow rates (see Figure 3). Since the difference in the activities at low v_{vol} is relatively small, curve 3 on Figure 3 (which shows the mobilities ratio) lies close to curve 2. Figure 3 shows also that the mobility of a catalyst depends on the method of preparation, which, in principle, makes it possible to find methods for the rational control of these factors.

The fact that the porous structure does not determine the productivity of the catalysts in our experiments is evident also from Figure 4 and from the corresponding values in Table 2.

A certain idea on the degree of mobility of oxide-alumina catalysts in the above reaction may be obtained by measuring the adsorption under the conditions of the reaction, as described in /5/. At the same time, by comparing the data on the reaction rate and on the fraction of the catalyst surface occupied by the reactant it is possible to reach certain conclusions on the dynamics of the adsorption-desorption processes on this fraction of the surface, i.e., on the mobility of the active sections.

By comparing the kinetic parameters of the reaction obtained by different methods (see Table 2) we can see that the values of these parameters depend on the reaction conditions and may change markedly. This is not surprising, especially in the case of oxide catalysts for which the nature of the surface non-homogeneity and its changes during the reaction (under the effect of the products or of foreign substances) play an important role. Hence, we believe that in the selection of the optimum catalyst we should not confine ourselves to the use of any single kinetic method, but we should try to use different methods, if possible at the same time. Such a complex kinetic study could make it possible to evaluate the separate roles of the various factors affecting the activity of catalysts (number of centers, mobility, etc.) and to find their optimum values.

In conclusion, let us mention another possibility for the use of the non-homogeneity of active surfaces in the selection of oxide catalysts. In selecting the method of preparation of a catalyst it is necessary to improve the quality and increase the number of groups of centers that operate under the given conditions, rather than of all active sections on the surface. The activity of complex oxide catalysts, for instance, aluminosilicate catalysts in cracking and dehydration reactions, depends also on the activity and the nature of non-homogeneity of the starting alumina used for the preparation of these catalysts (this was observed also in our experiments). It seems that in the preparation of complex, promoted oxide catalysts it is necessary to try to make selective use of the active surface of the starting oxides, by placing the promoter or the second component of the catalyst not on the whole surface but only on that section of the surface that otherwise would remain inactive and would not contribute to the reaction. At the same time, it is necessary, if possible, not to affect the sections that have a sufficient activity without promotion.

BIBLIOGRAPHY

1. ROGINSKII, S.Z. Adsorbtsiya i kataliz na neodnorodnykh poverkhnostyakh (Adsorption and Catalysis on Non-homogeneous Surfaces).—Moskva, Izd. AN SSSR. 1948.

2. BALANDIN, A.A. Mul'tipletnaya teoriya kataliz (The Multiplet Theory of Catalysis). Part 2.—Moskva, Izd. MGU. 1964.

3. TEMKIN, M.I.—ZhFKh, Vol. 14: 1153. 1940; Problemy Kinetiki i Kataliza, Vol. 6: 54. 1949.

4. KIPERMAN, S.L. Vvedenie v kinetiku geterogennykh kataliticheskikh reaktsii (Introduction to the Kinetics of Heterogeneous Catalytic Reactions).—Moskva, Izd. "Nauka". 1964.

5. VASSERBERG, V.E. and A.A. BALANDIN.—Problemy Kinetiki i Kataliza, Vol. 10: 356. 1960.

6. VASSERBERG, V.E., A.A. BALANDIN, and T.V. GEORGIEVSKAYA.—DAN SSSR, Vol. 134: 371. 1960.

7. VASSERBERG, V.E., A.A. BALANDIN, and T.V. GEORGIEVSKAYA.—DAN SSSR, Vol. 140: 859. 1961.

8. VASSERBERG, V.E., A.A. BALANDIN, and T.V. GEORGIEVSKAYA.—DAN SSSR, Vol. 140: 1110. 1961.

9. VASSERBERG, V.E., A.A. BALANDIN, and M.P. MAKSIMOVA.—ZhFKh, Vol. 35: 858. 1961.

10. ROGINSKII, S.Z., M.I. YANOVSKII, and G.A. GAZIEV.—Kinetika i Kataliz, Vol. 3: 529. 1962.

11. VASSERBERG, V.E. Preprints of the 3rd International Congress on Catalysis. Amsterdam. 1964.

12. BORESKOV, G.K.—ZhFKh, Vol. 32: 2739. 1958.

13. BORESKOV, G.K.—ZhFKh, Vol. 33: 1969. 1958.

V. I. Yakerson, L. I. Lafer, and A. M. Rubinshtein

SELECTION OF CATALYSTS FOR THE CONVERSION OF ACIDS INTO KETONES

The problem of converting acids into ketones has become important with the recent development of a technological process for the synthesis of aliphatic acids by oxidation of paraffins /1/. The catalytic conversion of acids into ketones is of considerable interest from the point of view of the theory of intermediate compounds in catalysis. The reaction involves intermolecular condensation with simultaneous decarboxylation and dehydration:

$$RCOOH + R'COOH \rightarrow RCOR' + CO_2 + H_2O.$$

Although assumptions have been made concerning the mechanism of the above reaction, there are almost no papers dealing with the determination of the respective kinetic parameters, and very few papers have been dedicated to the determination of the reaction mechanism. We made an attempt to solve the problem of the mechanism, the role, and the principles of selection of catalysts for the conversion of acids into ketones, on the basis of a combination of the kinetic approach with physicochemical methods for the study of catalysts (X-ray diffraction, magnetic methods, surface area measurements, and the method of labelled atoms).

The kinetics of the ketonic decomposition of acetic acid on carbonates of the metals belonging to group II was studied by us in a continuous-flow system. The reaction was of the zero order with respect to the acid /2/. It was found that on all catalysts the conversion to ketone had a lower temperature limit, below which no reaction took place. X-ray diffraction studies of the catalysts after service revealed in all cases the presence of an acetate phase, whose amount increased with decreasing experimental temperature. The decomposition polytherms of the acetates indicate that the temperatures of the beginning of decomposition of the acetates were virtually the same as the lower temperature limit of the conversion to ketones.

Investigations of the kinetics of thermal decomposition of calcium, barium, cadmium, and magnesium acetates /3 — 5/, and a comparison with the kinetics of conversion of acetic acid into ketone on calcium and barium carbonates and on cadmium and magnesium oxides /2, 4, 6/ show that the catalytic conversion into ketones is a two-stage reaction: the first, rapid stage results in the formation of a salt, and the second, slow stage involves the decomposition of the salt into carbonate and ketone. The same has been observed in the case of conversion to ketones on the carbonates of metals belonging to group I /5, 7/, although there were certain differences, namely, that in the case of metals belonging to group II the decomposition of the salt took place in the solid phase, while in the case of metals belonging to group I it took place in a molten phase. The reaction kinetics are described by the Erofeev's topokinetic equation (in the case of a solid phase, for acetates of metals belonging to group II) or by a second-order equation (in the case of a liquid phase, acetates of metals belonging to group I).

Our data, as well as data from the literature, enabled us to present as follows the mechanism of decomposition of the salt at the stage determining the rate of the catalytic conversion to ketone:

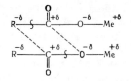

Bond formation and rupture occur simultaneously in the cyclic active complex composed of two molecules of the acetate of a monovalent metal; in this case the decrease in the energy of activation in the transition from lithium to rubidium is associated with a strengthening of the ionic nature of the metal-oxygen bond, which leads to a distribution of the charges and facilitates the dipole-dipole reaction between the two acetate molecules. The methanic decomposition of the acid, which occurs simultaneously with the above process on carbonates of metals belonging to group I (and which also passes through the salt-formation stage), is also associated with the ionic nature of the metal-oxygen bond. Thus, a reaction between the salt molecule and the strongly polar water molecule takes place during methanic decomposition:

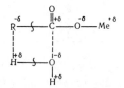

In the case of lithium, where the ionic nature of the bond is not strong, methanic decomposition is virtually absent; it becomes gradually more noticeable in the transition from sodium to rubidium.

Thus, the following cycle takes place on oxide and carbonate (of metals belonging to group I and II) catalysts in the course of the reaction: the acid reacts with the carbonate or oxide (of the metal) causing a disruption of the crystal lattice of the carbonate or the oxide, which is followed by a disruption of the crystal lattice of the salt (of the acid) and the formation of the crystal lattice of the oxide or carbonate. The rate of the last reaction is independent of the surface area of the catalyst and the polymorphic variety of the oxide or carbonate taken, and depends only on the chemical nature of the catalyst.

This leads to the conclusion that in the case of compounds with a high crystal lattice energy the disruption of the lattice is very unfavorable and the reaction will involve a different mechanism. A comparison of the crystal lattice energies of oxides of groups II and IV shows that in the case of oxides of group II it fluctuates between 700 and 1,000 kcal/mole, while for oxides of group IV it is much larger, i.e., 2,500 — 3,000 kcal/mole. In fact, an intermediate salt is not formed on oxides of the tetravalent metals (namely, on titanium, zirconium, tin, and cerium oxides) and the phase composition of the catalyst remains the same before and after the experiment /8/.

Moreover, according to our data and data from the literature, the surface area has a pronounced effect on the catalytic activity. Studies of the kinetics of catalytic conversion of acetic acid to ketone on tetravalent-metal oxides have shown (for a zero-order reaction) that the specific catalytic activity of these oxides decreases in the transition from cerium to zirconium, titanium, and tin, while the energies of activation are approximately the same. No by-products are formed on these catalysts as a result of a splitting of the acid, and UV-irradiation has no effect on the catalytic activity. On the basis of these data, and taking into account the presence of hydroxyl groups on the surface of the catalyst, it can be assumed that the course of the reaction involves the formation of the following cyclic (six-atom) active complex:

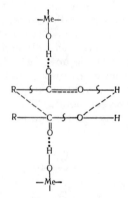

The orientation of two molecules required for the formation of the above complex is achieved during the adsorption of the acid on the surface as a result of the formation of hydrogen bonds between hydroxyl groups from the surface and the carbonyl oxygen from the acid. The advantages of such an orientation are as follows: a) carbonylic oxygen, which does not participate in the reaction, takes part in the adsorption; b) adsorption involving the creation of hydrogen bonds causes electron shifts followed by coordinated transfer of the electron in the cycle. The oxide of the metal serves as a "carrier" for its hydrated surface, and the nature of the metal has little effect on the energy of activation. The specific catalytic activity depends mainly on the preexponents whose values are determined by the number of hydroxyl groups per unit surface area. Let us mention that a disturbance of the conjugation chain (which occurs in cases in which the cation of the catalyst can change its valence) causes after a certain time a sharp drop in the activity; this was observed by us in the case of cerium dioxide. This is a good explanation of the fact that oxides of metals having a variable valence cannot serve as catalyst for the conversion of acids to ketones.

The data collected by us made it possible to select and prepare the most active mixed catalysts based on the presence of two groups differing with respect to the mechanisms of their activity.

Among the group of catalysts on which the reaction takes place with the intermediate formation of a salt of the acid, we selected and prepared the $CaCO_3 - Li_2CO_3$ system, for the following reason: each of the components of the above system catalyzes only the conversion to ketone, each of these components is the most active among the carbonates of metals of groups I and II respectively, and each forms the corresponding salt of the acid in the reaction, the difference between them being that the calcium salt is decomposed in the solid phase while the lithium salt is decomposed in the melt. The possibility of simultaneous participation (in the active complex) of the lithium and calcium acetates formed leads us to anticipate an increase in the catalytic activity, and such an increase was indeed observed in reality /9/.

Among the catalysts of the other group, on which the reaction occurs on the surface (where the surface area and the stability of the catalyst are of importance) we prepared the $ZrO_2 - Al_2O_3$ system. As we showed above, zirconium dioxide possesses the greatest specific catalytic activity /8/. Alumina was used as the second component because it has a large and hydrated surface, which resists sintering. This system was found to be extremely stable in the conversion of acetic acid to ketone. It could be used without regeneration over several months.

The laws established on the basis of the model reaction of conversion of acetic acid to ketone could be extended (because of their general nature) to cases that are much more complicated. The mixed alumina —zirconium oxide catalyst was used by us for the preparation of the rare alkyl pyridyl ketones, which have many uses. It is known that these ketones cannot be prepared by Friedel-Krafts synthesis. For the reaction we used esters of the aliphatic acids — from acetic to valeric — and of nicotinic or isonicotinic acids (the free carboxyl group is not required for adsorption on the surface). The yield of alkyl pyridyl ketones was 80% for the lower homologs and 30% for the higher. The stability of the catalysts was very high (several months of daily service without regeneration) /10/.

BIBLIOGRAPHY

1. TSYSKOVSKII, V.K. Sintez zhirnykh kislot i spirtov okisleniem zhirnykh parafinov (Synthesis of Aliphatic Acids and Alcohols by Oxidation of Aliphatic Paraffins). — Moskva, Goskhimizdat. 1960.
2. RUBINSHTEIN, A.M. and V.I. YAKERSON. — ZhOKh, Vol. 30: 2289. 1960.
3. RUBINSHTEIN, A.M. and V.I. YAKERSON. — DAN SSSR, Vol. 121: 664. 1958.
4. YAKERSON, V.I., E.A. FEDOROVSKAYA, and A.M. RUBINSHTEIN. — DAN SSSR, Vol. 140: 626. 1961.
5. YAKERSON, V.I. and A.M. RUBINSHTEIN. — Kinetika i Kataliz, Vol. 2: 172. 1961.
6. RUBINSHTEIN, A.M. and V.I. YAKERSON. — ZhOKh, Vol. 30: 3153. 1960.
7. RUBINSHTEIN, A.M. and V.I. YAKERSON. — Kinetika i Kataliz, Vol. 2: 118. 1961.

8. YAKERSON, V.I., E.A. FEDOROVSKAYA, A.L. KLYACHKO-GURVICH, and A.M. RUBINSHTEIN.—
Kinetika i Kataliz, Vol. 5: 319. 1964.
9. RUBINSHTEIN, A.M., V.I. YAKERSON, and L.I. LAFER.—Kinetika i Kataliz, Vol. 5: 319. 1964.
10. RUBINSHTEIN, A.M., V.I. YAKERSON, and L.I. LAFER.—Certificate of Authorship,* No. 158881.
1963; Byulleten' Izobretenii i Tovarnykh Znakov, No. 23. 1963.

* [Approximately equivalent to patent.]

III. RULES GOVERNING THE SELECTION OF OXIDATION CATALYSTS

A. I. Gel'bshtein, N. V. Kul'kova, S. S. Stroeva, Yu. M. Bakshi, and V. L. Lapidus

ON THE MECHANISM OF THE SELECTIVE OXIDATION AND OXIDATIVE AMMONOLYSIS OF THE C — H BOND IN THE METHYL GROUP OF PROPYLENE

The aim of our investigation was to collect data on the mechanism of the catalytic action of complex $MoO_3 - Bi_2O_3$ catalysts with different compositions in the oxidative ammonolysis of propylene to acrylonitrile (AN):

$$H_2C = CH - CH_3 + NH_3 + 1.5\ O_2 \rightarrow H_2C = CH - CN + 3H_2O \qquad (1)$$

and the partial oxidation of propylene to acrolein:

$$H_2C = CH - CH_3 + O_2 \rightarrow H_2C = CH - CHO + H_2O. \qquad (2)$$

In order to achieve the above aim, it was necessary to elucidate the effect of the chemical composition and the corresponding electrophysical properties of the $MoO_3 - Bi_2O_3$ system on the ability of this system to cause selective oxidation and oxidative ammonolysis of the C — H bond in the methyl group, and to obtain reaction products containing the double bond of propylene.

The catalysts were analyzed for their phase composition by X-ray diffraction and thermographic methods /1/. It was found that under the conditions of preparation and use of the bismuth-molybdenum oxide catalysts, the substance that was formed and exhibited a catalytic activity was not a solid solution of the oxides (MoO_3 and Bi_2O_3) but chemical compounds — bismuth molybdates. The compositions of those molybdates and their concentrations in the system can be characterized by the atomic Bi:Mo ratio. We found that the $MoO_3 - Bi_2O_3$ system contains several phases: MoO_3 (phase I), $3MoO_3 \cdot Bi_2O_3$ (phase II), $2MoO_3Bi_2O_3$ (phase III), a phase which was arbitrarily designated as phase IV and which consisted of several bismuth molybdates with a Bi:Mo ratio greater than unity, and a bismuth oxide phase (phase V). The approximate ranges of existence of these phases were established. The presence in the above system of a bismuth molybdate with a Bi:Mo ratio equal to unity (phase III) was observed for the first time. This result has been confirmed by E. P. Gel'perin /2/, who reported data on the lattice parameters of the above and other bismuth molybdates.

The catalytic activity of the various $MoO_3 - Bi_2O_3$ catalysts (evaluated on the basis of the specific rate constant for the total conversion of C_3H_6 in reactions (1) and (2); see Figure 1) and the ability to catalyze the selective oxidation and the oxidative ammonolysis of the C — H bond of propylene pass through a maximum for a composition corresponding to an atomic Bi:Mo ratio equal to unity, i.e., when the system contains the maximum amount of phase III (see Figure 2). Molybdenum oxide is characterized by a relatively low activity and selectivity; bismuth oxide does not catalyze the formation of acrolein and acrylonitrile.

The decrease in catalytic activity in the transition from the optimum composition to compositions with Bi:Mo < 1 and from there to MoO_3 is accompanied by a decrease in the selectivity, because of an increase in the relative contribution of reactions causing the destructive oxidation of propylene at the double bond, with the formation of aldehydes and nitriles containing less than three carbon atoms (acetaldehyde, acetonitrile, HCN). A transition to compositions with Bi:Mo > 1 causes a rapid decrease in the catalytic activity with respect to all types of propylene conversion except its complete oxidation to CO_2 (see Figure 2).

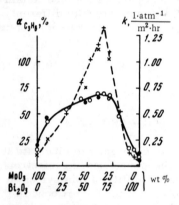

FIGURE 1. Dependence of the degree of conversion of the C_3H_6 (α) and the rate constant (k) of the overall conversion of C_3H_6 (at 450°C, τ = 0.75 sec) on the composition of the catalyst:

⊙ + oxidative ammonolysis; ●, x partial oxidation.

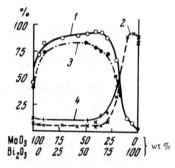

FIGURE 2. Dependence of the degree of conversion (based on the converted C_3H_6) at 450°C and τ = 0.75 sec on the catalyst:

1- oxidative ammonolysis of C_3H_6 to acrylonitrile; 2- the same to CO_2; 3- partial oxidation of C_3H_6 to acrolein; 4- the same to CO_2.

Kinetic studies of reactions (1) and (2) by the flow-circulation method revealed /3/ that on bismuth-molybdenum catalysts with a Bi:Mo ratio close to unity the above two reactions are of the first order with respect to propylene and of zero order with respect to oxygen if the partial pressure of the oxygen is not below a certain minimum value $(p_{O_2})_{min}$. Reaction (1) is not inhibited by the products, but reaction (2) is inhibited by acrolein. When the acrolein is frozen within the cycle of the flow-circulation system, the overall rates of the two reactions are virtually the same; the rates of formation of acrolein and acrylonitrile are also quite similar (see Figure 1). At temperatures not below 440° the overall degree of conversion of propylene in reaction (1) is independent of the partial pressure of ammonia. In the case of catalysts with an atomic Bi:Mo ≈ 1 and containing no additives the overall rate of reaction (1) is described by the equation:

$$r_1 = 3.8 \cdot 10^5 \exp\left(-\frac{16\,000}{RT}\right) p_{C_3H_6}.$$ (3)

The overall rate of reaction (2) when the acrolein is frozen within the cycle is:

$$r_2 = 1.0 \cdot 10^5 \exp\left(-\frac{15\,500}{RT}\right) p_{C_3H_6}.$$ (4)

The ratio of aldehydes to nitriles in the products of reaction (1) depends on the partial pressure of ammonia; this is valid only to $p_{NH_3} = 4 \times 10^{-2}$ atm, designated as $(p_{NH_3})_{min}$ (see Figure 3). An increase in p_{NH_3} from zero to $(p_{NH_3})_{min}$ causes a decrease in the yields of acrolein, acetaldehyde and CO_2, and an increase in the yields of acrylonitrile, acetonitrile, and HCN.

The results of the kinetic studies, including the data on the dependence of the composition of products of reaction (1) on the nature of the aldehyde added to the reaction mixture containing various amounts of ammonia /3/, lead to the following conclusions concerning the mechanism of the above reactions.

In the oxidative ammonolysis of propylene, the synthesis of nitriles (acrylonitrile, acetonitrile, and HCN) passes through an intermediate stage involving the formation of acrolein, acetaldehyde, and formaldehyde respectively; at $p_{NH_3} > (p_{NH_3})_{min}$ the stages of formation of the respective aldehydes and nitriles are preceded by the same limiting (slowest) stages.

It was assumed that in the formation of acrolein and acrylonitrile (products that retain the double bond and the number of carbon atoms of the starting olefin) the limiting stage is the dissociative adsorption of propylene with the formation of an adsorbed allyl radical and an adsorbed hydrogen atom:

$$H_2C{=}CH{-}CH_3 \rightleftarrows \left\{ \underset{S_1}{H_2C-CH-CH_2} \ldots \underset{S_2}{H} \right\}^{\neq} \rightarrow \underset{S_1}{H_2C-CH-CH_2} + \underset{S_2}{H}$$ (5)

(the sign $\neq$ in equation (5) denotes a transitory state, S_1 denotes the bismuth cation, and S_2 — the molybdenum cation). The above stage requires the participation of two cations from the surface of the catalyst as a doublet center for the dissociative adsorption of the propylene.

The fact that reactions (1) and (2) on a bismuth-molybdenum catalyst involve the formation of an intermediate allyl radical was proven recently /4 — 6/ by a tracer method. The dissociative adsorption of propylene must facilitate the formation of such a configuration of the transitory state in which one of the lattice cations is bound by coordination to the propylene (formation of a surface π-complex) and the other cation is bound (directly or by means of oxygen bound to it) to the hydrogen atom detached from the methyl group. The inductive polarization of the C — H bond in the methyl group, caused by the coordinative donor-acceptor interaction, facilitates the rupture of this bond.

The above data show that cations from the lattice of the catalyst must possess properties that enable them to fulfill the above functions. The maximum in the catalytic activity and selectivity in $MoO_3 - Bi_2O_3$ catalysts containing the maximum amount of bismuth molybdate with Bi:Mo = 1 (phase

III), the absence of selective catalytic properties in bismuth oxide, and the low catalytic activity and selectivity of molybdenum oxide may serve as a basis for the assumption that a doublet made of a bismuth cation (S_1) and a molybdenum cation (S_2) serves as a center for the dissociative adsorption of propylene, that is optimal from the standpoint of both the energetic and geometrical parameters. The peculiarities of the electronic structures of these cations, and the probable differences between the ionic natures of their bonds in the oxides and in bismuth molybdates of different compositions, agree with the concept that bismuth possesses the coordinating function in the composition of the doublet center, while the bond with the detached atom of hydrogen is formed with the participation of the molybdenum.

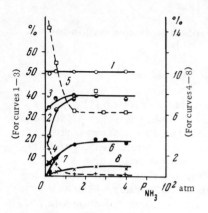

FIGURE 3. Effect of the partial pressure of ammonia at 460°C and τ = 2.8 sec on the yields of the products (α):

1- overall degree of conversion of the C_3H_6;
2- $\alpha_{AN} + \alpha_{CH_3CN} + \alpha_{resins}$; 3- $\alpha_{AN} + \alpha_{C_3H_4O} + \alpha_{CH_3CN} + \alpha_{resin}$; 4- $\alpha_{C_3H_4O}$;
5- α_{CO_2}; 6- α_{CH_3CN}; 7- $\alpha_{CH_3CN} + \alpha_{CH_3CHO}$; 8- α_{HCN}.

The coordinative donor-acceptor reaction between the catalyst and the olefin molecule may cause also a rupture of the double bond if the interaction energy is high enough. The formation of products of the destructive oxidation of propylene in reactions (1) and (2) (saturated aldehydes and nitriles containing less than three carbon atoms) is, most probably, a result of the adsorption of propylene with the rupture of its double bond.

The above concepts lead to the conclusion that the energy of donor-acceptor interaction is one of the factors that determine the probability of conservation or rupture of the double bond of the olefin during its interaction with the catalyst (i.e., the type of selectivity of catalytic action exhibited by the catalyst in the oxidation of unsaturated compounds).

According to widely accepted beliefs, the position of the Fermi level in the catalyst is a term in the expression for the surface interaction energy. Measurements have been made of the electron work function for $MoO_3 - Bi_2O_3$ catalysts of different compositions /7/. The measurements were made at 400° in a vacuum (10^{-6} mm Hg) and in air (400 mm Hg). A comparison of the data obtained in these measurements with the results of the kinetic study (Figure 4) show the absence of a simple relationship between the position of the Fermi level as determined by the electron work function and the catalytic properties of the different $MoO_3 - Bi_2O_3$ catalysts. The catalytic activity and selectivity have a maximum corresponding to a composition with Bi:Mo = 1, while the electron work function (at least for the various compositions with Bi:Mo < 4.6) has no extremum values but increases continuously with increasing molybdenum concentration in the system and reaches a maximum for pure MoO_3.

It was found also that the electrical conductivity of the different $MoO_3 - Bi_2O_3$ catalysts at the temperature ranges used in catalytic reaction is inversely proportional to the catalytic activity, namely, the compositions with the optimum catalytic properties are characterized by the lowest electrical conductivity. For instance, at 400° the specific resistance of MoO_3 is 8×10^6 ohm·cm., of the catalyst with Bi:Mo = 12×10^8 ohm·cm [sic, probably "of the catalyst with Bi:Mo = 1 it is 12×10^8 ohm·cm."], and of $Bi_2O_3 - 3 \times 10^6$ ohm·cm. This is in agreement with the concept according to which the individual peculiarities of the electronic structures of the lattice cations (which lead to the configuration described above for the transitory state in the limiting stages of reactions (1) and (2)) should be exhibited in the action between the catalyst and the adsorbed propylene molecules.

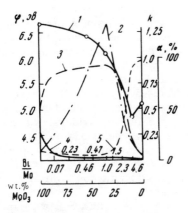

FIGURE 4. Dependence of the electron work function and the catalytic properties on the composition of the $MoO_3 - Bi_2O_3$ system:

1- work function; 2- overall rate constant k for the oxidative ammonolysis of C_3H_6; 3- yield of C_3 products; 4- yield of C_2H_3N + HCN; 5- yield of CO_2.

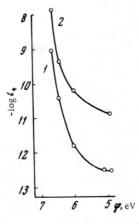

FIGURE 5. Dependence of the thermoemissive current of positive ions on the electron work function:

1- 410°C; 2- 450°C.

Thus, the change in the chemical composition of the $MoO_3 - Bi_2O_3$ system is accompanied by substantial changes in its catalytic and electrophysical properties. The catalytic activity decreases as a result of any change in the composition of the system that causes a decrease in the bismuth molybdate (with Bi:Mo = 1) concentration, although the extent of the decrease depends on the direction in which the composition is changed. At the same time, the nature of the changes in selectivity as well as the electrophysical properties depend to a much greater extent on the direction in which the composition changes (as compared with the optimum composition). A transition to compositions with Bi:Mo > 1 and farther to Bi_2O_3 is accompanied by an increase in the electrical conductivity and a decrease in the electron work function, and causes a decrease in selectivity as a result of the increased fraction of propylene completely oxidized to CO_2. A transition to compositions with Bi:Mo < 1 and then to MoO_3 is accompanied by an increase in both the electrical conductivity and the

165

electron work function, and causes an increase in the fraction of propylene subjected to destructive oxidation at the double bond.

The same conclusions are reached on the basis of measurements of the intensity of thermionic emission of positive ions from the surfaces of catalysts having different compositions when the catalysts are brought in contact with a current of air containing 1% C_3H_6 by volume, at 410 and 450° /7/. The catalysts were placed on the platinum disc (anode) of the diode lamp. The changes in the ionic current (i_+) and the electron work function caused by the variations in the catalyst composition were found to be in the same direction (Figure 5). However, the deviations from a linear relationship between log i_+ and the electron work function became more pronounced as the molybdenum concentration in the catalyst decreased. Hence, the electron work function is not the sole factor determining the rate of formation of products of the intermediate conversions of propylene in the presence of oxygen, and the rate of ionization of these products. The nature and rate of these conversions depend on the chemical composition of the catalyst, as well as on its electronic properties.

The true relationship between the chemical composition and the electrophysical and catalytic properties in the above and other mixed systems is more complicated. However, the nature of the changes in the selective catalytic effect with respect to the selective oxidation of the C — H bond or the double bond of unsaturated hydrocarbons as a result of changes in the chemical composition and corresponding electrophysical properties of systems such as V_2O_5 — MoO_3 /8/, MoO_3 — Co_3O_4 /9/, V_2O_5 — P_2O_5 /8, 9/, and WO_3 — Bi_2O_3 /1/ was found to be similar to those described above for the MoO_3 — Bi_2O_3 system.

The results of a study of the adsorption of oxygen on MoO_3 — Bi_2O_3 catalysts of various compositions showed that the adsorption is rapid. On these catalysts, an equilibrium adsorption is established almost instantaneously at p_{O_2} = 80 mm Hg. The adsorption kinetics at p_{O_2} = 0.2 mm Hg are described by the Zel'dovich-Roginskii equation. The activation energy for the adsorption at 400 — 450° decreases in the transition from MoO_3 (20 kcal/mole) to the catalyst with Bi:Mo = 1 (16 kcal/mole) to Bi_2O_3 (14 kcal/mole). The isosteric heat of adsorption decreases in the same direction (8.5, 5.8, and 3.1 kcal/mole respectively).

Preliminary data on the isotopic exchange between oxygen from the gaseous phase and oxygen from the crystal lattice showed that at 350 — 550° the fraction of the exchanged oxygen increases in the transition from molybdenum oxide to bismuth oxide. The exchange takes place with the participation not only of surface oxygen but also of oxygen from within the lattice. The exchange on all catalysts was studied after heat treatment in vacuo at 450°.

It was found also that the initial rates of reduction of the various catalysts (again after a preliminary heat treatment in vacuum at 450°) by propylene at 450° decrease rapidly in the transition from MoO_3 to the bismuth molybdate compounds.

On the basis of all the data discussed above, we reached the conclusion that the nature of the relationship established between the rates of reactions (1) and (2) and the partial oxygen pressure may be explained, in a formal manner, by using the concept of the so-called depletive adsorption of oxygen. The above explanation is similar to the one offered by V.A. Roiter /10/ in order to explain the observed differences in the kinetic relations for the oxidation of hydrogen and various hydrocarbons on a V_2O_5 catalyst.

In the case of the reactions (1) and (2) investigated on a bismuth-molybdenum catalyst with $Bi:Mo \approx 1$, and assuming that the adsorption of O_2 has a depletive mechanism, the zero kinetic order with respect to hydrogen means that at $p_{O_2} > (p_{O_2})_{min}$ the adsorption rate of oxygen is sufficiently high to cause the capture (by the adsorbed oxygen) of all electrons transferred to the catalyst by the propylene and the ammonia during their chemisorption. The above condition is not satisfied at $p_{O_2} < (p_{O_2})_{min}$, and this causes partial reduction of the catalyst and leads to a decrease in its activity. Furthermore, it is assumed that the adsorption of ammonia in the presence of oxygen causes its oxidative dehydrogenation with the formation of chemisorbed $=NH$ radicals.

The mechanism of reactions (1) and (2) which is in agreement with the kinetic data and the above concepts of the nature of intermediate chemical reactions between the reactants and the catalyst, may be represented roughly by the scheme below:

$$O_2 \underset{r_{-16}}{\overset{r_{16}}{\rightleftarrows}} (O_2) \overset{r_{17}}{\rightarrow} \qquad NH_3 \underset{r_{-18}}{\overset{r_{18}}{\rightleftarrows}} (NH_3) \overset{(O_2)}{\underset{r_{19}}{\rightarrow}} (=NH)$$

$$HCN \qquad CH_3CN$$

$$r_{14}\uparrow(=NH) \quad r_{15}\uparrow(=NH) \quad r_{12}$$

$$Z_2(H_2C=CH-CH_3) \overset{r_7}{\rightarrow} Z_2(H_2\dot{C}-CH-CH_3) \overset{r_3}{\rightarrow} (H\overset{|}{C}HO) + (CH_3CHO) \underset{r_{-12}}{\overset{}{\rightleftarrows}} CH_3CHO$$

$$r_6\downarrow\uparrow r_{-6} \qquad \qquad \qquad r_{10}\searrow \quad \nearrow r_{11}$$

$$C_3H_6 \qquad\qquad\qquad\qquad \overset{r_8}{} \rightarrow CO_2$$

$$r_{-1}\uparrow\downarrow r_1$$

$$\uparrow r_5$$

$$Z_1(H_2C=CH-CH_3) \overset{r_2}{\rightarrow} Z_1(H_2C=CH=CH_2) \overset{r_3}{\rightarrow} Z_1(H_2C=CH-CHO) \underset{r_{-4}}{\overset{r_4}{\rightleftarrows}} H_2C=CH-CHO$$

$$(=NH)\downarrow r_{13} \quad r_{-4}$$

$$H_2C=CH-CN$$

The above scheme is based on the concept of the existence of two types of chemical adsorption of propylene, determining the rates of the observed conversions on bismuth-molybdenum catalysts under the conditions of reactions (1) and (2): a) dissociative adsorption on the Z_1 centers with the formation of an allyl radical, and b) adsorption with the rupture of the double bond of the propylene on Z_2 centers. It is assumed that the Z_1 doublet center consists either of a bismuth cation and a molybdenum cation (the catalyst having the optimum composition, with $Bi:Mo = 1$) or of two molybdenum cations (MoO_3 catalyzes the formation of acrolein and acrylonitrile). The Z_2 centers may also have the same composition, but they are characterized by a greater energy of the coordinative acceptor-donor interaction with the propylene molecules, sufficient to cause rupture of their double bonds.

The kinetic equations derived on the basis of the above scheme of the mechanism are in good agreement with the experimental data.

BIBLIOGRAPHY

1. GEL'BSHTEIN, A.I., S.S. STROEVA, N.V. KUL'KOVA, Yu.M. BAKSHI, V.L. LAPIDUS, I.B.
   VASIL'EVA, and N.G. SEVAST'YANOV.—Neftekhimiya, Vol.4: 906. 1964.
2. GEL'PERIN, E.P.—ZhNKh, Vol.10: 349. 1965.
3. GEL'BSHTEIN, A.I., Yu.M. BAKSHI, S.S. STROEVA, N.V. KUL'KOVA, V.L. LAPIDUS, and A.S.
   SADOVSKII.—Neftekhimiya, Vol.5: 118. 1965.
4. SACHTLER, W.T.H.—Red. Trav. chim., Vol.82: 243. 1963.
5. VOGE, H.H., C.D. WAGNER, and D.P. STEVENSON.—J. Catalysis, Vol.2: 58. 1963.
6. ADAMS, C.R. and T.J. JENNINGS.—J. Catalysis, Vol.2: 63. 1963.
7. STROEVA, S.S., L.A. RUDNITSKII, O.K. FOMIN, N.V. KUL'KOVA, and A.I. GEL'BSHTEIN.—
   Kinetika i Kataliz, Vol.5: 355. 1964.
8. LYUBARSKII, A.G. Dissertation.—Moskva, NIIOPik. 1963.
9. KERNOS, Yu.D. Dissertation.—Moskva, MITKhT im. M.V. Lomonosova. 1963.
10. ROITER, V.A. and V.A. YUZA.—Kinetika i Kataliz, Vol.3: 343. 1962.

N. I. Popova, B. V. Kabakova, F. A. Mil'man, V. P. Latyshev,
E. E. Vermel', K. P. Zhdanova, and Yu. A. Poltavchenko

NEW CATALYSTS FOR THE GASEOUS-PHASE OXIDATION OF HYDROCARBONS AND HALOGENATED HYDROCARBONS TO UNSATURATED CARBONYL COMPOUNDS

The main reason for the lack of development of catalytic processes for the "soft" oxidation of hydrocarbons is the absence of a sufficient selection of catalysts with a group selectivity, i.e., with ability to carry out the selective oxidation of a larger number of hydrocarbons belonging to the same homolog series. The typical catalysts for the "soft" oxidation of hydrocarbons — silver and copper — oxidize only the lower olefins with a satisfactory selectivity.

The present investigation had as its aim the development of new catalysts for the oxidation of hydrocarbons and halogenated hydrocarbons containing methyl or methylene groups activated by conjugation with the double bond or the aromatic ring into unsaturated or aromatic carbonyl compounds. In addition, we made an attempt to elucidate certain aspects of the process mechanism associated with the selectivity. The introduction of additives (heavy metal oxides) improved the selectivity of the copper catalysts and led to the development of methods for the catalytic synthesis (see the table) of a number of rare substances: pentadienals — by oxidation of piperylene and isoprene, and hexadienal — by oxidation of hexadiene-2,4.

Halogenated hydrocarbons — methylallyl chloride and m-chlorotoluene — were oxidized for the first time into the corresponding aldehyde halides — chloromethyleneacrolein and chlorobenzaldehyde. The data shown in the table and published earlier /1/ indicate that from the standpoint of the courses of the reactions leading to the formation of aldehydes, CO_2 and H_2O, the catalytic reactions investigated by us may be classified into three groups. The first group, comprising the oxidation of $C_3 - C_4$ olefins, is characterized by a fairly selective reaction on copper catalysts without additives. In the case of the second group, comprising the oxidation of higher hydrocarbons ($C_5 - C_6$ dienes, $C_7 - C_8$ aromatic hydrocarbons, and $C_4 - C_7$ halogenated hydrocarbons) a satisfactorily selective reaction takes place only on copper catalysts containing oxides of the heavy metals. Finally, the oxidation of hydrocarbons in the third groups (ethylene, benzene, and methylacetylene) leads almost exclusively to the complete destruction of the molecules and the formation of CO_2 and H_2O, and the addition of heavy metal oxides does not change the nature of the process.

It has been established /2/ that the addition of heavy metal oxides to a copper catalyst does not change the energy of activation for the formation of carbonyl compounds (it equals $13 - 15$ kcal/mole) but increases the energy of activation for the formation of carbon dioxide, and in the case of a number of hydrocarbons its value is 20 — 23 kcal/mole. This indicates that the two processes have different limiting [rate-determining] stages. It would be of interest to compare the mechanisms of formation of carbon dioxide on copper catalysts containing no additives or containing heavy metal oxides. It has been shown by L. Ya. Margolis et al. /3/ (using the oxidation of propylene to acrolein as an example, by the tracer method) that even under moderate conditions the reaction proceeds mainly (up to 95%) through the consecutive formation of CO_2.

TABLE. New processes achieved by the oxidation of hydrocarbons and halogenated hydrocarbons on modified copper catalysts

Substance to be oxidized	Composition and yield (% on the basis of the converted hydrocarbon) of reaction products			
	main products		by-products	
$CH_2=CH-\underset{\underset{CH_3}{\vert}}{C}=CH_2$	$CH_2=CH-\underset{\underset{\underset{75.0}{CHO}}{\vert}}{C}=CH_2$		CO_2, H_2O CH_3CHO	25.0 Traces
$CH_2=CHCH=CHCH_3$	$CH_2=CHCH=CHCHO$ 75.0		CO_2, H_2O CH_3CHO	25.0 Traces
$CH_3CH=CHCH=CHCH_3$	$CH_3CH=CHCH=CHCHO$ 71.0		CO_2, H_2O CH_3CHO $OHCCH=CHCH=CHCHO$	25.0 Traces 5.0
$CH_2=C\underset{CH_2Cl}{\overset{CH_3}{<}}$	$CH_2=C\underset{\underset{90.0}{CH_2Cl}}{\overset{CHO}{<}}$		$CH_2=C\underset{CH_3}{\overset{CHO}{<}}$, CO_2, H_2O, Polymers	10.0
$H_3C-\!\!\!\bigotimes\!\!\!-Cl$	$OHC-\!\!\!\bigotimes\!\!\!-Cl$ 60.0		CO_2, H_2O	40.0
$CH_2=CH-CH_2-CH_3$ $CH_3-CH=CH-CH_3$	$CH_2=CH-CO-CH_3$ 50.0		CO_2, H_2O $CH_3-CH=CH-CHO$ Olefin oxides and saturated aldehydes	25.0 10.0 15.0

In the present paper we used the tracer method to study the mechanism of formation of CO_2 in the oxidation of toluene on a copper catalyst containing molybdenum and tungsten oxides. The experiments were carried out under rather moderate conditions, at contact times of 0.09 — 0.45 sec, at a $C_7H_8{:}O_2{:}N_2$ ratio of 10:15:75 and a temperature of 390°. Under these conditions we observed the same selectivity for different contact times, which is a common characteristic of reactions having a parallel course. According to the results of the radiometric measurements, in these experiments the CO_2 is formed by a successive-parallel scheme, with a marked predominance of the parallel path. When the contact time is reduced from 0.45 to 0.09 sec, the relative contribution of the parallel path increases from 68 to 95%. The conversion rates of toluene to benzaldehyde (w_1), of toluene to CO_2 (w_2), and of benzaldehyde to CO_2 (w_3), calculated by the kinetic method of Neiman [sic] are shown in Figures 1 and 2 as a function of the contact times. The different natures of these functions indicate different mechanisms of the corresponding processes.

As is evident from Figure 1, the changes in w_1 as a function of the contact time satisfies a bilogarithmic law — the curve for w_1 becomes a straight line when plotted on a log vs. log scale.

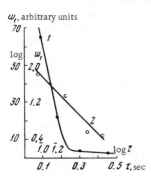

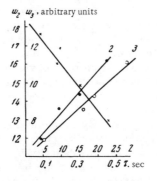

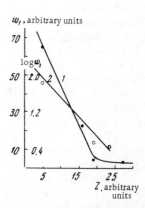

FIGURE 1. Dependence of the conversion rate of toluene to benzaldehyde w_1 on the contact time τ (1), and of log τ (2) in the oxidation of toluene on copper catalysts containing heavy metal oxides.

FIGURE 2. Dependence of the rate of formation of CO_2 from toluene w_2 (1) and from benzaldehyde w_3 (2), and dependence of w_3 on the amount of benzaldehyde adsorbed on the catalyst Z (3) in the oxidation of toluene on copper catalysts containing heavy metal oxides.

FIGURE 3. Dependence of rate of conversion of toluene into benzaldehyde w_1 on the amount of benzaldehyde Z adsorbed on the catalyst (1), and dependence of log w_1 on Z (2) in the oxidation of toluene on copper catalysts containing heavy metal oxides.

Such a shape of the curve indicates that the decrease in the rate of oxidation of toluene into benzaldehyde (w_1) with increasing time is caused by a decrease in the rate of adsorption of the starting substances — probably of oxygen, since under these conditions the reaction is of the first order with respect to oxygen. This decrease in the adsorption rate is caused by the blocking of active sections on the catalyst by the reaction products. This phenomenon is exhibited clearly on Figure 3, which shows the curves for w_1 and log w_1 as a function of the amount of benzaldehyde adsorbed on the catalyst under the given conditions. The difference between the laws governing the changes in w_1 (bilogarithmic in the first and logarithmic in the second case) can apparently be attributed to the fact that the effect of water (the second interfering reaction product) was not taken into account when the curves were plotted.

The rate of formation of CO_2 from toluene by the parallel mechanism (w_2) also decreases with increasing contact time; however, the data in Figure 2 show that this decrease is linear. Apparently, the oxidation of toluene to CO_2 takes place on surface sections that are more homogeneous than the sections catalyzing the conversion of toluene into benzaldehyde, and it is inhibited by water, since the second reaction product — CO_2 — does not affect the rate of the above process (according to the data of Ya.B. Gorokhovatskii et al. /4/).

Since w_2 also corresponds to a first-order reaction with respect to oxygen and a zero order with respect to the hydrocarbon, we may assume that the decrease in w_2 is also caused by the blocking of oxygen-adsorption centers by water on a catalyst surface that is more homogeneous (from the standpoint of energy) than in the case of w_1.

The change in the benzaldehyde oxidation rate w_3 is linear, but w_3 increases with the contact time. Apparently, the changes in w_3 are associated with the rate of desorption of benzaldehyde from the catalyst, which decreases with increasing contact time; this is confirmed by the fact that w_3 is directly proportional to the amount of adsorbed benzaldehyde. It should be noted that according to L.Ya. Margolis /3/ all acrolein and CO_2 formation rates in the oxidation of propylene on copper catalysts containing no additives decrease exponentially as a function of the contact time; this indicates that in this case the process takes place on non-homogeneous surfaces.

The formation of an energetically more homogeneous surface in the oxidation of toluene to CO_2 occurs probably through the blocking of the catalyst sections which are most active for this reaction by the heavy-metal oxides.

In an earlier paper /1/ we expressed the belief that the formation of aldehydes on copper catalysts (which in the equilibrium state contain both monovalent and divalent copper) takes place on the cuprous oxide, by adsorption of the hydrocarbon at the methyl group followed by the detachment of a hydrogen atom and the formation of an allyl radical; an aldehyde is formed when this radical reacts with adsorbed oxygen. The above mechanism of the process is supported by the data of U.S. scientists /5/, who used a tracer method. The same mechanism is supported also by the fact (revealed by us) that the same products are formed as a result of the oxidation of butene-1 and butene-2 on copper catalysts. In this case the oxidation of butene-2 takes place, apparently, according to the following scheme:

$$CH_3-CH=CH-CH_3 \rightleftarrows CH_2-CH=CH-CH_3 \rightarrow CH_2=CH-CH-CH_3.$$

We assumed also that total combustion on copper catalysts occurs mainly on the copper oxide, through a stage involving the adsorption of the hydrocarbons at the double bond or the aromatic ring, accompanied by a destruction of this bond or ring. This assumption is indirectly supported by the fact that CO_2 and H_2O are formed almost exclusively in the oxidation of ethylene and benzene (i.e., hydrocarbons containing no methyl groups), and by the almost complete absence of a reduction of cupric to cuprous oxide in these cases.

In order to check the validity of the above assumption we carried out an infrared spectroscopic study of the sorption of propylene on cupric and cuprous oxides. It was found (Figure 4) that in the case of cupric oxide the bands shifted in the direction of lower frequencies are almost exclusively those characterizing the $C=C$ bond oscillations ($1670 - 1640$ cm^{-1}); this indicates a deformation of the bonds. The oscillation bands of the $C-H$ bond ($1468 - 1396$ cm^{-1}) in the methyl group of the hydrocarbon are also shifted to the side of lower frequencies (by $20 - 30$ cm^{-1}) when cuprous oxide is used as the catalyst. These data support the above assumption on the different roles of cupric and cuprous oxides in the oxidation of hydrocarbons.

It is of interest to mention that an increase in the temperature above 320° or an increase in the contact time causes a shift of the band associated with the oscillations of the C — H bond in the methyl group when the reaction is carried out on cupric oxide, too; this is accompanied by reduction of the cupric oxide to cuprous oxide.

The above data lead to the following explanation of the effect of metal oxides on the selectivity of copper catalysts.

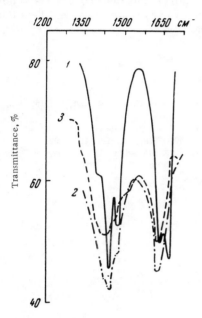

FIGURE 4. Infrared spectrum of pure propylene (1) (p = 38 mm Hg) and of propylene adsorbed on 1.5% CuO/Al_2O_3 (2) (p = 36 mm Hg) after two hours of heating at $180 - 200°C$, and on Cu_2O (3) (p = 39 mm Hg) after 30 min of heating at 320°C.

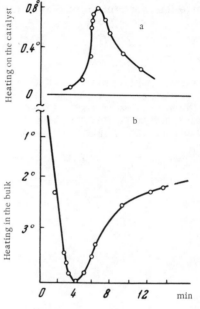

FIGURE 5.

a- heating curve for a copper catalyst surface in the oxidation of propylene to acrolein (370°C, p = 20 mm Hg); b- heating curve for the bulk of the gaseous mixture in the oxidation of methyl-acetylene on a copper catalyst (380°C, p = 120 mm Hg).

An increase in the molecular weight of the hydrocarbons to be oxidized is accompanied by an increase in the spatial hindrances for the orientation of the methyl group of the molecule on the catalyst, while at the same time and for the same reason the adsorption of dienes and aromatic hydrocarbons at the double bond or the aromatic ring, respectively, is facilitated.

The role of the heavy-metal oxide additives is reduced to the blocking (during the production of the catalysts) of the energetically most active surface sections on the copper oxide, and as a result the "exhaustive" oxidation takes place on copper oxide sections that are less active than in the case of additive-free catalysts and thus require a higher energy of activation. The introduction of additives does not affect the second process — the formation of aldehydes, since it occurs on active sections of the cuprous oxide that are formed in the course of the catalytic reaction, under the effect of the medium, and not during the production of the catalyst.

It should be stressed that under certain conditions (depending on the temperature and the nature of the substance to be oxidized) the oxidation of hydrocarbons on copper catalysts may be a homogeneous-heterogeneous process, with the formation of degradation products — mainly CO_2, CO, and H_2O; in such a case, a sharp decrease occurs in the yields of "soft oxidation" products. In the case of the homogeneous-heterogeneous scheme of the process (Figure 5), the introduction of heavy-metal oxides does not change the mechanism of the catalytic reaction.

BIBLIOGRAPHY

1. POPOVA, N.I., B.V. KABAKOVA, F.A. MIL'MAN, and E.E. VERMEL'.—DAN SSSR, Vol. 155: 149. 1964.
2. POPOVA, N.I. and R.N. STEPANOVA.—Kinetika i Kataliz, Vol. 2: 916. 1961.
3. ISAEV, O.V., L.Ya. MARGOLIS, and I.S. SAZONOVA.—DAN SSSR, Vol. 129: 141. 1959.
4. BELOUSOV, V.M., Ya.B. GOROKHOVATSKII, and M.Ya. BUBANIK.—Kinetika i Kataliz, Vol. 3: 221. 1962.
5. VOGE, H.H. and C.D. WAGNER.—J. Catalysis, Vol. 2: 58. 1963.

IV. RULES GOVERNING THE SELECTION OF METALLIC CATALYSTS

A.M. Sokol'skaya and S.M. Reshetnikov

ON THE EFFECT OF THE pH OF THE MEDIUM ON THE STRENGTH OF Pt − H AND Pt − C BONDS DURING HYDROGENATION IN BUFFER SOLUTIONS

The use of electrochemical methods for the investigation of hydrogenation catalysts has shown /1/ that the hydrogenation rate depends on the energy of the bond between the reactants and the catalyst surface.

The problem of the effect of the pH of the medium on the energy of the bond between the reactants and the catalyst is of great importance. We have shown /2 − 5/ that the pH of the medium affects the reaction kinetics and mechanism during hydrogenation in buffer solutions. We found that during the saturation of C = C bonds the reaction rate decreases with increasing pH. In the hydrogenation of compounds containing C ≡ C bonds or the nitro group the reaction rate remains virtually constant within the pH range between 2.5 and 13.0. It was assumed that the decrease in the hydrogenation rate with increasing pH is associated with the participation of hydrogen ions in the reaction. A case in which the reaction rate is independent of the pH is characteristic of compounds that can be adsorbed strongly on the catalyst surface and can displace from there a large fraction of other adsorbed species (adsorbed hydrogen, ions from the solution, reaction products). For compounds containing different functional groups, the dependence of the hydrogenation rate on the pH may not obey the above general laws. In such cases it is necessary to take into account the effect of pH on the state of molecules in the solution (solvation, prototropic transformations, salt formation, etc.).

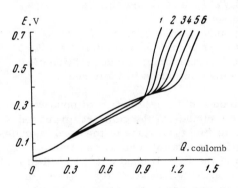

FIGURE. Charging curves for platinized platinum in sulfate solutions with a constant SO_4^{2-} ion-concentration:

1- pH 1; 2- pH 3; 3- pH 5; 4- pH 7.5; 5- pH 10; 6- pH 13.

By applying electrochemical /6, 7/ and kinetic research methods, we made an attempt (using the hydrogenation of certain unsaturated compounds as an example) to establish the effect of pH on the energy of the bonds between the reaction components* and the surface of the catalyst. We

---

* ["Reaction components" probably includes reactants, intermediate and final products; in some cases the term refers to reactants alone, and it is so translated.]

175

plotted the charging curves for platinized platinum in sulfate solutions. As is evident from the figure, an increase in pH is accompanied by an increase in the hydrogen region and the hydrogen desorption potential, which indicates that the degree of coverage of the platinum surface with hydrogen is increased and that the Pt — H bond is strengthened.

It is known /8/ that on a platinum charging curve the hydrogen region represents the hydrogen adsorption isotherm. In order to determine the heat of adsorption the isotherm is usually plotted at several temperatures. However, the heat of adsorption may be determined on the basis of a single isotherm, too /9/. Such a calculation based on the charging curves is perfectly acceptable for the determination of the heats of adsorption of hydrogen on metals of the platinum group /10/. The determination of the heats of adsorption of hydrogen makes it possible to calculate the catalyst-hydrogen bond energy. Since the heat of adsorption of hydrogen decreases with increasing degree of filling of the surface, the values calculated by us for the Pt — H bond energy would also change as the degree of filling of the surface changes. For instance, at pH 1.0, the Pt — H bond energy changes from 65.8 to 57.8 kcal/mole when the degree of filling is changed from 0 to 1.

Measurements of the potential of the catalyst in the course of the hydrogenation make it possible to evaluate the ratio of the reactants on the surface of the catalyst /7/ and to evaluate approximately the degree of filling of the surface with hydrogen /11/, and hence the bond energy with the hydrogen participating in the reaction.

Since the sorption of organic compounds on the surface of outgassed platinum surfaces is accompanied by their complete decomposition /1, 12 — 14/, the above method cannot be used for measuring the adsorption of the organic reactants, and hence for the determination of their heats of adsorption.

However, by using the kinetic method for the calculation of bond energies between the reactant molecules and the surface of the catalyst (proposed by A.A. Balandin /15/) we were able to find the values of the bond energies between platinum and hydrocarbons with double (hexene-1) and triple (phenylacetylene) bonds. The values of the Pt — H bond energy used in the above calculation were calculated by us in each case for degrees of filling of the platinum surface that corresponded to the potential of the functioning catalyst.

It should be noted that these values of the bond energies between the reactants and the catalyst surface should be regarded only as a first approximation, since the calculation of the Pt — H bond energy on the basis of the charging curves is of the same degree of accuracy as the calculation of the heats of adsorption of hydrogen /9/; moreover, the calculation of the degree of filling of the catalyst surface with hydrogen under the hydrogenation conditions is also only approximate /11/.

Data on the hydrogenation of hexene-1 are shown in Table 1. As is evident from the table, the hydrogenation rate (w, ml/min) decreases with increasing pH. This is accompanied by an increase in the degree of filling of the catalyst surface with hydrogen, as calculated from the shift of the potential (ΔE, mv) in the course of the reaction.

When the pH is increased the Pt — H bond energy increases somewhat while the Pt — C bond is weakened; however, the energy changes in both cases do not exceed 1 kcal/mole. Thus, in spite of the increase in pH, the hydrogenation is caused by hydrogen with only slight differences in the bond energies, and the adsorption potential of the catalyst remains constant with increase in pH. The reaction rate decreases as a result of the fact that the reaction of the more weakly bound hydrogen (which is most suitable for the hydrogenation of hexene-1) decreases as the pH is increased. Since the activation energy determined by us remains constant within the investigated pH range, it is evident that the decrease in the activity of the catalyst with increasing pH is associated with a decrease in the preexponential factor in the Arrhenius equation. Thus, it may be assumed that in the hydrogenation of hexene-1 the increase in pH causes a decrease in the number of active centers on the suface of the Pt catalyst.

TABLE 1. Hydrogenation of hexene-1 in a buffer solution on Pt-black

pH	w, ml/min	ΔE, mv	Degree of filling of the surface with hydrogen ω, %	q_{Pt-H}, kcal/mole	$q_{=C-Pt}$, kcal/mole
2.5	26.4	40	88.0	58.4	24.4
4.5	25.0	35	90.0	58.8	24.0
6.2	24.0	30	91.6	58.7	24.1
8.5	22.4	25	93.2	58.8	24.0
10.5	19.2	20	94.8	59.1	23.7
12.5	13.6	10	96.0	59.2	23.6
13.3	4.8	5	98.8	59.3	23.6

TABLE 2. Hydrogenation of phenylacetylene in a buffer solution on Pt-black

pH	w, ml/min	ΔE, mv	Degree of filling of the surface with hydrogen ω, %	q_{Pt-H}, kcal/mole	$q_{\equiv C-Pt}$, kcal/mole
2.4	9.0	60	81.8	59.2	34.3
4.2	10.0	60	82.9	59.4	34.1
6.5	11.2	65	82.5	59.6	33.9
9.0	10.4	70	82.4	60.3	33.2
10.4	10.4	75	81.5	60.6	32.9
12.9	11.2	80	81.0	61.2	32.3

Different rules govern the hydrogenation of phenylacetylene (Table 2). It can be seen that the hydrogenation rate of $C \equiv C$ bonds is not affected markedly by the pH. Phenylacetylene possesses greater adsorbability, as indicated by the higher values of ΔE for the reaction, than hexene-1. As a result, the hydrogenation of the $C \equiv C$ bond takes place at lower degrees of filling of the Pt surface with hydrogen. Since the strength of the $Pt - H$ bond increases with decreasing degree of filling, it is evident that the reaction involves the participation of hydrogen that is more strongly bound to the catalyst. The data in Table 2 indicate also that a carbon with a triple bond is bound to the platinum surface more strongly than a carbon with a double bond, and as a result phenylacetylene can displace from the catalyst surface a larger amount of hydrogen and other adsorbed species than hexene-1. For this reason, the pH of the medium has no marked effect on the hydrogenation rate of $C \equiv C$ bonds. As in the case of the hydrogenation of hexene, the pH of the medium has opposite effects on the $Pt - H$ and $Pt - C$ bond energies, but the adsorption potential of the catalyst is not changed as a result.

Similar relationships are observed in the hydrogenation of nitrobenzene (Table 3). In this case, too, the pH of the medium has little effect on the process kinetics, while the ΔE for the reaction is fairly large and increases with increasing pH.

Calculations show that the reaction occurs on a surface most of which is free of adsorbed hydrogen; in this case the hydrogen is bound to the surface even more strongly than in the previous cases.

Thus, the hydrogenation of the $C = C$ bond (which is weakly bound to the surface of the catalyst) is most rapid under conditions when a smaller fraction of the surface is occupied by the substance to be hydrogenated and hydrogen is rather weakly bound to the catalyst. The hydrogenation of $C \equiv C$ bonds, which are more strongly bound to the surface, takes place with the participation of hydrogen that is also more strongly bound to the catalyst. The hydrogenation of nitrobenzene, which has an extremely high adsorption potential, is accomplished with the participation of even more strongly bound hydrogen.

TABLE 3. Hydrogenation of nitrobenzene in a buffer solution on Pt-black

pH	w, ml/min	ΔE, mv	Degree of filling of the surface with hydrogen ω, %	q_{Pt-H}, kcal/mole
2.4	11.2	230	30.0	63.3
4.3	11.2	240	25.5	63.7
6.3	10.4	250	32.0	64.0
8.1	10.8	260	31.5	65.0
10.1	12.0	300	25.0	66.2
13.0	12.0	330	22.0	66.8

Thus, the greater the adsorption potential of the substance to be hydrogenated, the more strongly bound is the hydrogen used to hydrogenate it.

Changes in the hydrogen-ion concentration in the solution have opposite effects on the $Pt - H$ and $Pt - C$ bond energies. Depending on the ratios of the changes in these bond energies, the pH has a different effect on the rate of the process as a whole and on its stages. Thus, it is possible to control (by changing the pH) the bond energy between the reacting molecules and the surface of the catalyst, and hence, to affect not only the process rate but also its mechanism, selectivity, and the direction of the hydrogenation reaction. Thus, the pH of the medium should be taken into account in the selection of catalysts for liquid-phase hydrogenation reactions.

BIBLIOGRAPHY

1. SOKOL'SKII, D.V. Gidrirovanie v rastvorakh (Hydrogenation in Solutions), p.425.—Alma-Ata, Izd.
   AN KazSSR. 1962.
2. SOKOL'SKAYA, A.M., S.M. RESHETNIKOV, and D.V. SOKOL'SKII.—DAN SSSR, Vol.152: 1369.
   1963.
3. SOKOL'SKAYA, A.M. and S.M. RESHETNIKOV. —In: Sbornik "Kataliticheskie reaktsii v zhidkoi
   faze", p.33. Alma-Ata, Izd. AN KazSSR. 1963.
4. SOKOL'SKAYA, A.M. and S.M. RESHETNIKOV.—Vestnik AN KazSSR, No.2: 50. 1964.
5. RESHETNIKOV, S.M. and A.M. SOKOL'SKAYA.—Izv. VUZov SSSR, Khimiya i Khimicheskaya
   Tekhnologiya, No.2: 217. 1964.
6. FRUMKIN, A.N. and A.I. SHLYGIN.—IAN SSSR, OKhN, Vol.5: 773. 1936.
7. SOKOL'SKII, D.V. and V.A. DRUZ'.—ZhFKh, Vol.26: 364. 1952.
8. FRUMKIN, A.N.—ZhFKh, Vol.14: 1200. 1940.
9. BERING, B.P. and V.V. SERPINSKII.—DAN SSSR, Vol.114: 1254. 1957.
10. BARSOVA, L.I., A.A. BALANDIN, and V.I. SPITSYN.—In: Sbornik "Kataliticheskie reaktsii v zhidkoi
    faze", p.235. Alma-Ata, Izd. AN KazSSR. 1963.
11. SOKOL'SKII, D.V.—Vestnik AN KazSSR, No.8: 66. 1954.
12. MANZHELEI, M.E. and A.F. SHOLIN.—DAN SSSR, Vol.141: 897. 1961.
13. SOKOL'SKII, D.V. and T.M. BELOSLYUDOVA.—DAN SSSR, Vol.145: 834. 1962.
14. FRUMKIN, A.N. and B.I. PODLOVCHENKO.—DAN SSSR, Vol.150: 349. 1963.
15. KIPERMAN, S.L. and A.A. BALANDIN.—ZhFKh, Vol.33: 2045. 1959.

L.Kh. Freidlin and E.F. Litvin

ON THE SELECTIVITY OF CATALYSTS — METALS BELONGING TO GROUP VIII — IN THE HYDROGENATION OF DIENES AND OLEFINS

The following reaction may take place in the hydrogenation of dienes in the presence of metallic catalysts (Ni, Pd, Rh, Pt):

$$C_nH_{2n-2} \left\{ \begin{array}{l} \xrightarrow[(1)]{2H} C_nH_{2n} \downarrow 2H \\ \xrightarrow[4H]{(3)} C_nH_{2n+2} \end{array} \right. \quad (2) .$$

The monoolefins formed in the above reaction may undergo isomerization (shifts of the double bond and cis-trans transformations).

For a long time scientists accepted the view that compounds containing a system of conjugated double bonds are hydrogenated exclusively by reaction (3), through the addition of two moles of hydrogen without the formation of an intermediate ethylene compound (C. Paal /1/, M. Böeseken /2/, and others). Subsequently, it was established that in reality the addition of hydrogen to diene systems involves several stages with the formation of intermediate olefins /3/.

S.V. Lebedev /3, 4/ gave special attention to the study of the effect of diene structure on the direction of the attachment of hydrogen to the conjugated system. B.A. Kazanskii et al. showed /5— 8/ on the basis of a large amount of experimental data that dienes of various structures are hydrogenated in all possible directions, but the ratio of the olefins formed depends on the nature of the catalyst (Ni, Pt, Pd) and the structure of the starting hydrocarbon.

It remained, however, unclear to what extent the composition of the product depends on the secondary hydrogenation reaction or the isomerization of the olefins formed in the reaction, and also whether the direction of the attachment of hydrogen to the system of conjugated bonds can be determined on the basis of the ratio of reaction products.

Two possible paths for the formation of the saturated hydrocarbons have been discussed already in /3, 4/: directly from the diene and as a result of the hydrogenation of the intermediate ethylene compounds. The authors reached the conclusion that in the first reaction stage the saturated hydrocarbon is formed from molecules of the starting diene, which takes up two hydrogen molecules at the same time. If a monsubstituted ethylene is formed during the hydrogenation of the conjugated system, this may participate in the formation of the saturated molecules.

W. Young et al. /9/ reported a linear increase in the butene and butane concentrations during the hydrogenation of butadiene on Pt and Pd. On this basis he reached the conclusion that the saturated hydrocarbon is formed directly from the diene rather than by hydrogenation of monoolefins. The authors assumed that the olefins are not hydrogenated in the presence of the diene because of preferential adsorption of the latter.

On the basis of their own results and literature data on the isomerization of olefins during hydrogenation on Pd and Pt, Kazanskii et al. /8, 10/ reached the conclusion that shifts in the position of the double bond in the olefins formed in the reaction may affect the composition of the products of partial hydrogenation of dienes. The author did not take into account the possibility of adsorptive displacement of the olefins by the starting dienes.

In a series of papers /11 — 13/ on the mechanism of hydrogenation of acetylenic and diene unsaturated hydrocarbons G. Bond et al. suggested that two types of selectivity be considered: selectivity determined by the mechanism of attachment of hydrogen to the diene, and selectivity associated with the adsorptive displacement. It was assumed /13/ that the monoolefins formed are displaced quantitatively from the catalyst surface by the diene, and that the selectivity of the process is determined mainly by the mechanism of attachment of hydrogen to the diene. It should be noted that, in general, the above scheme is in agreement with the assumption that two paths lead to the formation of a saturated hydrocarbon in the hydrogenation of dienes /4/.

In the present paper we have made an attempt to determine to what extent the secondary reactions (hydrogenation and isomerization of the monoolefins formed in the reaction) affect the composition of the diene hydrogenation products, and to evaluate separately the selectivity due to the diene hydrogenation mechanism and the selectivity due to adsorption factors. To that end we carried out liquid-phase hydrogenation of dienes and olefins of different structures and their binary mixtures in the presence of Pt, Pd, Rh, and Ni. The conditions were maintained constant: an alcoholic medium, temperature +5°, and vigorous mixing (800 oscillations per minute). The Pt, Pd, and Rh blacks were prepared by reduction of the respective metal salts by formaldehyde in an alkaline medium, while Raney nickel was prepared by leaching a 1:1 Ni:Al alloy by a 20% NaOH solution at 100°. In each experiment we used 0.01 mole of the substance to be hydrogenated, 25 ml of alcohol, and 0.025 — 0.05 g of the [metal] black or 0.2 g of Raney nickel. The composition of the catalyst [sic, probably of the products] was determined by gas-liquid chromatography. This made it possible to control accurately the composition of the products in the course of the process /14 — 19/.

Samples of the products were withdrawn for analysis during the hydrogenation, through the self-sealing rubber stopper of the long-necked hydrogenation flask. The sample (1 — 3 microliter) was introduced directly into the chromatograph, without separating the solvent. The analysis was carried out on the SKB IOKh chromatograph, fitted with a katarometer with tungsten filaments. β,β-hydroxydipropionitrile (supported on INZ-600 bricks) served as the liquid phase, helium served as the carrier gas, and the temperature was 20°.

The results were plotted as the dependence of the composition of the products on the amount of hydrogen used up in the reaction.

Figures 1 and 2 show the changes in the composition of the products during the hydrogenation of dienes with conjugated and non-conjugated double bonds (trans-piperylene and pentadiene-1,4) in the presence of Pt and Pd.

It is evident from the figures that in the hydrogenation on Pd the ratio of the reaction products remains constant until the absorption of 0.95 moles of hydrogen. The hydrogenation of the pentene-1 formed in the reaction, and its isomerization into cis- and trans-pentene-2 start only after the completion of the hydrogenation of the diene to the monoolefin.

The process has a different course in the presence of a platinum catalyst. The saturated hydrocarbon is formed from the very beginning of the reaction, and the selectivity of the process and the composition of the olefins remain constant only at relatively low degrees of conversion of the diene. When the diene concentration in the reaction mixture decreases to 50 — 40%, a break is observed on the reaction curves: the relative concentration of pentene-1 starts to decrease while that of the saturated hydrocarbon starts to increase. This peculiarity was not reported in earlier papers /3, 9/, which stated that the olefin-formation curves in the hydrogenation of dienes on Pt are linear. A similar shape of the curves was observed by us in the hydrogenation of other dienes — isoprene, cis-piperylene, 2,3-dimethylbutadiene. In all cases, independently of the diene structure, the ratio of the reaction products and the degree of selectivity of the processes remained constant until the degree of conversion of the diene reached 95 — 100% on Pd and Ni, and 50 — 60% on Pt and Rh.

The above data show that the secondary reaction — hydrogenation of olefins — may take place in the presence of the diene. Analyses of the compositions of the products of hydrogenation of single olefins show also that isomerization of the double bond (migration and cis-trans transformation) occurs simultaneously on all investigated catalysts (Figure 3). The ratio of the hydrogenation and isomerization rates depends mainly on the nature of the catalyst, but changes also as a function of the olefin structure. The data in Table 1 show that the above ratio decreases in the order Pt > Rh > Ni > Pd.

The possibility of hydrogenation and isomerization of the olefin in the presence of the diene depends on the relative adsorbability on the catalyst, and on the hydrogenation rates.

In order to evaluate the role of the secondary hydrogenation (and isomerization) reactions, we measured the rate constants of these reactions, which are of zero order. Dienes and α-olefins are hydrogenated at a constant rate. In the hydrogenation of β-olefins the rate was constant only at the beginning stages of the process.

On all investigated catalysts the hydrogenation rates of α-olefins are close to the hydrogenation rates of the dienes.

In agreement with the Lebedev rule, β-olefins are hydrogenated much more slowly. It is of interest to note that in the case of platinum the hydrogenation rate of α-olefins is somewhat higher than the hydrogenation rate of the corresponding diene. This affects also the shape of the kinetic curve for the hydrogenation of dienes. An increase in the rate on Pt is observed beyond the "critical point" /3, 4/, while on Pd and Ni the reaction rate decreases after the completion of the hydrogenation of the α-olefin.

It is evident from Table 2 that the specific activity of the catalysts decreases in the order Rh > Pd > Pt > Ni. The activities of the above metals in the hydrogenation of ethylene follow the same order /20/.

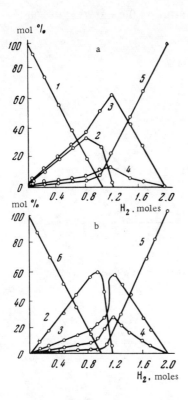

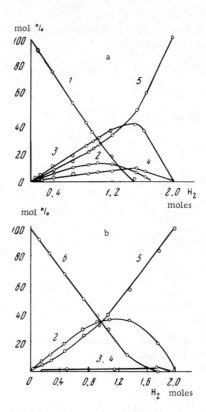

FIGURE 1. Changes in the composition of the products in the hydrogenation of trans-piperylene (a) and pentadiene-1,4 (b) on Pd:

1- trans-piperylene; 2- pentene-1; 3- trans-pentene-2; 4- cis-pentene-2; 5- n-pentane; 6- pentadiene-1,4.

FIGURE 2. Changes in the composition of the hydrogenation of trans-piperylene (a) and pentadiene-1,4 (b) on Pt

The designations are the same as in Figure 1.

TABLE 1. Isomerization of olefins under hydrogenation conditions (The [hydrogenation]/[isomerization] ratio)

Hydrocarbon	Catalyst			
	Ni	Pd	Rh	Pt
Pentene-1	1.1	0.17	2.6	12.5
cis-Pentene-2	0.43	0.20	0.7	19.0
3-Methylbutene-1 . . .	—	0.30	11.4	330

From the standpoint of the reaction rates, the hydrogenation of olefins (mainly of α-olefins) may, in fact, compete with the hydrogenation of dienes. However, studies of the hydrogenation of binary olefin-diene mixtures show

that the preferential adsorption of the diolefin on the catalyst surface is of
decisive importance.

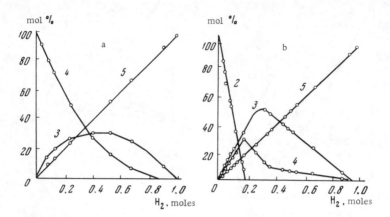

FIGURE 3.   Hydrogenation of cis-pentene-2 on Rh (a) and of pentene-1 on Pd (b)

The designations are the same as in Figure 1.

TABLE 2.   Rate constants for the hydrogenation of olefins and dienes ($k \cdot 10^{-2}$)

Catalyst	Dienes		Olefins		Diene	Olefins		Diene	Olefins	
	pentadi-ene-1,4	cis-pi-pery-lene	pen-tene-1	cis-pen-tene-2	iso-prene	3-methyl-butene-1	2-methyl-butene-2	2,3-di-methyl-butadi-ene-1,3	2,3-di-methyl-butene-1	2,3-di-methyl-butene-2
Pd	6.0	6.0	5.0	2.8	4.0	3.6	0.2	4.2	0.6	<0.01
Ni	1.1	0.9	0.8	0.4	0.9	0.6	—	1.0	0.2	<0.01
Rh	17.0	23.0	19.0	10.0	26.0	18.0	0.3	7.2	1.6	<0.01
Pt	3.2	2.4	3.4	1.0	2.0	2.2	0.1	1.0	0.7	<0.01

The changes in the composition of the reaction mixture during the
hydrogenation of a binary isoprene — pentene-1 mixture on Pd are shown in
Figure 4 a. The figure shows that in the presence of the diene the α-olefin
undergoes virtually no hydrogenation or isomerization. The hydrogenation
and isomerization of the pentene-1 starts only after the disappearance of
the isoprene from the solution. A similar behavior is observed in the
hydrogenation of binary piperylene — 3-methylbutene-1 and trans-piperylene
— cis-pentene-2 mixtures on palladium and Raney nickel.

The extent of the adsorptive displacement of the olefin by the diene is
markedly affected by the nature of the catalyst. For instance, in the
hydrogenation of isoprene — pentene-1 mixtures on Pt and Rh catalysts the
process is not selective (Figure 4 b).

For a rough evaluation of the extent of adsorptive displacement of olefins
by dienes, we carried out the hydrogenation of binary pentene-1 — isoprene,
3-methylbutene-2 — piperylene, and 3-methylbutene-1 — pentadiene-1,4
mixtures. Pentene-1 and 3-methylbutene-1 are olefins with rather similar

structures. In a binary mixture, these two olefins are hydrogenated simultaneously on all investigated catalysts. Thus, they are interchangeable as components of binary mixtures. Studies of the hydrogenation of the selected binary mixtures make it possible to evaluate the behavior of the α-olefin formed during the hydrogenation of the diene.

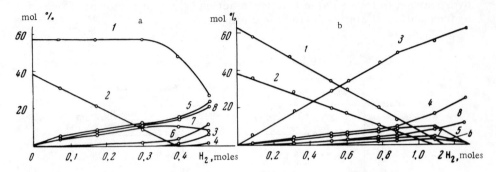

FIGURE 4. Hydrogenation of binary pentene-1 — isoprene mixtures on Pd (a) and Pt (b):

1- pentene-1; 2- isoprene; 3- n-pentane; 4- isopentane; 5- trans-pentene-2 and 2-methylbutene-1; 6- cis-pentene-2; 7- 3-methylbutene-1; 8- 2-methylbutene-2.

When binary diene — olefin mixtures are hydrogenated on the investigated catalysts, the selectivity remains constant until the diene disappears almost completely from the solution, although there are some exceptions. For instance, in the hydrogenation of an isoprene — 3-methylbutene-1 mixture on Pt the selectivity remains constant only until the degree of conversion of the diene reaches 50%, and afterwards the diene and the olefin are hydrogenated simultaneously.

The selectivity of hydrogenation (S) of an olefin in a mixture with a diene was determined experimentally on the basis of their relative degrees of hydrogenation in a binary mixture (v_{olefin}/v_{diene}) and may be expressed by the equation:

$$S = \frac{v_{olefin}}{v_{diene}} = \frac{b_{olefin}}{b_{diene}} \frac{k_{olefin}}{k_{diene}},$$

where k is the rate constant of the hydrogenation of the olefin and the diene taken separately. From here it is possible to calculate the ratio of the adsorption coefficients b_{olefin}/b_{diene}.

The data in Table 3 show that in the hydrogenation on Ni and Pd $b_{olefin}/b_{diene} = 0.04 - 0.06$, i.e., that the α-olefins are almost completely displaced from the catalyst surface by the diene. On Pt and Rh the value of b_{olefin}/b_{diene} reaches 0.5, i.e., the displacement is only partial.

This leads to several conclusions that are of importance for an understanding of the mechanism of hydrogenation of diene hydrocarbons.

It is evident that on catalysts like Ni and Pd the monoolefins formed in the reaction undergo no hydrogenation or isomerization in the presence of the diene, and the composition of the reaction mixture is determined by the transformations of the starting diene.

On Pt and Rh catalysts, the accumulating olefins are hydrogenated at a noticeable rate in the presence of dienes. For this reason, the direction of the primary reaction may be determined on the basis of the composition of the reaction mixture only in the case of low degrees of conversion of the diene. At the beginning of the reaction on these catalysts, the saturated hydrocarbon is formed directly from the diene by the addition of two molecules of hydrogen and without desorption of intermediate products in the bulk. At high degrees of conversion of the diene, the saturated hydrocarbon is formed also through reaction (2), as a result of the hydrogenation of olefins (mainly α-olefins).

TABLE 3. Hydrogenation of binary olefin—diene mixtures

Catalyst	Pentene-1 — isoprene		3-Methylbutene-1 — piperylene		3-Methylbutene-1 — pentadiene-1,4	
	S	$\dfrac{{}^b\text{olefin}}{{}^b\text{diene}}$	S	$\dfrac{{}^b\text{olefin}}{{}^b\text{diene}}$	S	$\dfrac{{}^b\text{olefin}}{{}^b\text{diene}}$
Pd	0.04	0.03	0.05	0.03	0.04	0.06
Ni	0.05	0.06	0.04	0.07	—	—
Rh	0.95	1.30	0.52	0.66	0.27	0.25
Pt	0.98	0.59	0.53	0.58	0.32	0.46

Data on the hydrogenation of dienes of different structures on Ni, Pt, Pd, and Rh catalysts are shown in Table 4. The selectivity of the process and the ratio of the monoolefins formed in the process were calculated from the slopes of the curves showing the dependence of the monoolefin concentrations on the amount of hydrogen absorbed in the initial stages of the reaction.

A comparison of the data in Tables 3 and 4 shows that Pd and Ni are characterized by a high selectivity associated with the reaction mechanism, as well as by a high selectivity associated with the adsorptive displacement of the olefins by the dienes. Rh, and especially Pt, are characterized by low selectivity of both types.

This conclusion is of practical importance. For instance, it is impossible to obtain a marked increase in the selectivity of a platinum catalyst by the introduction (into the reaction) of substances that displace the olefins formed in the reaction and that interfere with their hydrogenation. It is known /21/ that the introduction of an alkali hydroxide reduces the rate of hydrogenation of olefins on Pt. However, no marked increase in the selectivity is observed when isoprene is hydrogenated under these conditions: isopentane is formed from the very beginning of the reaction.

The hydrogenation of dienes is a complex, multistage transformations process occurring on the surface of the catalyst and involving the formation of semihydrogenated species that cannot be desorbed until the formation of the saturated hydrocarbon. The occurrence of a complex process on the catalyst explains, for instance, the formation of pentene-2 in the hydrogenation of pentadiene-1,4 in the presence of Pd, since pentene-2 cannot be formed on this catalyst by isomerization of the desorbed pentene-1 /22/.

TABLE 4. Composition of the reaction products (mol %) in the hydrogenation of dienes

Diene to be hydrogenated	Reaction products	Catalysts			
		Ni	Pd	Rh	Pt
Pentadiene-1,4	Pentene-1	63	62	48	54
	cis-Pentene-2	8	12	4	2
	trans-Pentene-2	20	23		
	n-Pentane	9	3	45	44
cis-Piperylene	Pentene-1	49	47	24	15
	cis-Pentene-2	16	18	24	35
	trans-Pentene-2	34	34	34	17
	n-Pentane	1	1	18	33
trans-Piperylene	Pentene-1	51	44	—	17
	cis-Pentene-2	8	8	—	8
	trans-Pentene-2	41	46	—	40
	n-Pentane	<1	2	—	35
Isoprene	3-Methylbutene-1	18.5	26	19	16
	2-Methylbutene-1	34	31	35	26
	2-Methylbutene-2	48	42	35	22
	iso-Pentane	0.5	1	11	36
2,3-Dimethylbutadiene	2,3-Dimethylbutene-1	61	66	55	65
	2,3-Dimethylbutene-2	39	34	31	14
	2,3-Dimethylbutane	0	0	14	21

In general, the composition of olefins formed from dienes of different structures is not determined by the thermodynamic stability of the olefins, but is probably associated with the behavior of intermediate forms.

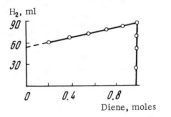

FIGURE 5. Extraction of hydrogen from the catalyst in the hydrogenation of 2,3-dimethylbutadiene on Raney nickel.

It is of interest to note the analogy in the nature of the influence of the catalyst on processes occurring during the adsorption of the olefin from the liquid phase, and on processes involving the transformation of intermediate species on the catalyst surface. Thus, the formation of pentene-2 from pentadiene-1,4 is most pronounced on Pd, which is also the most active catalyst for the isomerization of olefins.

We must also take into account the possibility of adsorptive displacement (by the diene) not only of the olefin from the "hydrocarbonic" surface of the catalyst, but also of hydrogen from the "hydrogenic" surface. Thus, our experiments showed that 2,3-dimethylbutadiene extracts from a Raney nickel catalyst a noticeable fraction (up to 30%) of the hydrogen, and the hydrogenation of the diene takes place on such a partially dehydrogenated catalyst, while 2,3-dimethylbutene-1 is not hydrogenated in the presence of the diene. When the hydrogenation of the diene is completed the catalyst again adsorbs hydrogen and the hydrogenation of the 2,3-dimethylbutene-1 begins (see Figure 5).

BIBLIOGRAPHY

1. PAAL, C.—Ber., Vol. 45: 2221. 1912.
2. BÖESEKEN, M.J., O.B. van der WEIDE, and M.C. MOM.—Ber., Vol. 35: 260. 1916.
3. LEBEDEV, S.V. and A.I. YAKUBCHIK.—ZhRFKhO, Vol. 59: 981. 1927.
4. LEBEDEV, S.V. and A.I. YAKUBCHIK.—ZhRFKhO, Vol. 60: 793. 1928.
5. KAZANSKII, B.A., I.V. GOSTUNSKAYA, and A.M. GRANAT.—IAN SSSR, OKhN, p. 670. 1953.
6. GOSTUNSKAYA, I.V., G.V. LOZA, and B.A. KAZANSKII.—IAN SSSR, OKhN, p. 863. 1955.
7. GOSTUNSKAYA, I.V., E.A. KRASNYANSKAYA, and B.A. KAZANSKII.—ZhOKh, Vol. 25: 1448. 1955.
8. KAZANSKII, B.A., I.V. GOSTUNSKAYA, N.I. POPOVA, and N.B. DOBROSERDOVA.—Vestnik MGU, No. 3: 207. 1958.
9. YOUNG, W.G., R.L. MEIER, J. VINOGRAD, H. BOLLINGER, L. KAPLAN, and S.L. LINDE.—J. Am. Chem. Soc., Vol. 60: 2046. 1947.
10. GOSTUNSKAYA, I.V., N.B. DOBROSEDOVA, and B.A. KAZANSKII.—ZhOKh, Vol. 27: 2396. 1957.
11. BOND, G.C., J. NEUHAM, and P.B. WELLS. Actes du 2-me Congrès International de Catalyse, Vol. 1: 1177.—Paris, Technip. 1960.
12. BOND, G.C., C. WEBB, P.B. WELLS, and J.M. WINTERBOTTOM.—J. Catalysis, Vol. 1: 74. 1962.
13. BOND, G.C. Catalysis by Metals. London. 1962.
14. FREIDLIN, L.Kh., E.F. LITVIN, and I.F. ZHUKOVA.—Neftekhimiya, Vol. 1: 213. 1961.
15. FREIDLIN, L.Kh. and E.F. LITVIN.—IAN SSSR, OKhN, p. 1307. 1963.
16. FREIDLIN, L.Kh. and E.F. LITVIN.—Neftekhimiya, Vol. 3: 326. 1963.
17. FREIDLIN, L.Kh. and E.F. LITVIN.—Neftekhimiya, Vol. 4: 374. 1964.
18. FREIDLIN, L.Kh., E.F. LITVIN, and L.M. KRYLOVA.—Neftekhimiya, Vol. 4: 185. 1964.
19. FREIDLIN, L.Kh, E.F. LITVIN, and Yu.Yu. KAUP.—DAN SSSR, Vol. 139: 6. 1961.
20. BEECK, O.—Review of Modern Physics, Vol. 7: 61. 1945.
21. SOKOL'SKII, D.V. Gidrirovanie v rastvorakh (Hydrogenation in Solutions).—Alma-Ata, Izd. AN KazSSR. 1962.
22. FREIDLIN, L.Kh, E.F. LITVIN, and L.M. KRYLOVA.—Neftekhimiya (in print).

E.I. Klabunovskii

ON THE PROBLEM OF THE SELECTION OF CATALYSTS
FOR ASYMMETRIC HYDROGENATION AND HYDROGENOLYSIS

The creation of general principles for the selection of asymmetric
catalysts (i.e., catalysts for reactions leading to the formation of optically
active compounds), as well as the more general problem of the selection of
stereospecific or morphological catalysts, are associated with much
greater difficulties than the selection of conventional (not stereospecific)
catalysts. This is due primarily to the need to take into account the fine
spatial relations in the structure of the non-reacting parts of the molecule
and the surface of the catalyst. In asymmetric catalysts the process is
governed by the interaction of extraindicial substituents (e.g., R', R'',
R''', R'''' in the case of hydrogenation) with the adsorbing center of the
catalyst (A):

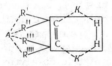

A stereospecific catalyst cannot exist without an asymmetric reaction
between its surface and the extraindicial components of the molecule.

In spite of the great theoretical and practical interest in asymmetric
catalysis as a means for modelling the action of enzymes, no systematic
research has been carried out in this field. There are a few known
examples of asymmetric reactions and catalysts whose selection was
based on analogies adopted from enzymology and immunochemistry.

Enzymatic catalysis under the effect of isolated enzymes was the first
example of the realization of asymmetric catalysis in the laboratory.
Many catalytic asymmetric syntheses have been carried out by using
oxynitrilase, reductase, carboxylase, ketoaldomutase, and their chemical
models — optically active organic catalysts /1/.

In addition to microheterogeneous, there are also heterogeneous
asymmetric catalysts: amines on cellulose, metals and oxides on quartz,
etc. /2/.

It has been concluded on the basis of experimental data that asymmetric
catalysis requires the presence of an asymmetric carrier and that
asymmetric adsorption takes place on the surface of such a carrier; the
catalysis proper is not optically specific /3/. Catalysts without
asymmetric carriers are unknown, and attempts to prepare them have
been unsuccessful /4/.

The interest in asymmetric catalysts has recently become greater, especially with respect to polymerization and hydrogenation catalysis. The asymmetric adsorption on the carrier plays the main role in asymmetric catalysis, and for this reason the selection of a catalyst should be confined to the selection of the carrier. However, in spite of the fact that the selective adsorption of optical isomers on a number of organic and inorganic adsorbents has been studied fairly extensively, the use of such adsorbents in catalysis encounters difficulties (only catalysts based on quartz and cellulose have been found to be active /2/). An active asymmetric catalyst is prepared by reducing the chelate compound of a metal with silk protein /5/. After the reduction, the chelate is decomposed leaving the metal in a highly dispersed state strongly bound to the surface. In addition to its asymmetric influence, the nature of the carrier affects also the general properties of the catalyst: it causes no hydrogenation of benzene, and its ability to hydrogenate $C = O$ bonds is weakened; however, there is no change in its activity with respect to $C = C$ bonds. The asymmetric activity of Pd catalysts is exhibited just in the hydrogenation of $C = O$ and $C = N$ bonds.

The manner of arrangement of the components of the molecule with respect to the catalyzing and adsorbing centers of the catalyst, within a rather confined space, is of importance in asymmetric catalysis. For this reason, according to the model discussed in /3/, the distances between the centers of these two types must be greater than or at least equal to the size of the reacting molecules.

The above point of view has been confirmed by studies of asymmetric catalysts prepared by the application of optically-active amino acids on the surface of Raney nickel or a Pd catalyst /6/. In such cases there was also a decrease in the activity with respect to the hydrogenation of $C = O$ bonds with the appearance of asymmetric catalytic activity; the modification did not lead to a loss of catalytic activity in the hydrogenation of $C = C$ bonds, which indicates differences in the active centers.

A detailed study of the effect of the structure of modifying agents on the asymmetric activity of catalysts in the hydrogenation of methyl acetoacetate and acetophenone showed that the modifier has the most beneficial effect in cases in which its molecules are adsorbed readily on the surface of the catalyst; this leads to the formation of stable bonds with the participation of free, non-substituted COOH, NH_2, and OH groups. For example, a proline molecule, which is adsorbed at two points only, is a poor modifying agent.

Thus, a strong bond between the optically active compound and the catalyst surface is the main requirement in the selection of a modifying agent. This should cause the formation of a structure that is the reverse of the structure adopted formerly to explain the asymmetric action of "quartz catalysts" /3/. In order to obtain the optimum catalyst it is necessary to create dilute catalysts with a low metal concentration on the surface of the carrier. "Free areas" should be left on the surface of the carrier between the catalyzing centers for the asymmetric adsorption and subsequent migration of the molecules over the surface towards these centers.

An almost complete filling of the surface of the catalyst is probably acceptable in the case of modified catalysts. The adsorbed amino and hydroxy acids shield the sextets (the largest and best organized active centers) and in this way prevent the hydrogenation of the six-atom rings. The doublets (on which hydrogenation of the $C = C$ bonds takes place) remain unchanged.

These facts indicate that the suface of the catalyst is geometrically non-homogeneous, as mentioned in a number of earlier papers. It is known, in fact, that molecules with spatial hindrances (e.g., substituted diphenyl and paracyclophane) cannot be hydrogenated; at the same time, triptycene derivatives of type I, which are shown below

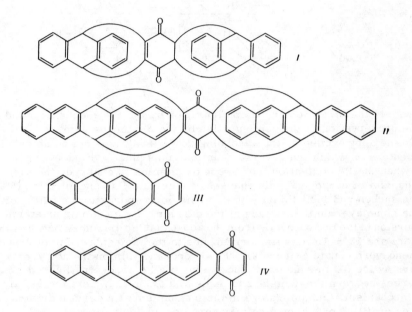

are hydrogenated under relatively moderate conditions, in spite of their complex bicyclic structure.

Compound II should be hydrogenated less readily than I, but III and IV are hydrogenated equally readily, since the spatially branched part of the molecule is not in contact with the surface of the catalyst (the quinoid system takes part in the reaction). The investigation of such structures may provide valuable (for the selection of catalysts) data on the geometric arrangement of the active centers of the catalyst /7/.

Systematic investigations of the active surface, and its adsorbing and catalyzing centers in the hydrogenolysis of optically active compounds, may be of great help in the selection of catalysts for asymmetric reactions.

The derivatives of the optically active atrolactic acid undergo hydrogenolysis at the $C - O$ bond on Ni, Pd/C, or Pd/Al$_2$O$_3$ catalysts; depending on the structure of the starting compound and the nature of the catalyst, the process takes place with the racemization, preservation, or inversion of the configuration formally by the S_N1, S_{Ni}, or S_N2 mechanisms (on the surface of the catalyst) /8/, as shown in the following multiplet schemes:

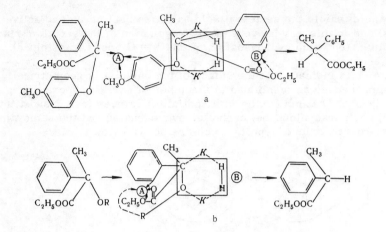

a

b

where *a* is the inversion of the configuration by the S_N2 mechanism and *b* is the preservation of the configuration by the S_Ni mechanism.

On the above scheme, the adsorbing centers (*A*) need not coincide with the centers on which the reverse reaction takes place. Figure 1 shows that when the Pd content on the carbon or alumina is changed, the mechanism of hydrogenolysis changes at a certain Pd concentration (8% Pd on carbon and 1.2% Pd on Al_2O_3). This corresponds to the filling of 3% of the monolayer on the surface of the carrier. By assuming an atomic dispersion of the Pd, we obtain from the above that the distances between the centers are 13 — 15 Å; this corresponds to the molecular size of 2-phenyl-2-phenoxypropionate (Figure 2). The hydrogenolysis on the above catalysts occurs by the S_Ni mechanism. Increasing the Pd concentration reduces the distances between the centers and leads to a transition from the S_Ni to the S_N2 mechanism. Such a change in the mechanism at a certain critical degree of filling of the surface may serve as an indication of the stereospecific nature of the adsorption during catalysis, providing that the group to be adsorbed also contains an asymmetric atom, or that the starting compound is a diastereoisomer or racemate.

Moreover, the type of adsorption may provide data on the nature of the surface activity. Both a strong adsorption of the group and steric hindrances during adsorption on Ni lead to the non-specific S_N1 mechanism involving the removal of an asymmetric C atom from the surface, and hence a great geometric and energetic non-homogeneity of the surface.

The absence of strong adsorption of polar groups on the surface of the catalyst (Pd) indicates a homogeneous surface. At the same time, the reaction is stereospecific (S_Ni or S_N2 mechanisms) since the asymmetric C atom is close to the surface, in accordance with the multiplet scheme (see above).

The establishment of the configuration relationships is of importance for both heterogeneous and homogeneous catalysis. Systematic work in this field is required, since the available data are very scarce. Such relationships were recently established by us for the inversion of *l*-menthone under the catalytic effect of (+), (-), and (±) alcoholates /9/.

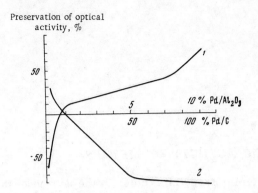

Preservation of optical activity, %

FIGURE 1. Dependence of the extent of preservation of the optical activity on the Pd concentration on the carrier in the hydrogenolysis of phenoxyatrolactate (according to /8/):

1- Pd/C; 2- Pd/Al$_2$O$_3$.

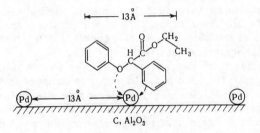

FIGURE 2. Scheme of the adsorption of phenoxyatrolactate molecules on the surface of a Pd/C (or Pd/Al$_2$O$_3$) catalyst.

BIBLIOGRAPHY

1. KLABUNOVSKII, E.I.—Khimicheskaya Nauka i Promyshlennost', Vol. 2: 197. 1957.
2. KLABUNOVSKII, E.I. Asimmetricheskii sintez (Asymmetric Synthesis), p. 90. —Moskva, Goskhimizdat. 1960.
3. KLABUNOVSKII, E.I. and V.V. PATRIKEEV.—DAN SSSR, Vol. 78: 485. 1951.
4. GHOSH, J.—J. Indian Chem. Soc., Vol. 16: 51. 1939.
5. AKABORI, S.—J. Chem. Soc. Japan, Pure Chem. Sect., Vol. 72: 1374. 1956.
6. IZUMI, Y.—Bull. Chem. Soc. Japan, Vol. 36: 21. 1963.
7. KLABUNOVSKII, E.I., A.A. BALANDIN, and L.V. ANTIK. Kataliticheskie reaktsii v zhidkoi faze (Catalytic Reactions in the Liquid Phase).—Trudy Vsesoyuznoi Konferentsii, p. 135. Alma-Ata, Izd. AN KazSSR. 1963.
8. MITSUI, S.—Juki gosay kagaku kekaisy, Vol. 17: 640. 1959.
9. KLABUNOVSKII, E.I., A.A. BALANDIN, and L.F. GODUNOVA.—IAN SSSR, OKhN, p. 886. 1963.

M.A. Landau

THE CATALYTIC ACTIVITY OF METALS

The vacant atomic d-orbitals (holes in the d-band of the metal) play an important role in some catalytic reactions on metallic catalysts. The activity of metals and alloys whose atoms (in the bulk) have no vacant d-electrons is lower (by several orders of magnitude) than the activity of catalysts having such electrons; in many cases the catalytic activity of binary alloys decreases linearly with decreasing paramagnetic susceptibility and becomes virtually zero when the number of vacant d-electrons in atoms in the bulk of the crystal becomes equal to zero /1 — 16/. Hence, at a first approximation, it is possible to associate the catalytic properties of metals with the electronic structure of their atoms in the bulk of the crystal. The author /17 — 20/ (see also /21/) used for this purpose the Pauling theory of metals /22 — 25/, which has recently been extensively used in research on heterogeneous catalysis.

The chemisorption of the reactants is a necessary stage of any heterogeneous catalytic reaction. In order to conduct the reaction, the catalyst must be able to chemisorb the reacting molecules, i.e., its atoms must possess the required number of free valencies, which is determined by the nature and the number of bonds between the reacting and catalyzing atoms in the intermediate state. For instance, the chemisorption of ethylene takes place on a doublet active center, and each atom of the catalyst forms a single simple bond with the carbon atom /11/; hence, the polymerization of ethylene requires only the existence of one unpaired d-electron in each of two adjacent atoms of the catalyst /26/. In the case of reactions that are limited by the chemisorption of trivalent nitrogen it is necessary to use a catalyst whose atoms have three unpaired valence d-electrons /17, 18/, since the chemisorption of nitrogen at the reaction temperature involves the rupture of the $N \equiv N$ bond /11/. In fact, among all metals in the fourth period, only iron, manganese and cobalt (whose atoms possess three unpaired d-electrons at one of their main valency states*, according to L. Pauling /24, 25/) have a marked catalytic activity in ammonia synthesis. Reactions accompanied by the chemisorption of hydrogen or deuterium require the presence of two free valences at each atom of the active center /17, 18/.

---

* The Pauling specification /25/, according to which one of the three vacant d-electrons in a Fe(B) atom forms a one-electron bond with the adjacent iron atom does not change the general conclusion on the causes of the catalytic activity of iron in ammonia synthesis: this electron remains unpaired, and the energy needed for the rupture of the relatively weak one-electron bond is readily obtained at the expense of the heat of chemisorption. Moreover, in view of their unsaturation, the surface Fe(B) atoms may not form the one-electron bond.

The same conclusion with respect to hydrogenation reactions was reached (simultaneously with the author) by Zh. V. Strel'nikova and V.P. Lebedev /28/, although they discussed carried catalysts with a subcrystalline phase of the metal (platinum) and, accordingly, the electronic structure of isolated Pt atoms. The decomposition of hydrogen peroxide on platinum

involves the formation of the intermediate $Pt {\displaystyle <} {\overset{O}{\underset{O}{|}}}$ compound, which also

requires a catalyst whose atom has two free electrons /29, 30/.

If the number of unpaired valence d-electrons in the catalyst atom is greater than the number required for the chemisorption of the reactants, this would lead to the creation of a relatively strong bond between the reactant atoms and the catalyst /8 — 10/ and the desorption of the reaction products would be hindered. Such a strengthening of the bond is caused probably by additional exchange forces exhibited in the exchange of an electron participating in the bond with the adsorbed atom, with the unpaired electron remaining on the atomic d-orbital of the catalyst atom. For this reason iron, for instance, is less active than nickel in hydrogenation reactions, and the decrease in the reaction rate is due only to the difference in the preexponential factors, if the energies of activation are the same /6, 15, 31/ (the heats of chemisorption of hydrogen on iron and nickel are equal — see below). The number of $Fe(A)$ atoms containing two unpaired d-electrons, which are the main factor determining the catalytic activity, decreases markedly in the course of the reaction, due to $Fe(A) \rightarrow Fe(B)$ transitions; the $Fe(B)$ atoms containing three unpaired electrons are captured by the adsorbed molecules, and the $Fe(A):Fe(B)$ ratio for the free atoms at the given temperature must remain constant. According to Pauling, nickel consists of $Ni(A)$ atoms with two valence electrons and $Ni(B)$ atoms having no valence electrons (see /19/); the number of active centers depends only on the amount of $Ni(A)$ atoms in the starting catalyst.*

When the atoms of the catalyst in the main valence state do not have the necessary number of unpaired d-electrons, the catalysis takes place only through the participation of atoms of the catalyst that are in excited valence states; reactions on such catalysts need an additional expenditure of energy. The above point of view provides a simple explanation of the changes in the catalytic activity of metals in the fourth period with respect to the above reactions /17, 18, 26/.

Thus, there exist two groups of metallic catalysts.

The first group comprises catalysts whose atoms possess (already in the ground valence state) the number of free valences required for the realization of the reaction (for instance — iron in ammonia synthesis and nickel in hydrogenation reactions). In the case of such catalysts the temperature-induced changes in the ratios of the various normal and excited valence states must not (to a first approximation) have an effect on the catalytic activity. Therefore, let us assume for example that the new valence states are created as a result of the rupture of one of the cohesive bonds between adjacent cobalt atoms. The energy of a single Co — Co bond (i.e., the atomization heat /32/ divided by the average valence of a cobalt atom in the crystalline state) equals 17,500 cal/mole. Hence, the ratio of

---

* The treatment of this problem in /17, 18/ is not strictly accurate.

the number of ruptured $Co - Co$ bonds to the total number of such bonds at $875°K$ will be equal to $e^{-\frac{17500}{875R}}$ or 0.0045%.

The energy of activation of heterogeneous catalytic reactions on such catalysts (E_{app}) at low degrees of filling of the surface is determined from the usual equation:

$$E_{app} = E_r - \sum_i v_i q_i, \qquad (1)$$

where E_r is the true energy of activation of the reacting molecules; q_i are the initial heats of chemisorption of these molecules; and v_i are stoichiometric coefficients.

The number of active atoms should not differ markedly from the number of catalyst atoms possessing the required number of valence electrons in the ground state. This conclusion is supported by investigations on the poisoning of platinum and nickel catalysts. V.P. Lebedev et al. /33, 34/, and T.I. Gorokhova, A.N. Mal'tsev and N.I. Kobozev /35/, who studied the effect of various poisons on platinum black in the decomposition of hydrogen peroxide, found that only $30 - 35\%$ of the surface platinum atoms are active; this value is identical with the number of $Pt(A)$ atoms possessing two unpaired valence electrons (30%).* D.V. Sokol'skii /21, 37/ studied the effect of various poisons on Raney nickel catalyst in the hydrogenation of cinnamic acid. He found that only $10 - 15\%$ of the surface atoms are active. This is less than the number of $Ni(A)$ atoms but is of the same order of magnitude. At the same time it should be recalled that the decomposition of hydrogen peroxide occurs on a single Pt atom /29, 30/, i.e., all surface $Pt(A)$ atoms may be active. Hydrogenation takes place on a doublet $Ni(A) - Ni(A)$ active center, and for purely geometrical reasons not all surface $Ni(A)$ atoms could form such doublets, i.e., the number of $Ni(A)$ atoms exhibiting a catalytic activity should be smaller than the total number of surface $Ni(A)$ atoms. In the oxidation of ethanol on platinum black /35/ the number of active atoms is also smaller than the number of $Pt(A)$ atoms. Hence, the data of Sokol'skii should be regarded as a satisfactory confirmation of the views developed here.

The second group comprises catalysts whose atoms in the ground state do not possess the number of free valences required for the given reaction (e.g., copper in hydrogenation).

In order to exhibit a catalytic activity, such catalysts require activation, which may be accomplished, for instance, at the expense of thermal energy. The author of /19/ found that the most probable path for the activation of metallic catalysts leading directly to the formation of a doublet active center (not of a single active atom) involves the rupture of the cohesive metal $-$ metal bond. This made it necessary to specify more

---

* The first results on the poisoning of platinum black by mercuric chloride in the decomposition of hydrogen peroxide /36/ showed that the total number of atoms on the surface of one gram of platinum black $g_n > 1 \cdot 10^{20}$, while the number of active atoms $z_n = 0.489 \cdot 10^{20}$, i.e., less than 50% of the total number of surface atoms; subsequent more accurate measurements of the surface of platinum black /34/ made it possible to improve the accuracy of these data: it was found that $g_n = 1.4 \cdot 10^{20}$, i.e., that z_n is 35% of the total number of surface atoms.

accurately the physical meaning of the energy of activation of chemisorption and heterogeneous catalytic reactions taking place on such catalysts. A mathematical analysis /20/ showed that at low degrees of filling of both homogeneous and non-homogeneous surfaces, the energy of activation of reactions on such catalysts equals:

$$E_{app} = E_r + \sum_i v_i \varepsilon - \sum_i v_i q_i, \qquad (2)$$

where ε is the energy of the cohesive metal — metal bond. In particular, for reactions of the first order we have:

$$E_{app} = E_r + \varepsilon - q. \qquad (3)$$

TABLE. Energy of activation (E) of various reactions on metals belonging to groups VIII and IB of the periodic table, and energy of the cohesive bond (ε) of metals in the IB subgroup (kcal/mole)*

Reaction	E_{Cu}	E_{Fe}	E_{Co}	E_{Ni}	ΔE_{av}	$\frac{1}{2}\varepsilon_{Cu}$	ε_{Cu}
Acetylene hydrogenation /15, 31/	21.0	8.7	9.0	8.0	12.4	—	14.7
Ethylene hydrogenation /15, 41/	19.5	—	—	5.0	14.5	—	14.7
Hydrogen-deuterium isotopic exchange /44/	16	8.1	7.9	8.0	8	7.35	—
Ortho-para transformations of hydrogen /15/	12	—	—	5	7	7.35	—
Oxidation of hydrogen /45/	12.1	4.3	—	6.8	7.3	7.35	—

Reaction	E_{Ag}	E_{Pd}	ΔE	$\frac{1}{2}\varepsilon_{Ag}$	E_{Au}	E_{Pt}	ΔE	$\frac{1}{2}\varepsilon_{Au}$
Isotopic exchange between deuterium and hydrogen in acetone /15, 46/	14.6	10.1	4.5	6.2	13.9	3.4	10.5	8.5
Isotopic exchange between deuterium and hydrogen in ammonia /15, 47/	14.1	8.5	5.6	6.2	—	—	—	—

* The values of ε were calculated with the aid of the data of F. Zeits /40/;
$\varepsilon = \frac{Q}{n}$ where Q is the heat of atomization and n is the average valence of the metallic atom in a crystal, according to Pauling.

This conclusion has been confirmed by experimental data. It is of interest to mention the results of G. Bond, and of R. Mann /15, 31/ on the hydrogenation of acetylene on iron, cobalt, nickel, and copper powders. A kinetic analysis shows that the energy of activation of the above reaction should depend only on the heat of chemisorption of the hydrogen q_H (but not on that of the acetylene) /20/; the heats of chemisorption on iron, nickel, and copper powders are approximately equal (32, 31, and 35 kcal/mole respectively /11, 38, 39/), and no data for cobalt are available.* Hence, we should expect that the energies of activation of acetylene hydrogenation should also be equal. However, while iron, cobalt, and nickel have the necessary number of unpaired electrons in the ground state /40/, a copper catalyst requires activation. An analysis of different

* It is of interest to mention that the initial heats of chemisorption of hydrogen on these four metals carried on silica gel are also fairly similar, i.e., $(24 - 28) \pm 4$ kcal/mole; a somewhat higher value (32 ± 4 kcal/mole) was obtained only for iron /15/.

reaction mechanisms leads to the conclusion that in all cases the rupture of a single Cu — Cu bond is sufficient for the hydrogenation of acetylene on copper /20/. In fact, the energies of activation of the hydrogenation of acetylene on iron, nickel, and cobalt (E_{VIII}) are virtually equal, while E_{Cu} is much larger, and the difference $\Delta E = E_{VIII} - E_{Cu}$ almost coincides with the energy of the cohesive Cu — Cu bond (see the table). Moreover, the existing small differences between ΔE and ε caused by the small differences in the heats of chemisorption of hydrogen on copper, nickel, and iron have been explained quantitatively /20/.

In the hydrogenation of ethylene on nickel and copper foil /15, 41/ ΔE was again equal to the energy of the cohesive bond of copper, which also agrees with the reaction kinetics (of the first order with respect to hydrogen, and of zero order with respect to ethylene /7/). Thus, in the case of a catalyst that requires activation the adsorption coefficient will equal /20/:

$$a = a_0 e^{q/RT} e^{-\varepsilon/RT} \tag{4}$$

and in the case of a reaction of zero order with respect to one of the reactants (i.e., when the degree of filling of the surface is close to unity) the value of ε, as well as the heat of chemisorption of this reactant, will not enter in the expression for E_{app}. For this reason E_{Cu} in the hydrogenation of ethylene is larger than E_{Ni} by ε rather than by 2ε, although a catalyst atom requires the presence of two valence electrons for the realization of the above reaction.

It is of interest to mention that hydrogen is not chemisorbed on pure copper at low temperatures /7, 42, 43/; however, free valences appear on the copper surface as the temperature is increased, and chemisorption of hydrogen on the copper catalyst begins /38/. The formation of an active sextet center on copper as a result of the rupture of cohesive bonds is rather improbable from the point of view of energy; evidently, this is the reason why copper catalyzes the hydrogenation of acetylene /15, 31/ but not of benzene (for example, see /11/).

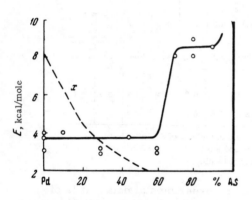

FIGURE. Energy of activation of the ortho-para transition of hydrogen as a function of the alloy composition (according to A. Couper and D. Eley /4/)

Curve x shows the changes in paramagnetic susceptibility.

The energies of activation of the ortho-para transition of hydrogen, the isotopic exchange of deuterium with hydrogen, acetone, and ammonia, and the oxidation of hydrogen on metals of subgroup IB are also greater than the energies of activation of the same reactions on metals of group VIII prepared by the same method, and the difference ΔE is equal to half the energy of the cohesive bond between the atoms of subgroup IB (see the table). It is known that in a number of cases the adsorption isotherm of hydrogen has the form $\theta = \dfrac{\sqrt{ap}}{1 + \sqrt{ap}}$, or at low degrees of filling of the surface

$\theta \simeq \sqrt{ap}$; the order of the reaction in the ortho-para transformations of hydrogen and in the isotopic exchange of hydrogen and deuterium is close to 0.5 /11 — 13/, i.e., in accordance with equations (2) and (3), when the values of q_{H} are equal the energies of activation of these reactions on copper should be greater than E_{VIII} by exactly $\frac{1}{2}\varepsilon$. It is of interest to mention that in the case of isotopic exchange of deuterium with ammonia the order of the reaction with respect to the deuterium is also 0.5 /12, 15/. However, because of the absence of more detailed data on the heats of chemisorption of the reactants and the kinetics of this reaction (and the other reactions listed in the table) we confined ourselves only to a statement of the fact that for all these reactions the energies of activation on metals of subgroup 1B are larger (by $\frac{1}{2}\varepsilon$) than the corresponding energies of activation on metals of group VIII.

It is of interest to compare the catalytic activities of nickel and germanium in the isotopic exchange of molecular hydrogen. From the equal values of the preexponential factors for the two cases, G.K. Boreskov /8, 9/ reaches the conclusion that on both germanium and nickel the reaction occurs on a large fraction of the surface, i.e., that the chemisorption of hydrogen involves the participation of electrons from the surface atoms of the germanium rather than from the donor impurities. In its ground state germanium has no vacant d-electrons, i.e., germanium, like copper, requires activation. The energy of activation of the isotopic exchange of hydrogen and deuterium on germanium (17 kcal/mole) is higher than on nickel (8 kcal/mole) and $\Delta E = 9$ kcal/mole again coincides with $\frac{1}{2}\varepsilon_{\mathrm{Ge}}$ (9.8 kcal/mole); unfortunately, data on the heat of chemisorption of hydrogen on germanium are not available.

The views developed here have been confirmed by the observed changes in the energy of activation of the ortho-para transformations of hydrogen on palladium—gold alloys of different compositions /4, 13/. As is evident from the figure, in the presence of an excess of palladium the value of E_{app} is independent of the composition of the alloy and coincides with the value of the energy of activation on pure palladium. However, a sudden jump in E_{app} is observed at a composition (of the alloy) corresponding to a paramagnetic susceptibility equal to zero (i.e., when all vacant atomic d-orbitals of the palladium have been used for binding the gold atoms): a catalyst possessing no vacant atomic d-orbitals requires activation. When the gold content is increased further, the energy of activation again remains constant and a new jump in E_{app} is observed only for pure gold: the Pt — Au and Au — Au bond do not have the same energies.

Similar results have been obtained also in the hydrogenation of ethylene, benzene, styrene, and cinnamic acid on the respective alloys of metals belonging to groups VIII and IB of the periodic table /6, 13/.

Thus, a discussion of the electronic structure of the atoms of a metal (in its crystalline state) makes it possible to explain the observed qualitative relations in the changes of the catalytic activity of metals belonging to a given period of the periodic table, and to give a quantitative correlation of the energies of activation of heterogeneous catalytic reactions on various metallic catalysts.

In conclusion, the author expresses his gratitude to V.P. Lebedev for valuable advice in the discussion of this paper.

BIBLIOGRAPHY

1. DOWDEN, D.A. and P.W. REYNOLDS.—Disc. Faraday Soc., Vol.8: 184. 1950.
2. DOWDEN, D.A.—J. Chem. Soc., p.242. 1950.
3. REYNOLDS, P.W.—J. Chem. Soc., p.265. 1950.
4. COUPER, A. and D.D. ELEY.—Disc. Faraday Soc., Vol.8: 172. 1950.
5. REYNOLDS, P.W.— Chem. a. Ind., p.320. 1949.
6. DOWDEN, D.A.—Ind. Eng. Chem., Vol.44: 977. 1952.
7. BEECK, O.—Disc. Faraday Soc., Vol.8: 118. 1950.
8. BORESKOV, G.K.—Problemy Kinetiki i Kataliza, Vol.10: 128. 1960.
9. BORESKOV, G.K.—In: Sbornik "Problemy fizicheskoi khimii". Trudy nauchno-issledovatel'skogo
        fiziko-khimicheskogo instituta im. L.Ya. Karpova, No.1: 101. 1958.
10. BORESKOV, G.K.—ZhFKh, Vol.31: 937. 1957.
11. TRAPNEL, B. Chemisorption. [Russian translation. 1958.]
12. GERMAIN, J. Heterogeneous Catalysis. [Russian translation. 1961.]
13. BAKER, M. and H. JENKINS. Catalysis. Electronic Phenomena. [Russian translation. 1958.]
14. BOUDART, M.—Chem. Eng. Progr., 57(8): 33. 1961.
15. BOND, G.C. Catalysis by Metals.—London-N.Y., Academic Press. 1962.
16. GARNER, W. Kataliz (Catalysis).—Proceedings of the 1st International Congress, p.198. Moskva, IL.
        1960.
17. LANDAU, M.A. and V.V. SHCHEKIN.—Trudy Instituta Nefti AN SSSR, Vol.14: 118. 1960.
18. LANDAU, M.A. and V.V. SHCHEKIN.—IAN SSSR, OKhN, p.430. 1961.
19. LANDAU, M.A.—IAN SSSR, OKhN, p.582. 1962.
20. LANDAU, M.A.—IAN SSSR, OKhN, p.789. 1962.
21. SOKOL'SKII, D.V. Gidrirovanie v rastvorakh (Hydrogenation in Solutions), p.461, 469.—Alma-Ata,
        Izd. AN KazSSR. 1962.
22. PAULING, L.—Phys. Rev., Vol.54: 899. 1938.
23. PAULING, L.—J. Am. Chem. Soc., Vol.69: 542. 1947.
24. PAULING, L.—Proc. Roy. Soc., Vol.A 196: 343. 1949.
25. PAULING, L. The Nature of the Chemical Bond. 3rd Ed., Chapter 11.—N.Y., Cornell Univ. Press.
        1960.
26. LANDAU, M.A. Dissertation.—Moskva, INKhS AN SSSR im. A.V. Topchieva. 1963.
27. MITTASCH, A.—Adv. Cat., Vol.2: 82. 1950.
28. STREL'NIKOVA, Zh.V. and V.P. LEBEDEV.—Vestnik MGU, No.1: 38. 1961.
29. LEBEDEV, V.P. and E.A. TROSMAN.—ZhFKh, Vol.34: 687. 1960.
30. LEBEDEV, V.P. and Zh.V. STREL'NIKOVA.—Vestnik MGU, No.5: 25. 1960.
31. BOND, G.C. and R.S. MANN.—J. Chem. Soc., p.3566. 1959.
32. GOLUTVIN, Yu.M. Teploty obrazovaniya i tipy khimicheskoi svyazi v neorganicheskikh kristallakh
        (Heat of Formation and Types of Chemical Bonds in Inorganic Crystals), p.77.—Moskva, Izd.
        AN SSSR. 1962.
33. STREL'NIKOVA, Zh.V. and V.P. LEBEDEV.—ZhFKh, Vol.37: 920. 1963.
34. EMEL'YANOVA, G.I. and V.P. LEBEDEV.—ZhFKh, Vol.38: 2293. 1964.
35. GOROKHOVA, T.I., A.N. MAL'TSEV, and N.I. KOBOZEV.—ZhFKh (in print).
36. ZYKOVA, G.I., Yu.P. SIMANOV, and V.P. LEBEDEV.—In: Sbornik "Kinetika i kataliz", p.227.
        Moskva, Izd. AN SSSR. 1960.
37. SOKOL'SKII, D.V.—Problemy Kinetiki i Kataliza, Vol.6: 157. 1949.
38. KWAN, T. Catalysis. Investigation of Heterogeneous Processes.—Collection of translated papers,
        p.314. Moskva, IL. 1956.
39. deBOER, J.H. Catalysis. Some Problems of the Theory and Technology of Organic Reactions.—
        Collection of translated papers, p.18. Moskva, IL. 1959.
40. ZEITS, F. Sovremennaya teoriya tverdogo tela (Modern Theory of Solids).—Moskva-Leningrad,
        Tekhteorizdat. 1949.
41. RIENÄCKER, G.—Z. anorg. Chem., Vol.236: 263. 1938.
42. BEECK, O., A. SMITH, and A. WHEELER.—Proc. Roy. Soc., Vol.A 177: 62. 1940.
43. KINGTON, G.L. and J.M. HOLMES.—Trans. Faraday Soc., Vol.49: 417. 1953.
44. AVDEENKO, A.A., G.K. BORESKOV, and M.G. SLIN'KO.—Problemy Kinetiki i Kataliza, Vol.9: 61.
        1957.
45. BORESKOV, G.K., M.G. SLIN'KO, A.G. FILIPPOVA, and R.N. GUR'YANOVA.—DAN SSSR, Vol.94:
        713. 1954.
46. KEMBALL, C. and C.T.H. STODDART.—Proc. Roy. Soc., Vol.A 241: 208. 1957.
47. KEMBALL, C.—Proc. Roy. Soc., Vol.A 214: 413. 1952.

E.I. Evzerikhin and G.D. Lyubarskii

THE CATALYTIC ACTIVITY OF ALLOYS OF THE TRANSITION METALS

   Investigations of the relationship between the catalytic activity of the transition metals and their electronic structure is conveniently carried out on alloys of these metals, since alloying makes it possible to control smoothly the electronic structure. The investigation of the nickel — copper and nickel — cobalt systems is of special interest, since in the first system the number of unpaired electrons in the d-band of the alloy decreases with increasing copper content, while in the second system it increases with increasing cobalt content.

   Our first paper in this field was dedicated to the study of the catalytic activity, chemisorption capacity and magnetic characteristics of a series of nickel — copper alloys /1/. The catalysts were prepared by coprecipitation of copper and nickel carbonates with subsequent reduction to the metals. X-ray and magnetic methods showed that this leads to the formation of the same solid solutions that are formed in the alloying of these metals. Magnetic measurements on the obtained alloys showed that the magnetic moment of the samples decreases as the copper concentration in the alloy is increased, and that it reaches a value of zero (filling of the d-band of the alloy) at a copper concentration of 80%. The specific catalytic activity (in benzene hydrogenation) and the chemisorption capacity (based on the adsorption of sulfurous compounds) changed in a similar way (Figure 1).

   Thus, for the above system of alloys we established the existence of a distinct correlation between the changes in specific activity (per unit surface of the samples), the chemisorption capacity, and the magnetic properties of these catalysts. This indicates that a certain relationship exists between the presence of unpaired d-electrons in the metals and their catalytic properties. It was shown that when the composition of the alloy is changed the energy of activation of the hydrogenation of benzene remains constant (about 14 kcal/mole), and that the kinetic rules governing the reaction also remain constant. This leads to the conclusion that the change in the catalytic activity of the above alloys is associated with changes in the values of the preexponents in the Arrhenius equation.

   Subsequent studies dealt with a system of nickel — cobalt alloys prepared by the same method as the copper — nickel catalysts, i.e., by coprecipitation of the carbonates. The catalytic activity was determined by measuring the rate of hydrogenation of benzene in the continuous-circulation setup described in a previous paper /2/. Kinetic studies showed that under these conditions the reaction rate is described by a zero-order equation with respect to the benzene. The surface area of the samples was determined by low-temperature adsorption of krypton; these measurements showed that the addition of cobalt to the nickel causes a marked increase in the specific surface area.

X-ray spectra obtained by us for nickel — cobalt catalysts reduced at 250 and 350° showed that these catalysts are homogeneous solid solutions, and that alloys with a cobalt content of 0 to 60% have a face-centered cubic lattice; alloys with 60 — 70% cobalt contain two phases — face-centered cubic and close-packed hexagonal; alloys with a cobalt content of 70 — 100% have a hexagonal lattice. The above results agree with literature data on the alloys prepared by high-temperature fusion of these metals /3/. The magnetic moment of nickel — cobalt alloys increases almost linearly with increasing cobalt content in the alloy, from 0.6 for nickel to 1.7 Bohr magnetons for cobalt, which corresponds to the increase in the number of unpaired d-electrons per atom of the above metals.

The nickel — cobalt catalysts were reduced for 2 hours at 250 and 350°. Increasing the reduction time to 13 hours had no effect on the activity of the catalysts.

The highest activity and specific surface of the samples were obtained when the reduction was carried out at 250°. Hence, the above temperature was selected as the optimum reduction temperature in our studies on the catalytic properties of nickel — copper and nickel — cobalt alloys.

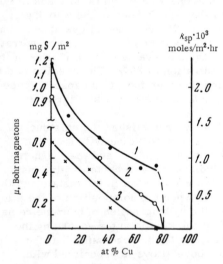 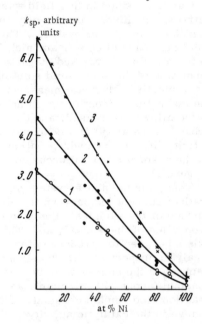

FIGURE 1. Relationship between the catalytic, chemisorption and magnetic properties of nickel-copper alloys:

1- specific chemisorption of carbon disulfide;
2- specific activity k_{sp}; 3- magnetic moment μ.

FIGURE 2. Dependence of the specific activity of nickel-cobalt alloys on the nickel content:

1- 140°C; 2- 150°C; 3- 160°C.

The activity of the nickel — cobalt catalysts was measured at 140 — 170°. The catalytic activity and the surface area (per one gram of the catalyst) increased with increasing cobalt concentration in the alloy. The specific catalytic activity increased almost linearly with increasing cobalt concentration in the alloy, and the activity of cobalt was more than 20 times the activity of nickel (Figure 2). The energy of activation of the reaction on all catalysts (independently of the composition) was practically constant and had the same value as the energy of activation on nickel — copper catalysts. It should be noted that the above-mentioned change in the lattice type (as a function of increasing cobalt concentration in the catalyst) did not affect the activity of the alloys; this should be expected, since certain planes of the face-centered cubic lattice correspond to planes with other indices in the close-packed hexagonal lattice. The collected data lead to the conclusion that a distinct correlation between the specific activity of the catalyst and the number of unpaired d-electrons per one atom of the metal exists in the cases of both nickel — cobalt and nickel — copper alloys.

Thus, investigations of the catalytic activities of nickel — cobalt and nickel — copper alloys revealed the following.

1) The energy of activation of all working catalysts is virtually constant, independently of their composition and electronic structure.

2) A sharp decrease in the catalytic activity (by a factor of at least 100) is observed in the case of a nickel — copper alloy with a copper content of about 80%, i.e., when the d-band is filled.

3) The changes in the preexponent in the expression for the rate constant of the investigated reaction follow the changes in the number of unpaired d-electrons in the metallic catalyst.

When the hydrogenation is carried out on nickel — cobalt or nickel — copper catalysts, it might be expected (on the basis of the concepts of D. Dowden /4/) that the energy of activation will increase with increasing cobalt or nickel content, since the electron work function and electron level density at the Fermi level should decrease with increasing copper or nickel concentration in the alloy. According to Dowden, a decrease in the values of these two parameters must lead to an increase in the energy of activation of the adsorption, and to a decrease in the surface concentration of molecules that during the adsorption transfer their electrons to the metal or form a covalent bond with it. According to the results of magnetic measurements made by P. Selwood et al. /5/, hydrogen and benzene do belong to the above type of molecules. However, the above concepts of Dowden concerning the changes in the energy of activation on nickel — copper and nickel — cobalt alloys cannot evidently be applied to processes whose rate is determined by the rate of reaction between the adsorbed molecules or the surface atoms rather than by the adsorption rate. It is commonly accepted that the molecules participating in the reactions on the surface of the catalyst are those with average bond energies. At the same time, the working fraction of the occupied surface ($\Delta\theta$) corresponding to the "working" range of bond energies between the adsorbed molecules and the catalyst is independent of the initial heat of adsorption (at $\theta = 0$), which is determined (according to Dowden) by the electronic structure of the catalyst. Catalysts having a crystal lattice of the same type and with close values of the lattice parameters would apparently have the same "working" range of bond energies for a given reaction. Hence, if the activated complex on such catalysts is of the same type, the height of the energy barrier for the reaction should also be the same. This leads to the conclusion that geometrically similar catalysts with different electronic structures should be characterized by a constant value of the energy of activation of processes whose rate is determined by the rate of surface interactions.

As a result of the above investigation of the kinetics of benzene hydrogenation on nickel catalysts it was found that the process rate is determined by the rate of the successive surface stages of the reaction between the adsorbed hydrogen and the semihydrogenated state of the benzene (of the surface radicals type). In view of our observation that the kinetic equation for the above reaction on nickel — cobalt and nickel — copper catalysts remains unchanged, it may be assumed that the above mechanism also remains unchanged. In such a case, the energy of activation of the process should be the same on all alloy catalysts, independently of their composition; this has been confirmed experimentally for alloys with an unfilled d-band (from cobalt to a nickel alloy with ~ 75% copper).

The gradual filling of the d-band as a result of increasing copper concentration in the alloy causes a deterioration in the adsorption conditions, and the energy of activation of the adsorption increases sharply, which causes a decrease in the adsorption rate so that the adsorption may become the limiting [slowest] stage of the process. This evidently occurs on the surface of nickel — copper catalysts with a copper content of 80% or more; this leads to a sharp decrease in the catalytic activity and chemisorption capacity in the above range. The above point of view is supported by the data of /6/ on the energy of activation of hydrogen adsorption: on nickel it is close to zero while on copper it equals about 20 kcal/mole. The latter value is much higher than the energy of activation of benzene hydrogenation as determined in this paper and assigned to the stage of surface interaction. Moreover, if the filling of the d-band at copper concentrations of about 80% causes such an increase in the energy of activation of hydrogen adsorption that the adsorption begins to limit the process rate, the sharp decrease in activity in the above range of compositions should

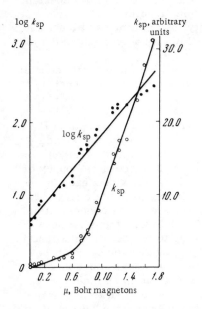

FIGURE 3. Dependence of the specific activity of alloy catalysts on the magnetic moment

be a general feature of most hydrogenation processes conducted on nickel — copper catalysts. Experimental data /7/ on the hydrogenation of ethylene and cinnamic acid or the ortho-para conversion of hydrogen confirm the above conclusion.

According to the collected data, the specific activity of copper — nickel alloys increases with increasing nickel content, while that of nickel — cobalt alloys increases with increasing cobalt content; however, correlation exists between this increase in activity and any of the physical characteristics of the metallic catalyst (electron work function, lattice parameter, % of d-state, etc.), except the magnetic moment or the number of unpaired d-electons per one atom of the metal. Figure 3 shows the dependence of the logarithm of the specific activity of all investigated catalysts on their magnetic moment, i.e., on the number of unpaired electrons in the alloys; it is evident that the dependence is almost linear.

Since the energy of activation on these catalysts remains unchanged, the increase in activity is associated with an increase in the preexponents. In the theory of transitional states with respect to heterogeneous processes, the preexponent is $A = \varkappa$ const $e^{\Delta S^*}$, where $\varkappa$ is the transmission coefficient and ΔS^* is the entropy of activation. The increase that we observed in the preexponent with increasing number of unpaired d-electrons may be associated with an increase in $\varkappa$ or ΔS^*. The above-mentioned increase in the values of the preexponents for the series of investigated alloys corresponds to a change in the entropy of activation of nearly 10 entropy units, which is rather improbable for an unchanged energy of the activated complex. In such a case the change in the preexponent is associated with an increase in the value of $\varkappa$, which by its nature is a term that takes into account the electronic changes in the course of the reaction. By using the method of V.A. Roiter and G.I. Golodets /9/ we made a statistical calculation of the values of the preexponents for the rate constants of this reaction, assuming that $\varkappa = 1$. The resulting values of the preexponents are higher (by a factor of three and a half orders of magnitude) than the experimental values for the most active catalyst — cobalt (and by a factor of five and half orders of magnitude for the least active — a 25% Ni + 75% Cu alloy). Such a substantial difference between the experimental and calculated results indicates that $\varkappa$ has a very small value (i.e., that the process is apparently non-adiabatic), and supports the conclusion according to which the transmission coefficient may change in the above process as a result of changes in the electronic structure of the catalyst.

Thus, the experimental results show the existence of a distinct connection between the catalytic and chemisorption properties of metal and alloys on the one hand, and their electronic structure on the other. In discussing this connection, it is necessary to take into account the kinetic features of the investigated reaction; in the case of benzene hydrogenation, the concepts of Dowden do not describe the observed relationships and require further development.

BIBLIOGRAPHY

1. LYUBARSKII, G.D., E.I. EVZERIKHIN, and A.A. SLINKIN.—Kinetika i Kataliz, Vol. 5: 311. 1964.
2. LYUBARSKII, G.D., L.B. AVDEEVA, and N.V. KUL'KOVA.—Kinetika i Kataliz, Vol. 3: 123. 1962.
3. TEYLOR, R.—J. Inst. Metals, Vol. 77: 585. 1950; SAMAMOTO, M. Sci. rep. Tohoku imp. univ., Vol. A 4: 14. 1952.
4. DOWDEN, D.A.—J. Chem. Soc., p. 242. 1950; Ind. Eng. Chem., Vol. 44: 977. 1952.
5. MORRIS, H. and P.W. SELWOOD.—J. Chem. Sco., Vol. 65: 2245. 1943; DIETZ, R.E. and P.W. SELWOOD. J. Chem. Phys., Vol. 35: 270. 1961; SELWOOD, P.W. J. Chem. Phys., Vol. 37: 2709. 1962; J. Am. Chem. Soc., Vol. 79: 4637. 1957.
6. KWAN, T. Catalysis. Investigation of Heterogeneous Processes.—Collection of translated papers, p. 314. Moskva, IL. 1956.
7. HALL, W.K. and P.W. EMMETT.—J. Phys. Chem., Vol. 63: 1102. 1959; RIENÄCKER, G. Z. Anorg. Chem., Vol. 283: 287. 1956.
8. TEMKIN, M.I.—ZhFKh, Vol. 11: 169. 1938.
9. GOLODETS, G.I. and V.A. ROITER.—Kinetika i Kataliz, Vol. 4: 177. 1963.

Ya. T. Eidus and T. F. Bulanova

COBALT CATALYSTS FOR REACTIONS WITH THE PARTICIPATION OF CARBON MONOXIDE, HYDROGEN AND OLEFINS, AND THEIR PROMOTION BY METAL OXIDES

The development of a scientific basis for the selections of catalysts, using the principles of structural and energetic correspondence /1/, electronic and other concepts /2/ is of great practical and theoretical value. Such a selection, like the empirical one, requires the accumulation of a large amount of experimental data on various parameters, and in particular on the bond energy between the reacting atoms and the catalyst, which depends on the composition of the catalyst and the method of preparation. The problem of the selection may also be solved in a doubtful manner, so that further experiments may be required in order to reach final conclusions.

For the time being, the practical selection of catalysts for actual processes (which usually are multistage ones and which as a rule need the use of multicomponent catalysts) outstrips the theory. Catalysts and their components are selected by trial-and-error methods, on the basis of experience accumulated over more than a hundred years of development of catalytic processes. In essence, the correlation of this experience is also one of the scientific principles of the selection; for this reason, in the investigation of catalytic and promoting properties it is necessary to expand the range of chemical elements and their compounds as well as the number of model reactions, which by nature rarely differ from hydrogenation-dehydrogenation and hydration-dehydration reactions /3/.

The aim of this paper is to correlate some data on the selection of catalysts for reactions involving the participation of CO, namely, the hydrogenation of CO to higher hydrocarbons (by the Fischer-Tropsch method), its hydrogenation-condensation with olefins, and the hydrogenation-polymerization of olefins under the influence of small amounts of CO in the presence of H_2. These reactions are complex and have many stages, which necessitates the use of polyfunctional, multicomponent catalysts, that cannot be selected on the basis of the existing theories of catalysis. We discuss only the data on the most important (for the practical realization of the above processes) precipitated Co catalysts. The results are shown as graphs in which comparisons are made between the yields of liquid hydrocarbons of the benzine (gasoline) and oil (b + o) type, or between the total yields of C_3 and higher hydrocarbons (b + o + z) and which show the b/o weight ratios or the $\frac{o + b}{2}$ weight ratio (where z is "gazol'", $C_3 - C_4$ hydrocarbons)*.

_____
* ["Gazol" is not gas oil, which is much heavier.]

PRECIPITATED Co CATALYSTS FOR THE FISCHER-TROPSCH PROCESS

It was found that the Co catalysts for the above process required the following components: a metal of group VIII and its oxide, an oxide that is reduced with difficulty, and a carrier. The most important data obtained in this field by F. Fischer /4/ are shown in Figure 1.* These data were collected in 1932, when some experience existed already on the investigation of certain Ni, Fe, and ignited Co catalysts, and it was known that it is necessary to use a carrier of the kieselguhr type. However, the catalyst (100 weight parts of Co per 100 weight parts of kieselguhr) had a low activity (b + o = 35 g/m^3 at 210°) and yielded light hydrocarbons (b:o = 17). The addition of 20 parts of Zn or Mg (as the oxides) per 100 parts of Co did not improve, while the addition of Al or Cr impaired, the properties of the catalyst when the reaction was carried out at 215°. The activity was increased by adding Mn or by using soda ash instead of potash for the precipitation of the catalyst. The reaction could then be carried out at 200° (b + o 104 g/m^3, b:o = 1.1). The most important promoter was ThO$_2$: its optimum concentration is 18 parts per 100 parts Co (at 190° b + o = 100 g/m^3, b:o = 0.5). Many investigations were carried out on the above catalyst. In 1939 O. Roelen replaced part of the ThO$_2$ by MgO and doubled the kieselguhr content, producing in this way the catalyst in its commercial form (about 125 g/m^3 of liquid hydrocarbons at room temperature) /5/.

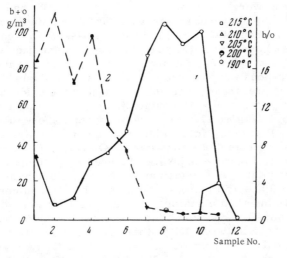

FIGURE 1. Effect of various additives on the activity of a catalyst (100 wt parts Co per 100 wt parts kieselguhr) in the synthesis of hydrocarbons from CO and H$_2$:

1- total yield of b+o; 2- b:o ratio. Description of the samples:
No. 1- starting catalyst (I); No. 2- I+20Al; No. 3- I+20Cr;
No. 4- I+20Zn; No. 5- I+20Mg; No. 6- I+20Mn; No. 7- I+
15Mg; No. 8- I+15Mn; No. 9- I+12ThO$_2$; No. 10- I+18ThO$_2$;
No. 11- I+24ThO$_2$; No. 12- I+48ThO$_2$. (All catalysts except
No. 8 were precipitated by K$_2$CO$_3$, while No. 8 was precipitated
by Na$_2$CO$_3$).

* The graph was plotted and the yields were converted from ml/m^3 to g/m^3 on the basis of the data of /4/.

Subsequently interest arose in an investigation of the possibility of complete exclusion of ThO_2 from the composition of the Co catalyst, as this would eliminate the harmful biological effects of the catalyst and free the thorium for other uses. On the basis of the principle of chemical similarity (which is derived from the arrangement of the elements in the periodic table, and is often used as one of the fundamentals of scientific selection), it could be assumed that dioxides of the elements belonging to the titanium subgroup would act (like ThO_2) as effective promoters for Co catalysts /6/.

We investigated the possibility of replacing the ThO_2 by ZrO_2, TiO_2, HfO_2, and CeO_2. Figures 2 and 3 show the results of experiments on the synthesis of hydrocarbons from a $CO + 2H_2$ mixture, in a continuous-flow system at atmospheric pressure, in a glass tube 10 mm in diameter containing 30 cm^3 of the catalyst (5 g Co) at a velocity of 100 volumes/hr. Catalysts No. 1 — 5 (see Figure 2) and 1 (see Figure 3) were prepared from Hannover diatomaceous earth /5/ (grain size before the reduction 4×4 mm); the remaining catalysts were carried on kieselguhr (kisatibi [sic]) with a grain size of 2×3 — 4 mm). Catalysts No. 1 — 7 (see Figure 2) and 6 — 7 (Figure 3) were precipitated with potash, while the remaining catalysts were precipitated with soda ash. Catalysts No. 1 (Figures 2 and 3) are identical; there is little difference between them and the other catalyst of the same composition (see Figure 1). Of the catalysts containing ZrO_2 (catalysts No. 2 — 4, Figure 2) the most active had a ZrO_2 content of 18%, as in the case of ThO_2-containing catalysts (see Figure 1). Catalysts No. 1 — 5 (Figure 2) were much more active at 205 — 210° than at 190° (curves 1a and 1). No liquid hydrocarbons were formed within the first 10 — 20 hr when the gaseous $CO - H_2$ mixture was passed over catalysts No. 6 — 8 (see Figure 2) and 2 — 10 (Figure 3) at 190°; the surface was "developed", and CO_2, CH_4 and H_2O were formed. A gradual increase in the yields of liquid hydrocarbons was observed afterwards. Catalysts of different activities were prepared by varying the quantitative oxide carrier ratio and the amount of precipitant. The catalysts precipitated with soda ash (No. 8, Figure 2; No. 4, Figure 3) were more active than those precipitated with potash (No. 7, Figure 2; No. 6, Figure 3), and the catalysts containing ZrO_2 were more active than those containing TiO_2 (No. 7, Figure 2 and No. 6, Figure 3; No. 8, Figure 2 and No. 4, Figure 3). A comparison of three catalysts precipitated with potash and having similar compositions (No. 7, Figure 2; No. 6 and 7, Figure 3) shows that the catalyst containing zirconia is more active than that containing thoria, and the latter is more active than the one containing titania. Doubling the concentration of the carrier caused a marked increase in the activity of the zirconium catalyst (No. 6 and 7, Figure 2) but only a very small increase in the activity of the titanium catalyst (No. 3 and 4, Figure 3). The $100Co:18CeO_2:100$ kieselguhr catalyst (No. 8, Figure 3) had a low activity, while the $100Co:10CeO:6MgO:200$ kieselguhr catalyst was much more active (b + o 70 g/m^3, b/o 0.5, see No. 9, Figure 3), and the catalyst of a similar composition but containing HfO_2 (No. 10, Figure 3) had about the same activity.

Thus, ZrO_2 and TiO_2, like ThO_2, act as promoters for Co — kieselguhr and Co — MgO — kieselguhr catalyst in the formation of hydrocarbons from CO and H_2. Less pronounced properties as promoters are exhibited by CeO_2 and HfO_2 with respect to Co — MgO — kieselguhr catalysts.

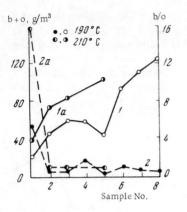

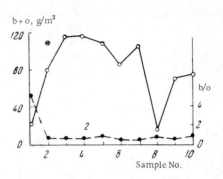

FIGURE 2. Effect of the addition of ZrO_2 and MgO on the activity of a Co-kieselguhr (100:100) catalyst in the synthesis of hydrocarbons from CO and H_2:

1, 1a- total yield of b+o; 2, 2a- b/o ratio. Description of the samples: No. 1- starting catalyst (I); No. 2- $I+24ZrO_2$; No. 3- $I+18ZrO_2$; No. 4- $I+12ZrO_2$; No. 5- $I+10ZrO_2+6MgO$; No. 6- $I+6ZrO_2+10MgO+100$ kieselguhr; No. 8- $I+6ZrO_2+10MgO+100$ kieselguhr. (Catalysts No. 2—7 were precipitated with K_2CO_3, No. 8 with Na_2CO_3).

FIGURE 3. Effect of the addition of TiO_2, CeO_2, and MgO on the activity of Co-kieselguhr (100: 100) catalyst in the synthesis of hydrocarbons from CO and H_2:

1- total yield of b+o; 2- b/o ratio. Description of the samples: No. 1- starting catalyst(I); No. 2- $I+18TiO_2$; No. 3- $I+6TiO_2+10MgO$; No. 4- $I+6TiO_2+10MgO+100$ kieselguhr; No. 5- $I+10TiO_2+6MgO+100$ kieselguhr; No. 6- $I+6TiO_2+10MgO+100$ kieselguhr; No. 7- $I+6ThO_2+10MgO+100$ kieselguhr; No. 8- $I+18CeO_2+100$ kieselguhr; No. 9- $I+10CeO_2+6MgO+100$ kieselguhr; No. 10- $I+10HfO_2+6MgO+100$ kieselguhr. (Catalysts No. 1—5 and 9—10 were precipitated with Na_2CO_3, while No. 6—8 were precipitated with K_2CO_3).

PRECIPITATED Co CATALYSTS FOR THE HYDROGENATION POLYMERIZATION OF OLEFINS UNDER THE EFFECT OF SMALL AMOUNTS OF CO IN THE PRESENCE OF H_2

The effect of the nature of the carrier of a standard $100Co:18ThO_2$ catalyst in the hydrogenation polymerization of ethylene (in a gasesous 1:1 $C_2H_4:H_2$ mixture containing 5% CO) has been studied earlier /7/. The study encompassed silica gel, activated carbon, alumina, and muslyumian and red clays previously heated to 450° in a current of air /8/. In the experiments with Al_2O_3 the Co:carrier weight ratio was 1:5, while in the other experiments it was 1:2 (see Figure 4). Catalyst No. 4 was used after one cycle involving reaction and regeneration by H_2 at 450°. On Figure 4, the yield of gazol' is represented by the distance (along a vertical line) between curves 1 and 2. The most active catalysts were those supported on the clays (especially on red clay) and on Al_2O_3 after regeneration. The latter catalyst yielded liquid hydrocarbon with the greatest specific gravity (b/o = 1.35). The catalyst on silica gel showed no activity.

Co catalysts containing no additives were tested also on different carriers, in the hydrogenation polymerization of ethylene at 190°, using a starting $C_2O_4 + H_2$ mixture containing 5% CO /9 — 11/. Catalytic activity was exhibited by the catalysts on Al_2O_3 and clay (Figure 5) and especially by the catalyst with a Co:red clay ratio of 100:200 (b + o + z = 380 g/m³; (b + o)/z = 4.3). The addition of Mg, Ca, Zn, Cr, Ba, and Mn oxides as well as metallic Cu at concentrations of 5% of the Co reduced the catalytic activity /11/, and only the addition of Al_2O_3 (Figure 6) had an effect as a promoter /9/.

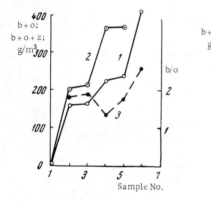 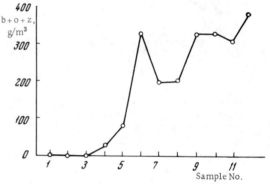

FIGURE 4. Effect of the nature of the carrier on the activity of a catalyst containing 100 parts of Co and 18 parts of ThO_2 in the hydrogenation polymerization of ethylene:

1, 2- total yields of b+o and b+o+z; 3- b/o ratio. Description of the samples: No.1- SiO_2; No.2- activated carbon; No.3- Al_2O_3; No.4- regenerated Al_2O_3; No.5- muslyumian clay; No.6- red clay.

FIGURE 5. Effect of the nature of the carrier on the activity of a Co catalyst in the hydrogenation polymerization of ethylene:

Description of the samples (amount of carrier per 100 parts of Co): No.1- 400 $Ca(OH)_2$; No.2- 300 $BaCO_3$; No.3- 100 MgO; No.4- 200 $CaCO_3$; No.5- 400 Cr_2O_3; No.6- 500 Al_2O_3; No.7- 100 kieselguhr; No.8- 200 kieselguhr, No.9- 500 muslyumian clay; No.10- 200 muslyumian clay; No.11- 400 red clay; No.12- 200 red clay.

We studied also the effect of the addition of dioxides of metals belonging to the titanium subgroup (Zr, Ti, and Ce) on the 1 Co:2 kieselguhr (kisatibi) (Figure 7) and 1 Co:2 clay (Figure 8) catalysts in the hydrogenation polymerization of ethylene at 190°, using $2C_2H_4 + H_2$ mixtures containing 5% CO. The catalysts were prepared by precipitation with soda ash ("pure" grade) in the presence of kieselguhr or red clay (fired in air at 450°) and were reduced by H_2 flowing at a velocity of 100 volumes/hr at 450°. The grain size prior to the reduction was 2×3 —4 mm. In this case the catalyst [surface] was "developed" twice as fast (5 — 9 hr) as in the synthesis of hydrocarbons from CO and H_2. The formation of liquid hydrocarbons started at once, but the yields were low. The activity of the Co — kieselguhr catalyst increased sharply upon the addition of 10 parts of ZrO_2 or ThO_2, and the b/o ratio decreased simultaneously. The further addition of 6 parts of MgO caused a decrease in the activity of the Co —Zr catalyst with an increase in the b/o ratio, or an increase in the activity of the Co —Th catalyst with a small increase in b/o. The addition of 10 parts of TiO_2 caused a decrease in the yield of hydrocarbons and an increase in b/o, but the subsequent addition of 6 parts of MgO caused a sharp increase in the yield of hydrocarbons and a decrease in b/o. Thus, the simultaneous addition of TiO_2 and MgO had a promoter effect on the Co—kieselguhr catalyst (at a TiO_2:MgO ratio of 10:6, b + o = 245 g/m³, b/o = 0.9, and b + o + z = 335 g/m³, while at TiO_2:MgO = 6:10, b+ o = 203 g/m³, b/o = 2.4, and b + o + z = 270 g/m³). The addition of CeO_2 or CeO_2 + MgO to the Co—kieselguhr catalyst caused its deactivation (see Figure 7).

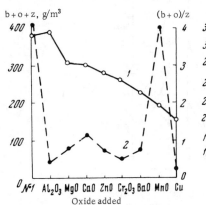

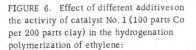

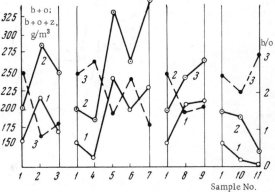

FIGURE 6. Effect of different additives on the activity of catalyst No. 1 (100 parts Co per 200 parts clay) in the hydrogenation polymerization of ethylene:

1- total yield of b+o+z; 2- (b+o)/z ratio.

FIGURE 7. Effect of the addition of ZrO_2, TiO_2, ThO_2, CeO_2, and MgO on the activity of Co-kieselguhr catalysts in the hydrogenation polymerization of ethylene:

1,2- total yields of b+o and b+o+z; 3- b/o ratio. Description of the samples: No. 1- starting catalyst (I); No. 2- I+ 10 ZrO_2; No. 3- I+ 10 ZrO_2 + 6 MgO; No. 4- I+ 10 TiO_2; No. 5- I+ TiO_2 + 6MgO; No. 6- I+ 6 TiO_2 + 10 MgO; No. 7- I+ 6 TiO + 10 MgO; No. 8- I+ 10 ThO_2; No. 9- I+ TiO_2 + 6 MgO; No. 10- I+ 18 CeO_2; No. 11- I+ 10 CeO_2 + 6 MgO. (In samples No. 1—6, 8—9, and 11 the Co:kieselguhr ratio was 100:200, while in samples No. 7 and 10 the ratio was 100:100).

The effect of the addition of oxides of metals belonging to the Ti subgroup to the Co—clay catalysts was altogether different. The addition of ThO_2, TiO_2, or ZrO_2 (10 parts per 100 parts Co) caused a decrease in the activity and a slight increase in b/o. The further addition of 6 parts of MgO caused a further drop in the activity of the Co—Th catalysts and a slight increase in the activity of the Co—Ti catalysts, but the Co—clay catalyst containing no additives was always the most active (see Figure 8). This catalyst (b + o = 330 g/m³, b/o = 0.64, b + o + z = 420 g/m³) was twice as active as the Co—kieselguhr catalyst (b + o = 160 g/m³, b/o = 2.5, b + o + z 200 g/m³).

The above results show that the effect of the additive depends on the nature of the carrier and may differ in different reactions. In spite of the similarity between the reaction mechanisms in the formation of hydrocarbons from CO and H_2, and the hydrogenation polymerization of ethylene under the effect of CO, the optimum catalysts for these two reactions have different compositions, and the same additives have different effects.

In the synthesis of hydrocarbons from CO and H_2 the addition of ZrO_2, ThO_2, and TiO_2 to Co—kieselguhr and Co—MgO—kiselguhr was very effective, while CeO_2 and HfO_2 were less effective. In the hydrogenation polymerization of ethylene (under the effect of small amounts of CO in the presence of hydrogen) ZrO_2 and ThO_2 acted as promoters for both catalysts, while TiO_2 had a promoter effect only on the $Co-MgO-$ kieselguhr catalyst. Both catalysts were deactivated by the addition of CeO_2. All the oxides mentioned above reduced the activity of the $Co-$ clay catalyst in the above reaction.

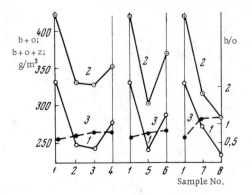

FIGURE 8. Effect of the addition of ZrO_2, TiO_2, ThO_2, and MgO on the activity of the Co-kieselguhr catalyst in the hydrogenation polymerization of ethylene:

1,2- total yield of b+o and b+o+z; 3- b/o ratio. Description of the samples: No. 1- starting catalyst (I); No. 2- I+10 ZrO_2; No. 3- I+10 ZrO_2+6 MgO; No. 4-I+10 ZrO_2+6 MgO; No. 5- I+10 TiO_2; No. 6- I+10 TiO_2+6 MgO; No. 7- I+10 ThO_2; No. 8- I+ 10 ThO_2+6 MgO. (In all samples except No. 4 the Co:clay ratio was 100:200 while in sample No. 4 it was 100:100).

In both reactions, the oxygen from the CO molecule was separated mainly in the form of water. Apparently, this is favored by the presence of the Th, Zr, and Ti oxides, which have dehydrating properties. Processes leading to the formation of water are of more importance in Fischer-Tropsch synthesis than in hydrogenation polymerization, since the CO concentration in the starting gas mixture is $6-7$ times greater. For this reason, the hydrogenation polymerization is catalyzed by the $Co-$ clay catalyst which contains no oxide promoter but whose carrier has dehydrating properties. According to A.A. Balandin, A.A. Tolstopyatova, and I.R. Konenko /12/, the specific dehydration activity of dioxides of metals belonging to the titanium subgroup is characterized by the ratio ZrO_2:TiO_2: HfO_2 = 5:2.5:1. According to our results, the promoter effectiveness of these oxides in the $Co-$ kieselguhr catalyst for Fischer-Tropsch synthesis corresponded to the same ratio.

BIBLIOGRAPHY

1. BALANDIN, A.A. Mul'tipletnaya teoriya katalyza (The Multiplet Theory of Catalysis). Part 1.—
   Moskva, Izd. MGU. 1963.
2. ROGINSKII, S.Z.— Problemy Kinetiki i Kataliza, Vol. 10: 5. 1960.
3. EIDUS, Ya.T.—Vestnik AN SSSR, No. 2: 22. 1961.
4. FISCHER, F. and H. KOCH.—Brennstoff. Chem., Vol. 13: 61. 1932.
5. STORCH, H., N. GOLUMBIC, and R.A. ANDERSON. Synthesis of Hydrocarbons from Carbon Monoxide
   and Hydrogen. [Russian translation. 1954.]
6. EIDUS, Ya.T., T.F. BULANOVA, and N.S. SERGEEVA.—DAN SSSR, Vol. 147: 1105. 1962; Vol. 153:
   101. 1963; Neftekhimiya, Vol. 4: 61. 1964.
7. EIDUS, Ya.T., K.V. PUZITSKII, and I.V. GUSEVA.—IAN SSSR, OKhN, p. 2213. 1959.
8. EIDUS, Ya.T., N.I. ERSHOV, and V.R. EROKHINA.—IAN SSSR, OKhN, p. 1874. 1961.
9. EIDUS, Ya.T., K.V. PUZITSKII, and N.I. ERSHOV.—IAN SSSR, OKhN, p. 331. 1960.
10. EIDUS, Ya.T. and N.I. ERSHOV.—IAN SSSR, OKhN, p. 120. 1960.
11. EIDUS, Ya.T., N.I. ERSHOV, K.V. PUZITSKII, and I.V. GUSEVA.—IAN SSSR, OKhN, p. 913. 1960.
12. BALANDIN, A.A., A.A. TOLSTOPYATOVA, and I.R. KONENKO.—IAN SSSR, OKhN, p. 2096. 1960;
    pp. 38, 45. 1961.

Yu. N. Artyukh, R. F. Lavrentovich, and M. T. Rusov

INVESTIGATION OF THE CATALYTIC PROPERTIES OF METALS AND ALLOYS AND THEIR ELECTRONIC STRUCTURE

The existing data on the activity of some transition metals in the synthesis (decomposition) of ammonia may be interpreted (with a certain degree of approximation) from the standpoint of the effect of the number of unpaired d-electrons per atom of the catalyst on the course of the reaction. For instance, according to the ideas of D. Dowden /1/, a change in the number of unpaired d-electrons in the catalysts affects reactions whose limiting stage involves the formation (or rupture) of a covalent bond between one of the reactants and the surface of the catalyst.

It has been established recently that for a number of hydrogenation /2 — 4/, dehydrogenation /5/ and hydrogen ortho-para conversion /6/ reactions the catalytic activity of metals and alloys decreases when the magnetic susceptibility of the metal decreases with the filling of the d-band of the catalyst. D. Dowden and P. Reynolds /7/ investigated the hydrogenation of styrene, the decomposition of formic acid and methanol and the decomposition of hydrogen peroxide on iron-nickel and nickel-copper alloys and found that the catalytic activity in the first three reactions decreased as the d-band was filled. The reverse relationship was observed in the decomposition of hydrogen peroxide. The work of H. Kunz and L. Rienäcker /8/ on the hydrogenation of acetone on nickel-iron alloys is of great interest. In this reaction, the maximum catalytic activity was possessed by alloys containing 75 — 90% nickel. A marked increase in the catalytic activity of alloys containing less than 75% nickel (i.e., having a large number of d-vacancies) was obtained by substituting copper for part of the nickel (i.e., by reducing the number of d-vacancies).

In the synthesis (decomposition) of ammonia, a change in the number of unpaired d-electrons could affect the rate of adsorption (desorption) of nitrogen in the catalyst surface, which limits the rate of the process.

In this paper we discuss the results of a study of the catalytic activity of some transition metal alloys in the decomposition of ammonia, and we make an attempt to relate the changes in the activities of these alloys with changes in other parameters such as the number of unpaired d-electrons per one atom of the catalyst and the electron work function.

Our investigation was carried out on iron-nickel, cobalt-nickel, and iron-cobalt alloys. It is well known that these metals form a continuous series of solid solutions within a wide temperature and concentration range /9/.

The alloys were prepared in an arc furnace in an argon atmosphere. For the catalytic studies, some of the ingots obtained were worked into turnings.

For the magnetic measurements we made (on a lathe) cylindrical samples
20 — 30 mm long and 1 mm in diameter. All catalysts were annealed in
quartz ampuls under vacuum, at 1100°, in order to obtain an equilibrium
structure.

The catalytic activity of the alloys was determined by a continuous-
circulation method at atmospheric pressure, in the temperature range
between 550 and 680°. A stoichiometric nitrogen-hydrogen mixture
containing about 25% ammonia by volume was used as the working mixture.
In all experiments, the volume of the mixture was constant — 1,300
volumes/hr. The circulation velocity was 450 1/hr. The volume of
immersed catalyst was 5.5 — 6 ml. The temperature within the reactor
was measured by a thermocouple. The rate constant of the ammonia
decomposition was calculated by the Temkin-Pyzhev equation /10/ applied
to the prevailing conditions:

$$k_2 = C \frac{z_1 v_1 - z_2 v_2}{T z_1 \omega} (1 - z_2),$$

where k_2 is the rate constant of ammonia decomposition; C is a constant,
equal to $\dfrac{0.75 \times 1.5 P^{1.5}}{R}$ (P is the pressure of the gaseous mixture in atm,

R is the gas constant, $1 \cdot \text{atm/deg} \cdot \text{mole}$); z_1 and z_2 are the mole fractions of
ammonia in the gas mixture at the entrance and exit of the reaction space;
v_1 and v_2 are the flow rates of the gas mixture at the entrance and exit of
the reaction cycle, 1/hr; T is the temperature of the experiment °K; and
ω is the volume of the catalyst, 1.

The rate constant of ammonia decomposition (k_2) referred to unit surface
of the catalyst was used as a measure of the catalytic activity of the alloys.
The surface area of the catalysts was measured by low-temperature
adsorption of krypton. Catalyst samples weighing about 10 grams were
used in the adsorption measurements.

The number of unpaired d-electrons per one atom of the alloys was
determined by extrapolation of the experimental data on the magnetization
of the samples. The magnetization was measured by a differential
magnetometric method /12/. The measurements were made at room
temperature in a 5,500-oersted field. The contact potential difference of
Fe — Ni and Co — Ni alloys was determined by the oscillating capacitor
method in a nitrogen-hydrogen-ammonia medium at 420°, using the apparatus
built by V.I. Lyashenko and A.M. Pavlenko /13/. A silver plate was used
as the reference electrode. The accuracy of measurment was ± 30 mv.

The possibility of using the Temkin-Pyzhev equation for the calculation
of the rate of decomposition of ammonia at $\alpha = 0.5$ was examined by us on
a number of Co — Ni and Fe — Ni alloys. The values of k_2 for four samples
of different compositions calculated for flow rates of 670 and 1,330 hr^{-1}
are shown in Tables 1 (for Co — Ni) and 2 (for Fe — Ni alloys).

These data show that the best agreement between the values of k_2 is
obtained at $\alpha = 0.5$, i.e., at medium degrees of filling. The fact that the
above equation is valid indicates, in particular, that the nitrogen adsorption
stage in the decomposition of ammonia determined the reaction kinetics on
the alloys investigated by us, too.

The Fe — Ni s y s t e m (Table 3). Figure 1 shows the dependence of the
specific catalytic activity of Fe — Ni alloys (curve 1) and their magnetic

saturation moments (curve 2) on the composition. The continuous curve 2 is from /14/, while the dots show the values of η_0 calculated by us. The good agreement between our results and the data from the literature indicates, in particular, that the alloys used by us had, in fact, an equilibrium structure.

TABLE 1. Rate constants of the decomposition of ammonia on Co—Ni alloys at 650°C

Composition of the cata- lyst, wt% Ni	α	k_2		Deviation
		$v_1 = 670\ \mathrm{hr}^{-1}$	$v_1 = 1330\ \mathrm{hr}^{-1}$	
30	0.1	8.5	11.7	27
	0.5	50.2	50.2	0
	0.8	192.5	50.5	22
70	0.1	4.6	6.1	25
	0.5	24.6	23.5	4.5
	0.8	85.3	65.0	24

TABLE 2. Rate constants of the decomposition of ammonia on Fe—Ni alloys at 650°C

Composition of the cata- lyst, wt% Ni	α	k_2		Deviation
		$v_1 = 670\ \mathrm{hr}^{-1}$	$v_1 = 1330\ \mathrm{hr}^{-1}$	
30	0.1	6.4	7.7	17.0
	0.5	21.8	21.4	1.8
	0.8	54.6	46.0	15.7
70	0.1	11.1	14.3	22.4
	0.5	51.3	50.5	1.6
	0.8	162.5	129.0	20.5

TABLE 3. Heats of activation for the decomposition of ammonia (E_p) on Fe—Ni catalysts

% Fe	$S \cdot 10^3$, m²/g	E_p kcal/mole	% Fe	$S \cdot 10^3$, m²/g	E_p kcal/mole
100	6.3	54	45	2.6	52
80	4.0	53	35	1.8	51
70	3.9	50	30	1.9	51
65	3.2	52	20	1.6	52
55	2.9	50	0	1.0	53

The curve showing the changes in the magnetic saturation moment of the above system has a small maximum for nickel concentrations between 10 and 20%; a further increase in the nickel content causes a gradual drop of the line.

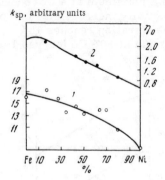

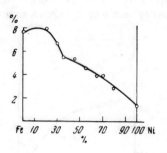

FIGURE 1. Changes in the catalytic activity k_{sp} (1) and the magnetic saturation moment η_0 (2) of Fe—Ni alloys as a function of the composition

FIGURE 2. Output (%) of Fe—Ni alloys

In our opinion, the observed scattering of the values of k_2 could be attributed to inaccuracies in the determination of the surface area of the iron-nickel catalysts, in view of its small magnitude. As is evident from Table 3, the specific surface of the catalysts decreases with increasing Ni content, which is caused probably by an increase in the ductibility of the alloy. (The same relationship is observed also in the case of the cobalt-nickel catalyst in the shape of turnings; see below). Naturally, this increases the relative error in the measurement of the surface area. If in the above case we use a parameter such as the output of the catalyst per one gram, we see (Figure 2) that it changes in exactly the same way as the magnetic saturation moment (as a function of the composition of the alloy).

The changes in the contact potential difference of iron-nickel catalysts are shown in Figure 3. In spite of the marked scattering of the points, a trend towards an increase in the contact potential difference is clearly evident — an increase in the nickel content of the alloy causes a decrease in the electron work function from the surface of samples in the nitrogen-hydrogen-ammonia mixture at 420°; this causes a decrease in the activity of the alloys.

The Co — Ni system (Table 4). Figure 4 shows the changes in the specific catalytic activity of Co — Ni alloys (curve 1) and their magnetic saturation moments (curve 2). As in the case of the Fe — Ni system, these changes are in the same direction. The electron work function also decreases with increasing nickel content (Figure 5).

The compositions of the investigated catalysts, their specific surfaces, and the heats of activation of ammonia decomposition on their surfaces are listed in Table 4.

The Fe — Co system (Table 5). On the basis of the results obtained by us in the study of iron-nickel and cobalt-nickel catalysts, an agreement should be expected between the changes in the magnetic saturation moment and the specific activity of iron-cobalt alloys. However, a more complicated pattern is observed in the case of the Fe — Co system. The magnetic moment changes smoothly, passing through a maximum at a Co concentration of 35% (Figure 6, curve 3). The catalytic activity increases (as compared with the activity of iron) until the cobalt concentration reaches 15%, then decreases and again passes through a maximum at 50% Co (curves 1 and 2).

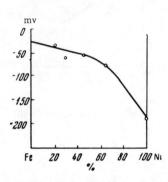

FIGURE 3. Contact difference (mv) of Fe—Ni alloys in the nitrogen-hydrogen-ammonia mixture at 420°C

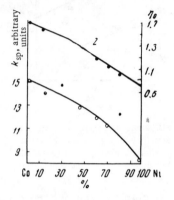

FIGURE 4. Changes in the specific catalytic activity (1) and the magnetic saturation moment (2) of Co—Ni alloys as a function of the composition

TABLE 4. Heats of activation of ammonia decomposition on Co—Ni catalysts

% Ni	$S \cdot 10^2$, m²/g	E_p kcal/mole	% Ni	$S \cdot 10^2$, m²/g	E_p kcal/mole
0	5.9	52	60	2.0	50
15	5.4	53	70	2.4	52
30	3.8	51	80	2.3	52
45	2.1	53	100	1.0	53

Let us now discuss the experimental results. It has been assumed /15, 16/ that the shift in the catalytic activity (in ammonia synthesis) towards iron in the Cr—Fe—Co—Ni—Cu series is caused by the presence of atoms containing three unpaired d-electrons in the iron crystal. In the opinion of the authors, this number of electrons provides for the strongest bond between the nitrogen atoms and the catalyst. The authors believe also that the assumption of a continuous change in the catalytic activity with the changes in the average number of unpaired d-electrons /6, 17, 18/ is less acceptable. Indeed, from the standpoint of Pauling's theory of the metallic bond /19, 20/, an iron crystal has atoms containing in their "atomic" orbitals either two [Fe(A)] or three [Fe(B)] unpaired d-electrons, the ratio of these forms being 78:22. These electrons take no part in the metallic bond, they are relatively free and could probably react with electrons from gas atoms (molecules) adsorbed on the surface of the catalyst.

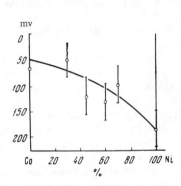

FIGURE 5. Changes in the contact potential difference (mv) of Co−Ni alloys as a function of the composition

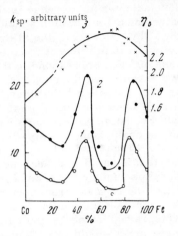

FIGURE 6. Specific catalytic activity k_{sp} of Fe−Co alloys at 630 (1) and 650°C (2), and their magnetic saturation moment η_0 (3)

TABLE 5. Heats of activation for the decomposition of ammonia (E_p) on Fe−Co catalysts

% Co	$S \cdot 10^2$, m²/g	E_p kcal/mole	% Co	$S \cdot 10^2$, m²/g	E_p kcal/mole
100	5.9	52	40	4.4	53
90	3.2	52	30	6.3	52
80	4.2	50	25	3.3	54
70	4.0	52	20	4.8	54
60	4.6	51	15	6.2	55
50	3.5	54	10	3.6	55
45	2.8	52	0	6.3	54

However, if we assume that the synthesis (decomposition) of ammonia occurs specifically on atoms with three unpaired d-electrons, it is not clear why the activity of cobalt in the above reaction should be lower (or, in any case, not higher) than the activity of iron /3, 11/. Surely the amount of atoms containing three unpaired d-electrons is higher (about 35%) in cobalt than in iron crystals.

A discussion of the results obtained by us in the investigation of the catalytic activity of Fe − Ni and Co − Ni alloys leads to the conclusion that for these systems the concept that atoms with three unpaired d-electrons have a higher catalytic activity is acceptable. An increase in the concentration of nickel (whose crystals in the ideal state cannot have three unpaired electrons in the "atomic" orbits) causes a decrease in the number of iron (cobalt) atoms having three d-electrons; this leads to a decrease in the catalytic activity. However, when we pass to the Fe — Co system we encounter serious difficulties in our attempt to treat the changes in the catalytic activity from the above point of view. In fact, the increase in the magnetic saturation moment of Fe — Co alloys at Co concentrations up to 35% indicates an increase in the number of atoms containing three unpaired electrons, which should lead to an increase in the catalytic activity of the alloy. However, the alloys with $\eta_0 > 2.40$ (20 — 40% Co) show a low activity. It is of interest to note that the two maxima in the catalytic activity (15 and 50% Co) correspond to the same value of η_0.

We assume that the unpaired d-electrons are not strictly localized on their "own" atom, but that they interact to some extent with similar electrons from adjacent atoms. The smaller the number of atoms (in a crystal) containing three unpaired d-electrons, the smaller is the number of active centers and the smaller is the adsorption capacity of these centers. At $\eta_0 < 2.40$ the bond between nitrogen and the surface is weak, the desorption is rapid, but because of the decrease in the number of active centers the number of decomposing ammonia molecules is small. At $\eta_0 > 2.40$ the bond is strengthened and the reaction becomes slower in spite of the increase in the number of active centers.

The gradual change in the catalytic activity of alloys (as a function of the changes in η_0) should be reflected in a gradual change in the heats of activation of the reaction (E_p). However, the similar values of E_p for ammonia decomposition on Fe, Co, and Ni /3, 11/ may completely obscure the changes in E_p caused by the transition from one alloy to another.

With respect to the agreement between the changes in the catalytic activities of Fe — Ni and Co — Ni alloys on the one hand and the contact potential difference (the electron work function) on the other, the data we have collected are not sufficient for us to come to a more or less definite conclusion as to whether the changes in the contact potential difference in the above case are caused by the overall effect of the nitrogen, hydrogen, ammonia, and probably the radicals formed in the course of the reaction. However, the very fact that such an agreement exists is worthy of attention.

BIBLIOGRAPHY

1. DOWDEN, D. A.—Ind. Eng. Chem., Vol. 44: 977. 1952.
2. ALCHUZHDAN, A.A. and M.A. INDZHIKYAN.—ZhFKh, Vol. 33: 983. 1959.
3. BORESKOV, G.K.—Problemy Kinetiki i Kataliza, Vol. 10: 128. 1960.
4. BEKER, M. and F. JENKINS. Catalysis. Electronic Phenomena.—Collection of translated papers, p. 34. Moskva, IL. 1958.
5. SCHWAB, L.M.—Disc. Faraday Soc., Vol. 8: 166. 1950.
6. COUPER, B.H. and D.D. ELEY.—Disc. Faraday Soc., Vol. 8: 172. 1950.
7. DOWDEN, D.A. and P.W. REYNOLDS.—Disc. Faraday Soc., Vol. 8: 184. 1950.
8. KUNZ, H. and L. RIENÄCKER.—Z. anor. allg. Chem., Vol. 310: 170. 1961.
9. KHANSEN, M. and K. ANDERKO. Struktury binarnykh splavov (Structures of Binary Alloys).—Moskva, Metallurgizdat. 1952.
10. TEMKIN, M.I. and V.M. PYZHEV.—ZhFKh, Vol. 13: 85. 1939.
11. ARTYUKH, Yu.N., O.A. STREL'TSOV, and M.T. RUSOV.—Kinetika i Kataliz, Vol. 4: 299. 1963.
12. PERMYAKOV, V.G., Yu. V. NAIDICH, and S.A. RYBAK.—Zavodskaya Laboratoriya, Vol. 21: 695. 1955.

13. LYASHENKO, V.I. and A.M. PAVLENKO. Kataliz (Catalysis).—Trudy Vsesoyuznogo Soveshchaniya po Katalizu, p.73. Kiev, Izd. AN UkrSSR. 1950.
14. BOZORT, R. Ferromagnetism. [Russian translation. 1956.]
15. LANDAU, M.A. and V.V. SHCHEKIN.—IAN SSSR, OKhN, p.430. 1961.
16. LANDAU, M.A.—IAN SSSR, OKhN, p.582. 1962.
17. DOWDEN, D.A.—J. Chem. Soc., p.242. 1950.
18. SCHWAB, L.M.—Trans. Faraday Soc., Vol.42: 689. 1946.
19. PAULING, L.—J. Am. Chem. Soc., Vol.69: 542. 1947.
20. PAULING, L.—Proc. Roy. Soc., Vol.A 196: 343. 1949.

V. SCIENTIFIC PRINCIPLES OF THE SELECTION AND SEARCH FOR NEW CATALYSTS

N. P. Keier

ON THE FACTORS DETERMINING THE CATALYTIC ACTIVITY OF CHELATE POLYMERS OF THE TRANSITION METALS

Chelate polymers belong to a class of substances whose catalytic properties (in heterogeneous catalysis) have been studied only recently and our present knowledge about them is inadequate. The chelate polymers differ in their structure, and electrical and chemical characteristics from metals, oxides, sulfides, and other inorganic substances that serve as heterogeneous catalysts.

It has been shown /1 — 5/ that chelate polymers possess a high catalytic activity in some reactions of the oxidation-reduction type. Investigations of the mechanism and the rules governing the catalysis on these polymers is of theoretical importance, since this is the chemical form of occurrence of the metals in enzymes.

We studied the catalytic activity of chelate polymers which contained (with rare exceptions) a divalent metal ion in the chelate center. The structure of the investigated polymers may be represented by the following general scheme:

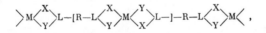

characterized by the fact that the metal M in the chelate center is bound to the donor atoms of the ligand (X and Y) determining the first sphere of the metal. Adjacent to it is a group of ligand atoms which may contain a variable part (designated by R) of organic molecules or, more accurately, radicals in the polymer chain; this group may be changed by synthesizing a ligand of the appropriate chemical composition. This part of the polymer will determine the second nearest sphere, i.e., the effect of groups of atoms that are not bound directly to the metal on the nature of the polymer. Thus, in a polychelate of a given structure it is possible to change either the metal (without changing the remaining part of the polymer) or the organic radical. Among the investigated polychelates there were several types that differed only in the composition of the donor atoms bound to the metal at the chelate center. By comparing the catalytic activities of these polymers it is possible to evaluate the effect of the first sphere. We studied polychelates of the following metals:

Cu, Ni, Co, Fe, Pt, Mn, Zn and Cd,

in which the short-range order was determined by donor atoms occupying chelate centers of the following compositions:

2 (O,O) Me; 2 (N,O) Me; 2 (N, S) Me; 2 (S, S) Me.

The laws governing the catalysis were studied on model reactions of the oxidation-reduction type: hydrazine decomposition, oxidation of cumene, and decomposition of hydrogen peroxide. The following three fundamental rules were established for the above catalytic processes, in spite of the differences in the absolute catalytic activities of the polychelates.

1) The catalytic activity is determined by the metal in the polychelate. This is illustrated by the data on the catalytic activity of polychelates differing only in the metal at the chelate center (the remaining part of the polychelate being the same in all cases):

Designation of the polychelate	Rate of decomposition of hydrazine at 104°C, $cm^3/m^2 \cdot min$
$1R_3Cu$	0.023
$1R_3Ni$	0.075
$1R_3Co$	0.014
$1R_3Zn$	0.000

It is evident that the catalytic activity varies within wide limits. In a polychelate of the above structure, the highest activity is obtained with nickel, while copper and cobalt are less active and zinc is not active at all. The lack of catalytic activity in Zn and Cd polychelates was observed also in the decomposition of hydrogen peroxide. In the oxidation of cumene these chelates show a negligible activity compared with copper polychelates. This leads to the conclusion that only the polychelates of transition metals exhibit catalytic activity. For a given metal, the catalytic activity depended strongly on the ligand, although the ligand itself had no catalytic activity.

2) The catalytic activity changes as a function of the nature of the donor atoms bound to the metal at the chelate center. The effect of the first sphere may be evaluated from the results of measurements of the catalytic activity in the oxidation of cumene on copper polychelates, by replacing the 2(N, O) Cu chelate center by 2(N, S) Cu (the polychelates were prepared from polyamides and polythioamides that differed mainly in the composition of the chelate center, the rest of the polychelate being the same):

Designation of the polymer	Rate of formation of cumene hydroperoxide at 122°C, %/hr
$2b(N, S)R_3Cu$	0.01
$2b(N, S)R_4Cu$	1.26
$1x(N, O)R_3Cu$	8.3
$1x(N, O)R_4Cu$	9.1

In this case, the substitution of oxygen for the sulfur causes a marked (more than two orders of magnitude) increase in the rate of the catalytic oxidation reaction. The strong influence of the second sphere is also exhibited here: substitution of methyldiphenyl R_4 for the diphenyl R_3 radical in the polymer chain increases the rate of the catalytic process. The table lists the results characterizing the influence of the replacement of nitrogen by oxygen in the chelate center, (i.e., of 2 (N, O) Me by 2 (O, O) Me) in the oxidation of cumene and the decomposition of hydrogen peroxide. In the case of copper and nickel polychelates such a replacement causes an increase in the catalytic activity in the oxidation of cumene and the decomposition of hydrogen peroxide. The reverse effect is observed in the case of iron polychelates. Thus, the first sphere has a strong influence on the catalytic properties, which may differ both qualitatively and quantitatively for different metals.

TABLE. Effect of the substitution of oxygen for the nitrogen in the chelate center on the rates of oxidation of cumene and decomposition of hydrogen peroxide (in arbitrary units)

Metal	Oxidation of cumene		Decomposition of hydrogen peroxide	
	Me (O,N)	Me (O,O)	Me (O,N)	Me (O,O)
Cu	1	3,3	1	5
Ni	1	3.4	0	1
Fe	—	—	3.7	1

3) Of greatest interest is the third effect observed in the study of the catalytic properties of chelate polymers, namely, the strong influence of the second sphere, i.e., of the organic radical R in the polymer chain, which is not bonded directly to the metal in the chelate center.

We believe that the elucidation of the nature of this effect is of substantial interest both for the theory of catalysis on chelate polymers and for homogeneous and enzymatic catalysis; in the first case the activity depends on the nature of the ligand, while in the second case we often observe a strong activating effect of the protein part of the enzyme on the cofactor containing the chelate-bonded metal.

The effect of R was investigated on polychelates of different structures. Substitution of an aromatic radical (phenylene or diphenylene) for an aliphatic radical (hexamethylene or dimethylene) in copper polychelates based on bis-dithiocarbamates reduces the rate of decomposition of hydrazine and increases the rate of decomposition of hydrogen peroxide. A similar effect is observed also in the case of other metals. Cobalt polychelates containing the R_2 radical (hexamethylene) are active catalysts in the decomposition of hydrogen peroxide, while those containing the R_3 radical (diphenyl) are not active.

Chelates of the above type have an electric conductivity which depends on the introduced radical. For this reason, it is possible to relate the changes in the catalytic properties to the changes in electric conductivity, and to assume that such an effect of the organic radical is a confirmation of the electronic nature of the mechanism of catalysis on chelate polymers. In our opinion, however (for the reasons described below), such a mechanism is rather improbable in the case of catalysts of the above type.

A correlation of the catalytic activities of polychelates of different chemical compositions and structures with their electrical conductivity indicates the absence of a relationship between them. As a result, we cannot assume that the mechanism of the catalytic action of polychelates

224

resembles that of catalysis by semiconductors, with the participation of a conductivity electron in the formation of intermediate reaction products. In our opinion, it is more probable that the changes in the catalytic activity of chelate polymers as a result of replacements of the organic radicals are associated with the effect of such a replacement on the electronic state of the metal. In order to check the validity of the above assumption, a study was made (by the method of X-ray K-spectroscopy) of polychelates of the above structure differing in the nature of the organic radical in the chain; the study was made at our laboratory in cooperation with the laboratory of Physical Investigation Methods of the Institute of Catalysis, SO of the USSR Academy of Sciences. The X-ray absorption spectra for copper, obtained by R.P. Akopdzhanov /6/ are shown in Figure 1. We can observe a marked change in the absorption intensity in the initial and middle regions as a result of the substitution of aromatic for aliphatic radicals. Compared with polymers containing aromatic radicals, polymers with aliphatic radicals (R_1 and R_2) show stronger absorption in the initial and middle regions. These results indicate a decrease in the intensity of $4p$-level transitions (permitted by the selection rule) in the presence of an aromatic radical in the polymer chain. Such a change may be attributed either to a greater utilization of the $4p$-state in the formation of the polymer (i.e., a strengthening of the π-bond with the ligand, with the participation of the $4p$-orbitals of the metal) or to a decrease in the degree of hybridization of the $4p$- and $4s$-states causing a decrease in the absorbance. The study by these methods continues and is being extended to polychelates of other structures.

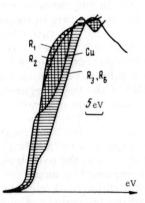

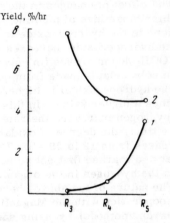

FIGURE 1. X-ray K-absorption spectra of copper in polychelates based on bis-dithiocarbamates and aliphatic (R_1-dimethylene, R_2-hexamethylene) and aromatic (R_6-phenylene, R_3-diphenylene) radicals.

FIGURE 2. Dependence of the rate of oxidation of cumene into the hydroperoxide on the nature of the organic radical in the polymer chain (polychelates prepared from bis-thioamides of picoline (1) and quinaldine (2)).

The above investigation shows unambiguously that the electronic state of the metal is changed as a result of the replacement of the organic radical in a polymer chain of a given structure.

An even finer effect involves the influence of the substitution of hydrogen in the donor groups in the phenyl rings of the organic radical (diphenyl) on the catalytic properties of polychelates prepared from the bis-thioamides of picoline and quinaldine:

Scheme I

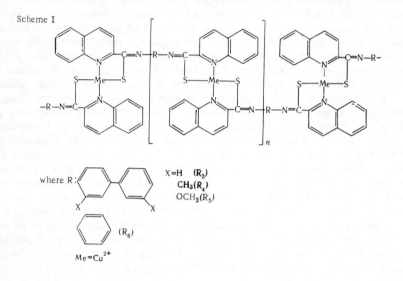

where R:

X=H   (R$_3$)
       CH$_3$(R$_4$)
       OCH$_3$(R$_5$)

(R$_6$)

Me=Cu^{2+}

The effect of changes in the organic radical in polychelates made from the bis-thioamides of picoline and quinaldine on the rate of oxidation of cumene to the hydroperoxide is shown in Figure 2. The rate of oxidation to the hydroperoxide increases when the hydrogen is replaced by the CH$_3$ and OCH$_3$ donor groups (in polychelates prepared from picoline).

In polychelates made from quinaldine bis-thioamides the rate of oxidation (to the hydroperoxide) is higher and the yield of the hydroperoxide at 100° reaches a higher value. In this case, the substitution of donor groups for the hydrogen increases the rate of the overall oxidation process; at the same time, the degree of oxidation of the cumene after 2 hours at 100° increases from 19 to 29.4%. Thus, for both types of polychelates we observe a marked (but not selective) acceleration in the oxidation process when the hydrogen in the organic radical is replaced by donor groups.

The nature of the above phenomenon was elucidated at our laboratory (in cooperation with the Magnetism Group of the laboratory of physical research methods) by using specially prepared complex compounds with a chemical composition corresponding to a monomer link of the polymer chain. We prepared chelate complexes with a wider variety of donor groups by substituting the hydrogen in the para-position; for the sake of comparison two of the groups were introduced also in the ortho-position (see Scheme II on next page).

According to our data, the catalytic activity of complexes of the above type is low (Figure 3); it is much lower than the activity of the least active polychelates.

In spite of the difficulties in the measurement of the catalytic activity of recrystallized monomers, it is possible to observe a trend towards a decrease in the catalytic activity (in the decomposition of hydrazine) as a

result of the introduction of donor groups in place of the hydrogen (Figure 4).
At the same time it was found that a change in the position of the group
replacing the hydrogen (from the para to the ortho position) has a strong
effect on the activity (Figure 5).

Scheme II

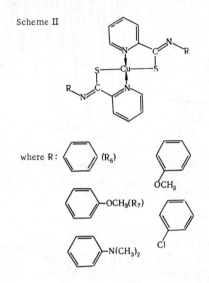

where R:

The electronic state of the metal was studied by the electron paramagnetic
resonance method. The spectra were traced for both solid substances and
their solutions in various solvents, which yielded more detailed information
on the electronic state of the chelate center and the effect of substituting
donor groups on it.

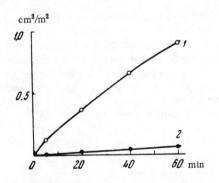

FIGURE 3. Comparison of the catalytic activities (product yields in cm^3/m^2) of a polychelate (1) and a recrystallized monomer
analog (2) in the decomposition of hydrazine.

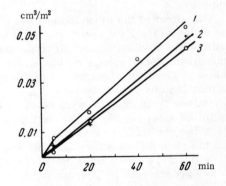

FIGURE 4. Catalytic activity (in the decomposition of hydrazine) of chelate complexes differing in the composition of the donor groups
that replace the hydrogen in the phenyl radical:

1- H, 75°C; 2- OCH_3, 75°C; 3- $N(CH_3)_2$,
108°C.

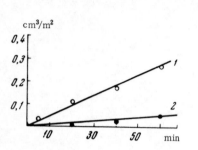

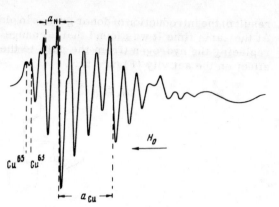

FIGURE 5. Influence of the nature and position of the donor group replacing the hydrogen on the catalytic activity:

1- OCH_3 in the ortho-position; 2- OCH_3 in the para-position.

FIGURE 6. Ultrasuperfine structure of the electron paramagnetic resonance spectrum of the complex with R_6 in a solution:

α_{Cu}- splitting on a copper nucleus; α_N- splitting on a nitrogen nucleus.

The study of complexes in solutions yielded a complex spectrum associated with splitting on the copper nucleus $(2I + 1) = 4 I_{Cu} = 3/2;$* this leads to the formation of superfine structure with a band width of $60 - 80$ oersted, and an ultrasuperfine splitting through the interaction of an unpaired electron with a nitrogen nucleus $(I_N = 1)$ which yields $(2 \times ny + 1) =$ 5 lines for $n = 2$, i.e., for two nitrogen nuclei. The ultrasuperfine structure (Figure 6) is superimposed on the superfine structure in each of the four bands. The magnitude of the splitting on the nitrogen is $16 - 15$ oersted. The ultrasuperfine structure found by us shows unequivocally that a covalent bond exists between the copper and nitrogen atoms in the complex.

The effect of the crystalline field of the ligand, exhibited as a change in the shape of the EPR spectrum lines of the above chelate complexes (in solid-state studies, is another important characteristic of the influence of substituent donor groups on the electronic state of the metal at the chelate center. The EPR spectrum of the complexes is characterized by three (rather than by two) g-factors: g_x, g_y, and g_z, i.e., $g_x \neq g_y$, which indicates deviations from an axial symmetry of the square (Figure 7). This is exhibited most clearly in the case of a substituent donor group (OCH_3) in the ortho position; in this case the deviation of g_x from g_y is greatest and the rhombic structure is exhibited clearly (Figure 8). If the value of $(g_x - g_y) = \Delta g$ is taken as a measure of the rhombic nature, this nature becomes more pronounced in the following order

$$H < OCH_3(para) < N(CH_3)_2 < Cl < OCH_3(ortho).$$

The above series characterizes the influence of the crystalline ligand field in the substitution of donor groups for the hydrogen in the phenyl rings of the organic radical (diphenyl). The above data require a detailed quantum-mechanical analysis that would make it possible to determine the quantitative

---

* I — magnetic moment of the nucleus.

influence of the outer sphere on the electronic structure of the copper in the chelate center.

Qualitatively, it is clear that the electronic state of the metal is affected strongly by the outer sphere, and that this is exhibited as a change in the crystalline field and is evidently responsible for the change in catalytic activity.

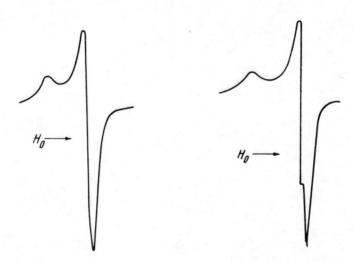

FIGURE 7. EPR spectrum of the solid complex with R_6.

FIGURE 8. EPR spectrum of the solid complex with R_7 (ortho).

A comparison of the EPR spectra of the complex compounds with the spectra of the polymer analogs indicates that a correlation exists between them and that the above conclusions may be applied to polychelates.

Thus, direct measurements with the use of X-ray spectroscopy and electron paramagnetic resonance methods show that not only the nearer sphere to the metal, but also the far-lying (from the metal) organic radicals of the ligand affect the electronic state of the metal, and cause changes in the crystalline field and the catalytic activity.

The investigation was carried out on polychelates and complex compounds prepared in the laboratory of A.P. Terent'ev (member-correspondent of the USSR Academy of Sciences) at the Moscow State University, and by the synthesis group of the Institute of Catalysis of the Siberian Department of the USSR Academy of Sciences (by E.K. Mamaeva).

BIBLIOGRAPHY

1. KEIER, N.P., G.K. BORESKOV, V.V. RODE, A.P. TERENT'EV, and E.G. RUKHADZE.—Kinetika i Kataliz, Vol. 2: 509. 1961.
2. BORESKOV, G.K., N.P. KEIER, L.F. RUBTSOVA, and E.G. RUKHADZE.—DAN SSSR, Vol. 144: 1069. 1962.

3. KEIER, N.P., G.K. BORESKOV, L.F. RUBTSOVA, and E.G. RUKHADZE.—Kinetika i Kataliz, Vol. 3: 680. 1962.
4. KEIER, N.P., M.G. TROITSKAYA, and E.G. RUKHADZE.—Kinetika i Kataliz, Vol. 3: 691. 1962.
5. KEIER, N.P.—In: Sbornik "Nauchnye osnovy podbora i prigotovleniya katalizatorov", Izd. SO AN SSSR, Novosibirsk. 1964.
6. AKOPDZHANOV, R.P., R.D. VAINSHTEIN, N.P. KEIER, L.M. KEFELI, and E.G. RUKHADZE.—Kinetika i Kataliz, Vol. 4: 257. 1964.

M.L. Khidekel'

ENZYME MODELS AND THE SELECTION OF NEW CATALYSTS

Important data on the structure and the mechanism of action of enzymes have been collected recently in enzymology. The question arises as to whether the existing data can be used for the selection of new catalysts. This is related to the problem of the creation of models that would not only describe the different aspects of enzymatic catalysis but could also be used directly in catalytic chemistry.

Enzyme models may correspond to the various levels of organization of biological catalysts.

The subject of this paper is the creation of models of the properties of the non-protein components that play an important role in the structure and action of enzymes. The problem of the extent to which the existing principles and the components themselves may be used for catalytic reactions is considered.

There are about 700 known enzymes, including about 200 oxidation-reduction enzymes that will be the main subject of this paper [1].

As is evident from the table, the non-protein part of hydrogen-transferring enzymes consists of a limited number of components. Flavinic, nicotinamidic, and porphyrinic systems are widespread among organic prosthetic groups. The metal-containing enzymes most often contain Zn, Fe, Mo, Cu, Mn, and Mg ions.

What are the properties of these components that make them so universal?

The conjugation energies of the main organic components of prosthetic groups and coenzymes are listed below:

Type of compounds	Conjugation energy, kcal/mole
Pyrimidines	30—45
Purines	50—80
Nicotinic acid derivatives	30—40
Naphthoquinone-1,4 derivatives	30—40
Isoalloxazone derivatives	100
Porphyrins	200

It is evident that these compounds are thermodynamically quite stable. As a rule, the metal complexes occurring in metal-containing enzymes, and in particular the copper complexes, are also stable [2, 3]. Thus, the universal components of biological catalysts are very stable species. This stability is attained through conjugation and through the formation of stable coordination bonds.

TABLE. Composition of the non-protein part of oxidoreductase (according to /1/)

Reaction type	Number of known enzymes with coenzymes and prosthetic groups	Fl*	NAD*	HEM*	Including the metal ions					
					Zn	Fe	Mo	Cu	Mn	Mg
Hydrogen transfer from N-containing groups	23	19			1	2	1	3		
−CHOH → −CO− ...	24	7			2	2			5	
−CH−CH₂ → C=CH..	4	3			2		1		1	
Hydrogen transfer from S-containing groups	2	1								
(Oxidases)	16	2	6				3	4		
(Peroxidases)	6	1		5						
Intramolecular hydrogen transfer	3									3

* Fl, HAD, HEM, Zn, Fe, etc. indicate that the enzyme contains flavinic, nicotinic, heminic systems and the respective metal ions.

Spectroscopic studies of enzymatic reactions show the stabilization of intermediate products of the enzymatic process /4/. The spectrum of semiquinone stabilized on the enzyme was recorded when pyrocatechol was oxidized in the presence of an enzyme, for instance, tyrosinase /5/. A flavinic radical stabilized as a result of complex formation with Cu^{2+} has been formed through the action of lipoyl dehydrogenase /6/. It seems that the direction of many enzymatic reactions is determined by the nature of the reaction between the intermediate products and the surface of the enzyme.

What are the methods by which the stabilized universal components participate in enzymatic reactions?

Schemes describing the action of the active portions of flavinic (a) and nicotinamidic (b) coenzymes are shown below:

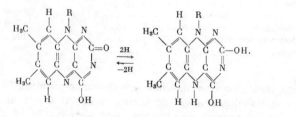

(a)

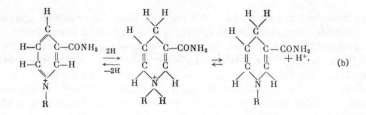

Calculations show /7/ that the reduced form possesses the greatest tendency towards electron donation, while the oxidized form possesses the highest electron-acceptor capacity.

As a result of this, flavinic and nicotinamidic systems are almost ideal hydrogen transfer agents from the standpoint of thermodynamics. A.A. Balandin and the author found /8/ that the rate constant of the catalytic addition of hydrogen decreases if conjugation energy is lost in the course of the process. The loss of conjugation energy during the functioning of flavinic and nicotinamidic coenzymes in the addition of hydrogen is very small /9/.

In certain cases the effect of energy stabilization is apparently cancelled by the preliminary effect of various groups in the biological catalyst.

Calculations made by us on the basis of /10 — 14/ and of our data show that the reduction of quinones, which is carried out both homogeneously and in the presence of heterogeneous catalysts in cases that are not complicated by other factors, is described by the Hammett equation:

$$\log k/k_0 = m\,(E - E_0),$$

where k and k_0 are the constants of the oxidation, E and E_0 are the oxidation-reduction potentials, and m is a constant. While in homogeneous transfer of hydrogen $m \simeq 2 \times 10^{-2}$ mv^{-1}, in catalytic and enzymatic reactions the value of the constant decreases to $m \simeq 1 \times 10^{-3}$ mv^{-1}.

Among the other principles of activation we must mention the following: the necessity for a coordinative unsaturation of the complex-bonded ion in the metal-containing enzyme (see, for instance, the figure), and the principle of catalytic chains (which is widely used in enzymatic catalysis), e.g.

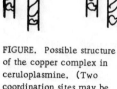

$$H \rightarrow \text{NAD}\cdot H_2 / \text{Protein} \rightarrow \text{Flavoprotein} \rightarrow \text{Cyt b} \rightarrow \text{Cyt c}_1 \rightarrow$$
$$\text{Cyt c} \rightarrow \text{Cyt a} \rightarrow O_2$$

where NAD$\cdot$H$_2$ is the reduced form of nicotinamide adenine dinucleotide (NAD) and Cyt b, Cyt c$_1$, Cyt c, and Cyt a are cytochromes.

In our opinion, the use of the above principles may extend the number of compounds used as catalysts and increase the number of catalytic reactions.

FIGURE. Possible structure of the copper complex in ceruloplasmine. (Two coordination sites may be utilized for the catalysis /3/).

For instance, it is known that under moderate conditions C_6H_5Li can attach molecular hydrogen by splitting at the metal-carbon bond. The addition of NiCl$_2$ to the system causes a sharp increase in the hydrogen absorption rate /15/. We showed that the reaction passes through an intermediate compound $(C_6H_5)_2(THF)_2$ which reacts rapidly with hydrogen (THF — trihydrofuran). When prepared separately, dimesitylnickel also reacts with hydrogen in a tetrahydrofuran solution. A whole series of organometallic complexes, (e.g., diallylnickel /16/) react very rapidly with hydrogen. The development and application (to these systems) of the principles of stabilization of coordination-unsaturated centers leads to a substantial increase in the number of possible catalysts. Some advances have been made already in this field. In the first place, this involves complexes formed by a reducing agent that functions at the same time as a stabilizing agent. Examples of such systems are catalysts based on $SnCl_2 +$ H_2PtCl_6 /17/, the carboxylate salts of Ni, Co, etc. and trialkylaluminum /18/, and the acetylacetonates of several metals and trialkylaluminum /19/. The solid phase may serve as an important stabilization agent, e.g., an active center of the dibenzeneplatinum type in a platinum catalyst on carbon.

The stabilization principle must be applied also to cases involving the use of coenzyme models. In this case a substituent may be used for the stabilization.

For instance, it has been shown that the reduction of maleic anhydride by models of the $NAD \cdot H_2$ coenzyme is possible only if the model is protected by a substituent /21/.

The principle of stabilization of the intermediate compounds by complexes or by the surface opens wide possibilities. The interaction of tetraphenylhydrazine with absolutely dry silica gel leads to the formation of a radical $[(C_6H_5)_2\dot{N} - N(C_6H_5)]_2^+X^-$ that is stabilized by the surface /22/. Such a reaction between the free valence and the catalyst may determine the direction of the reaction, as was shown in the hydrogenation of diphenylpicrylhydrazyl /23/. On account of the different effects on the intermediate radical, the oxidation of 2,4,6-triphenylphenol may be carried out in different directions /24/.

Even at this time, the use of the principles derived from enzymologic works, as well as of the enzyme models, may be very useful in catalytic chemistry.

The main functions of an enzyme, e.g., tyrosinase, are shown below:

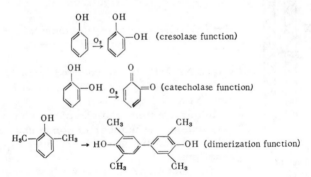

We have shown /25/ that the complex formed in the oxygenation of cuprous salts in a pyridine solutions is, in many respects, analogous to an enzyme — tyrosinase. The copper is monovalent both in the enzyme and in the model catalyst under anaerobic conditions; oxygenation occurs under aerobic conditions, and one mole of O_2 is absorbed per two copper atoms. The stage of formation of the oxygenated complex precedes the oxidation stage. Under aerobic conditions, part of the copper remains in the monovalent state. The enzyme and its model transfer to the substrate only one of the two atoms in the oxygen molecule. The substrate reduces part of the copper to Cu^+. The hydrogen peroxide does not participate in the process. An intermediate radical is formed and stabilized on the enzyme or the model. Coordinative $Cu - N$ bonds were presumed to exist in the enzyme and the absence of a hemine structure was proved, while EPR studies revealed the existence of $Cu - N$ bonds in the model; copper phthalocyanine does not catalyze the reactions that occur on the model.

We used the prepared catalyst in various processes, as a model of the tyrosinase function. We found that the model fulfills satisfactorily the catecholase and dimerization functions. The cresolase function is exhibited less strongly by the model. In the course of the investigation, we achieved new synthesis reactions: the preparation of para- and ortho-quinones (a, b), diphenols (c), polymers (d), and other derivaties (e) /26/:

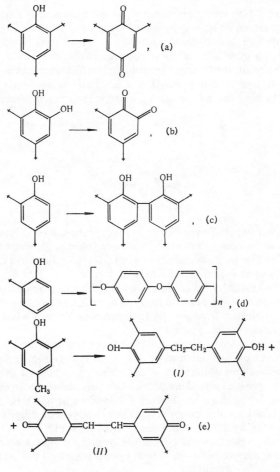

where $\longrightarrow = C(CH_3)_3$,

235

Great possibilities are opened by the use of the principle of stabilization of the intermediate compound on the enzyme model. In the oxidation of 2,4,6-tri-tert-butylphenol, the extent of the reaction between the intermediate radical and the complex may be different, depending on the composition of the catalyst, and this determines whether the reaction leads to the formation of the peroxide:

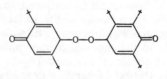

or of 2,6-di-tert-butylbenzoquinone /25/.

When the steric hindrances diminish, the intermediate radical has a greater tendency towards interaction with the complex, and hence in the oxidation of 2,6-di-tert-butyl-4-methoxyphenol the corresponding peroxide is formed in the presence of catalysts that in the previous case produced only the quinone /25/.

One of the main features common to the enzyme and the model is the preliminary formation of an oxygenated complex. In the absence of oxygen, the reaction between the radical and the catalyst may have some specific peculiarities which must affect the direction of the reaction. In fact, while the oxidation of 2,6-di-tert-butyl-4-methylphenol under aerobic conditions leads to the formation of diphenol (I) and stilbenequinone (II), a diphenoquinone having the following structure is formed under anaerobic conditions:

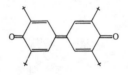

One of the main natural processes — the synthesis of lignin — occurs through a stage involving a reaction between phenoxyl radicals and an enzyme /27/. It can be assumed that today it may be possible to carry out the synthesis of the structural units of lignin.

Interesting possibilities have been revealed by the modelling of one of the main coenzymes for redox reactions by dihydronicotinamide dinucleotide (NAD·H_2) whose function involves hydrogen transfer and whose model consists of dihydropyridine systems.

We have demonstrated the possibility of using a system consisting of the dihydropyridine compound and a one-electron reducing agent for the reduction of ketones and aldehydes /28/. The direction of the reaction depends on the degree of stabilization of the intermediate product.

By using a model of the complexing properties of NAD·H_2 we prepared organometallic (lithium and magnesium) derivatives of dihydropyridine, and reduced ketones by the hydride-ionic mechanism.

By utilizing the reducing and complex-forming properties of the models, we carried out reactions between dihydropyridines and the salts and derivatives of a number of metals.

We found that the reduction of $RhCl_3$ produces a stable heterogeneous hydrogenation catalyst whose activity is higher than that of platinum (according to Adams), Rh/Al_2O_3 and Rh-boride catalysts. Thus, the reducing agents used to produce heterogeneous catalysts were supplemented by the addition of $NAD \cdot H_2$ models — dihydropyridine derivatives.

Subsequently, we prepared a series of homogeneous systems that activate oxygen under moderate conditions and are able to carry out the hydrogenation of cyclohexene. Homogeneous catalysts were produced by the reaction between N-benzyl-dihydronicotinamide and H_2PtCl_6, $RhCl_3$ in alcohol.

The NAD models may be included in the catalytic chain. We built the hydrogen transfer cycle from water to the substrate (2,4,6-tri-tert-butylphenoxyl-1) by using dihydropyridine derivatives as catalysts — hydrogen transfer agents:

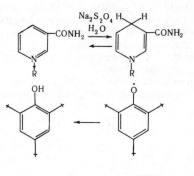

The above process can be used for the production of spatially-hindered deuterophenols.

This research was carried out with the participation of A.S. Astakhova, L.V. Gorbunova, O.N. Eremenko, V.V. Karpov, and Yu.A. Shvetsov.

BIBLIOGRAPHY

1. DIXON, M. and E. WEBB. Enzymes. [Russian translation. 1961.]
2. WILLIAMS, R.J. "Molecular Principles of the Action and Inhibition of Enzymes".—Collection of translated papers. Moskva, IL, No.4: 160. 1962.
3. FRIEDEN, E. Horizons in Biochemistry. Ed. M. Kasha, B. Pullman. N.Y. 1962.
4. BEMFORD, K. and A. JENKINS. "Formation and Stabilization of Free Radicals".—Collection of translated papers. Moskva, IL, p.503. 1962.
5. Le CLERK, A.M., J. MOUDY, P. DOUZON, and S. LISSITZKY.—Biochim. et biophys. acta, Vol.32: 499. 1959.
6. The Enzymes, Vol.7. 2nd Ed. N.Y. 1963.
7. PULLMAN, B. and A. PULLMAN.—Proc. U.S. Natl. Acad., Sci., Vol.45: 136. 1959.
8. BALANDIN, A.A. and M.L. KHIDEKEL'.—DAN SSSR, Vol.123: 83. 1958.
9. PULLMAN, A.—J. Theor. Biol., Vol.2: 259. 1962.
10. DIMROTH, O.—Z. angew. Chem., Vol.46: 571. 1933.
11. WALLENFELS, K. and M. GELLRICH.—Ann., Vol.621: 149. 1959.
12. NOST, N.—Rec. trav. chim., Vol.71: 857. 1952.

13. BRAUDE, E. A., L. M. JACKMAN, and R. P. LINSTEAD.—J. Chem. Soc., p. 3548. 1954.
14. MUSSO, H., K. FIGGE, and D. J. BECKER.—Chem. Ber., Vol. 94: 1107. 1961.
15. SARRY, B. and W. HANKE.—Z. anorg. allgem. Chem., Vol. 296: 228. 1958.
16. WILKE, G.—Angew. Chem., Vol. 75: 10. 1963.
17. CRUMER, R. D., E. L. JENNER, R. V. LINDSEY, and U. G. STOLBERG.—J. Am. Chem. Soc., Vol. 85: 1691. 1963.
18. LAPPORTE, S. J. and W. R. SCHUETT.—J. Org. Chem., Vol. 28: 1947. 1963.
19. SLOAN, M. F., A. S. MATLACK, and D. S. BRESLOW.—J. Am. Chem. Soc., Vol. 85: 4014. 1963.
20. NICOLAU, C., H. G. THOM, and E. POBITSCHAK.—Trans. Faraday Soc., Vol. 55: 1430. 1959.
21. ASTAKHOVA, A. S. and M. L. KHIDEKEL'.—IAN SSSR, Seriya Khimicheskaya, p. 1717. 1964.
22. RAZUVAEV, G. A. and M. L. KHIDEKEL'. Trudy konferentsii po problemam primeneniya korrelyatsionnykh uravnenii v organicheskoi khimii (Transactions of the Conference on the Problems of the Application of Correlation Equations to Organic Chemistry).—Riga, Izd. AN LatvSSR, Vol. 1: 365. 1962.
23. BALANDIN, A. A., M. L. KHIDEKEL', and V. V. PATRIKEEV.—IAN SSSR, OKhN, p. 361. 1959.
24. KHIDEKEL', M. L., G. A. RAZUVAEV, E. I. NOVIKOVA, L. A. SMIRNOVA, and A. P. KHRUSHCH.—IAN SSSR, Seriya Khimicheskaya, p. 948. 1964.
25. GORBUNOVA, L. V., O. N. EFIMOV, V. V. KARPOV, G. A. RAZUVAEV, V. B. TURCHANINOV, and M. L. KHIDEKEL'. Trudy konferentsii po mekhanizmu i kinetiki fermentativnogo kataliza (Transactions of the Conference on the Mechanism and Kinetics of Enzymatic Catalysis), p. 244.—Riga, Izd. AN LatvSSR. 1964.
26. KARPOV, V. V., M. L. KHIDEKEL', L. V. GORBUNOVA, and R. A. RAZUVAEV.—IAN SSSR, seriya khimicheskaya, pp. 1322, 1909. 1964.
27. FREUDENBERG, K. and B. LEHMAN.—Chem. Ber., Vol. 93: 1354. 1960.
28. ASTAKHOVA, A. S. and M. L. KHIDEKEL'.—IAN SSSR, seriya khimicheskaya, p. 1909. 1964.

Kh. M. Minachev, V. I. Garanin, and Ya. I. Isakov

NEW CATALYSTS — SYNTHETIC ZEOLITES — AND SOME PROBLEMS OF THE SELECTION OF ZEOLITE CATALYSTS

It is well known that synthetic zeolites are widely employed as effective and selective sorbents for the drying, purification, and separation of various gas and liquid mixtures. Recently, they have also been used as catalysts and catalyst carriers. The scientific literature and patents describe more than 15 organic and inorganic reactions in which zeolites are suggested as catalysts. These include such important reactions as cracking, isomerization, alkylation, etc.

The interest in the study of the catalytic properties of zeolites is explained by the fact that they possess a high thermal stability, are able to act as cation exchangers, have a large internal surface and a well-defined crystalline structure with uniform pores, exhibit a high selectivity because of their molecular-sieve properties, etc.

The above characteristics of the zeolites make it possible to use them for the preparation of polyfunctional catalysts of prescribed properties.

All natural and most synthetic zeolites consist of crystalline aluminosilicates*.

Zeolites of the A, X, Y, P, E, mordenite, and other types have been synthesized. All of them are built of silicon- or aluminum-oxygen tetrahedra, which in contrast to other aluminosilicates are arranged in such a way that channels of molecular dimensions remain between them.

In molecular sieves of the A, X, and Y** types, the SiO_4 and AlO_4 tetrahedra are grouped together forming cubooctahedra, which in the zeolites of the A type yield a simple cubic lattice and in the zeolites of the X and Y types a face-centered cubic lattice (Figure 1 /4/). Such packing leads to the formation of cavities that are separated from each other by aperture of definite dimensions.

The porous structure of the zeolites consists of small and large cavities (pores). The small cavities are formed by the volumes within the cubooctahedra and their dimensions are the same for zeolites of the A, X, and Y types (v_S = 150 $Å^3$, d_S = 6.6 Å), while the large cavities are formed by the spaces between the cubic octahedra and the corresponding four-atom (zeolite A) or six-atom (zeolites X and Y) oxygen bridges. The latter differ little in their dimensions /1/:

---

* Zeolites in which the silicon has been replaced by Ge, Ti, etc., and the aluminum has been replaced by B, Ga, Mg, Cr, and other elements have been prepared.

** Since we used these zeolites in our investigation, their structure is described in brief. More details on the structure of these and other zeolites may be found, for instance, in /1—5/.

239

for zeolites of the A type $v_L = 776Å^3$, $d_L = 11.4$ Å;
for zeolites of the X and Y types $v_L = 811$ Å^3, $d_L = 11.6$ Å.

The main difference between the structures of zeolites of the A, X, and Y types consists in the dimensions of the apertures of the large cavities.

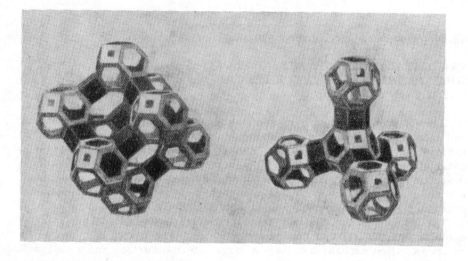

FIGURE 1. Spatial arrangement of the cubooctahedra and peculiarities of their mutual connections in the lattices of A (left) and X (right) zeolites. On the above models, the corners of the cubooctahedra correspond to the positions of the silicon and aluminum atoms in the lattice.

The large cavities in zeolites of the A type are interconnected through apertures (formed by eight oxygen atoms) with an average diameter of 4.2 Å (from X-ray diffraction data), while in zeolites of the X and Y types the apertures are formed by twelve atoms and have an average diameter of $8 - 9$ Å (in both cases — for the zeolites in the Na form). The chemical composition of these zeolites is characterized by different $SiO_2:Al_2O_3$ ratios. In a zeolite of the A type the above ratio is about 2, while in zeolite X it equals $2.4 - 2.8$ and in zeolites of the Y type it ranges within fairly wide limits ($3.5 - 6.0$) depending on the method and conditions of preparation. The variable $SiO_2:Al_2O_3$ ratio is explained by the isomorphous substitution of aluminum-oxygen tetrahedra for different fractions of the silicon-oxygen tetrahedra.

The zeolites contain cations (Na^+, K^+, Li^+, Ca^{2+}, Sr^{2+}, etc.) whose charges cancel the negative charges of the AlO_4^- tetrahedra. These cations may take part in ion exchange, and as a result the zeolites may be obtained in various cationic forms. The ion exchange may be used for the introduction of catalytically active elements, which after reduction are distributed very uniformly in the cavities and channels of the zeolite.

The high thermal stability of their crystal lattice (it remains stable even at $700 - 750°$) is an important property of synthetic zeolites of the A, X, and Y types.

240

The cavities of the zeolites are accessible only to those molecules whose dimensions (critical diameter) are smaller than those of the apertures (channels) leading to the cavities.

The molecules that are adsorbed on the walls of the cavities and channels in the zeolites are subjected to the polarizing action of the oxygen ions and the cations that cancel the negative charge of the AlO_4^- tetrahedra; as a result, these molecules may, under certain conditions, undergo chemical transformations.

In this paper we present results* showing the influence of: 1) the nature of the cation; 2) the $SiO_2:Al_2O_3$ ratio; and 3) the molecular-sieve properties of the zeolite catalyst, on the course of the isomerization of n-alkanes and cyclohexane, the hydrogenation and hydroisomerization of benzene, the dehydration of alcohols, and the alkylation of benzene by olefins.

The catalysts for the above reactions were prepared from zeolites of the X, Y, and synthetic mordenite types,** with different $SiO_2:Al_2O_3$ ratios and channel dimensions of $4 - 10$ Å.

The isomerization and hydrogenation of the hydrocarbons was carried out on zeolites containing 0.5% (by weight) Pt, Pd, Rh, or Ir, while the dehydration of alcohols and the alkylation were carried out on the pure zeolites.

We should mention that the isomerization of n-pentane and n-hexane on zeolite catalysts with the X and Y structures in various cationic forms and containing 0.5% Pd and Pt was studied for the first time by J. Rabo et al. /9, 10/. The hydrogenation of olefins on a 0.31% Pt/CaA catalyst and the dehydration of butanols on pure CaA and CaX zeolites was studied by P. Weisz et al. /11, 12/. In a recent paper, G. V. Tsitsishvili et al. /13/ showed (using the dehydration of isopropanol as an example) that the zeolites studied by them can be arranged in order of activity as follows: HX > NaX > CaA. With regard to the alkylation of benzene by olefins, there is a single patent /14/ which suggests the use of a zeolite of the X type in various cationic forms as a catalyst.

TABLE 1. Effect of the nature of the cation on the course of the isomerization of n-hexane and cyclohexane and the hydroisomerization of benzene

Reaction	Reaction conditions	Yield of isomers, wt %			
		type X		type Y	
		SiO_2/Al_2O_3 = 2.5		SiO_2/Al_2O_3 = 4.5	
		0.5% Pd/NaX	0.5% Pd/CaX	0.5% Pd/NaY	0.5% Pd/CaY
Isomerization of n-hexane	350°C; 30 atm; $v = 1$ hr^{-1}; H_2:CH = 3.2	0.0	12.5	0.0	70.3
Isomerization of cyclohexane	330°C; 30 atm; $v = 1$ hr^{-1}; H_2:CH = 3.2	0.0	14.3	0.0	57.0
Hydroisomerization of benzene	330°C; 30 atm; $v = 0.5$ hr^{-1}; H_2:CH = 5	0.0	16.3	0.0	67.3

* Part of the results used here were published in /6, 8/.

** The zeolites were synthetized at the VNIINP, and the mordenite — at the GEOKhI AN SSSR.

The effect of the nature of the cation is indicated by the data in Tables 1 and 2, which show the product yields corresponding to the optimum conditions. Thus, independently of the values of the $SiO_2:Al_2O_3$ ratio, the Na-forms of the zeolites are inactive under the above conditions in all investigated reactions. The substitution of Ca^{2+} for Na^+ (i.e., of a divalent for a monovalent cation) causes a sharp increase in the activity of the catalyst. In the alkylation reactions we studied the activity of a decationized form in addition to the activities of the Ca- and Na-forms (see Table 2). The decationized form is usually prepared by high-temperature decomposition of an ammonium zeolite that has been formed by ion-exchange substitution of NH_4^+ for Na^+. The nature of this form has not been established as yet. The structure of some zeolites (e.g., of the X type) is destroyed during their conversion to the decationized form, while other structures (e.g., of the Y type) remain substantially unchanged, as shown by adsorption and X-ray diffraction analyzes and by electrical conductivity measurements.

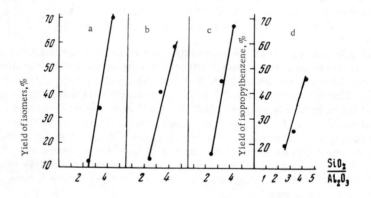

FIGURE 2. Effect of the $SiO_2:Al_2O_3$ ratio in the zeolite on the catalytic activity:

a- isomerization of n-hexane, 350°C, 30 atm, v_{vol} = 1 hr^{-1}, H_2:CH = 3.2;
b- isomerization of cyclohexane, 330°C, 30 atm; v_{vol} = 1 hr^{-1}, H_2:CH = 3.2;
c- hydroisomerization of benzene, 330°C, 30 atm, v_{vol} = 0.5 hr^{-1}, H_2:CH = 5;
d- alkylation of benzene by propylene, 200°C, 1 atm, v_{vol} = 0.3 hr^{-1}, C_6H_6: C_3H_6 = 2:1.

It has been assumed /10/ that the decationizing of zeolites of the Y type involves at first the formation of the hydrogen form which at $450 - 500°$ releases water leading to the transformation of part of the AlO_4^- tetrahedra to an acid alumina center (Lewis acid) with a coordination number equal to three.

The decationized form of a zeolite of type Y and the calcium form of the same zeolite possess a high activity (see Table 2).

The effect of the $SiO_2:Al_2O_3$ ratio on the activity of zeolite catalysts is shown in Figure 2. It is evident that a transition from a zeolite of type X (with a $SiO_2:Al_2O_3$ ratio of 2.5) to a zeolite of type Y ($SiO_2:Al_2O_3$ = 3.4) increases the degree of isomerization of the hydrocarbons from $10 - 15$ to $30 - 45\%$. A change in the $SiO_2:Al_2O_3$ ratio in zeolites of type Y from 3.4

to 4.5 increases the yield of isomers to 55 — 70%. A similar relationship is observed also in the alkylation of benzene by propylene.

TABLE 2. Effect of the nature of the cation on the course of aklylation of benzene by propylene: 300°C; 1 atm; $v_{C_6H_6} = 0.3$ hr^{-1}; $C_6H_6{:}C_3H_6 = 2{:}1$ (mol)

Catalyst	SiO$_2$/Al$_2$O$_3$	Yield of isopropylbenzene, % of theoretical
NaX	2.5	0.4
CaX	2.5	52.8
NaY	4.2	0.6
CaY	4.2	70.0
DY	4.2	50.0

TABLE 3. Hydrogenation of benzene: 200°C; 30 atm; $v_{vol} = 0.5$ hr^{-1}, H$_2$: $C_6H_6 = 5$

Catalyst	SiO$_2$/Al$_2$O$_3$	Composition of catalyzate, % by wt	
		cyclohexane	benzene
0.5% Rh/CaY	3.4	97.8	2.2
0.5% Ir/CaY	3.4	91.0	9.0
0.5% Pd/CaY	3.4	82.5	17.5
0.5% Pd/CaY	4.5	80.2	19.8
0.5% Pd/NaY	4.5	87.6	12.4
0.5% Pd/CaX	2.5	86.0	14.0

Data on the hydrogenation of benzene on zeolites of types X and Y (in the Na- and Ca-forms) containing metals of group VIII are shown in Table 3.

The data in the table show that the type of the zeolite, the nature of the cation, and the SiO$_2$:Al$_2$O$_3$ ratio have practically no effect on the degree of hydrogenation of benzene to cyclohexane (compare the Pd catalysts). Thus, in the above reaction the zeolite serves as an inert carrier having a large surface area.

It should be mentioned that the metals are arranged in the following order of catalytic activity for the hydrogenation reaction: Rh > Ir > Pd.

The reaction temperature is directly related to the SiO$_2$:Al$_2$O$_3$ ratio in the zeolite. Figure 3 shows that in order to obtain the same degree of conversion, a zeolite of type X (with the lowest SiO$_2$:Al$_2$O$_3$ ratio) requires a reaction temperature which is higher than the temperature needed by zeolytes of type Y (with a larger SiO$_2$:Al$_2$O$_3$ ratio). The reaction temperature is reduced by 60 — 100° when the SiO$_2$:Al$_2$O$_3$ ratio is increased from 2.5 to 4.5.

The effect of the molecular-sieve properties of zeolites on their catalytic activity is shown in Table 4. The data in the table show that the degree of conversion in the six investigated reactions depends on the ratios of the dimensions of the apertures in the zeolite to the critical diameters of the reacting molecules and the reaction products. Practically none of the investigated reactions occur on catalysts based on Ca-mordenite (4 — 5 Å). However, dehydration of ethanol with a yield of 100% becomes possible under the same conditions, by substituting H$^+$ for the Na$^+$ in the mordenite (this is accompanied by an increase in the dimensions of the channels).

It should be mentioned that such a selectivity of the zeolite catalysts depends on the reaction conditions. Thus, Weisz et al. /12/ found that sec-butyl alcohol, whose dimensions are greater than those of an aperture in the CaA zeolite, is not dehydrated at 130° (while the degree of dehydration on CaX is 82%); when the temperature is increased to 210°, the degree of conversion reaches 45%. According to the authors, the above effect is due to surface catalysis.

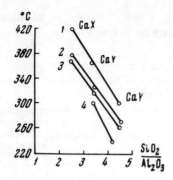

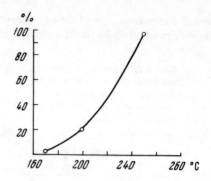

FIGURE 3. Dependence of the temperature of equal degrees of conversion on the $SiO_2:Al_2O_3$ ratio:

1- isomerization of n-hexane;
2- isomerization of cyclohexane;
3- hydroisomerization of benzene;
4- alkylation of benzene by propylene.

FIGURE 4. Dehydration of cyclohexanol (%) on the outer surface of Ca-mordenite as a function of the temperature:

1 atm, v_{vol} = 3.9 g-mole/l·hr.

TABLE 4. Selectivity of zeolite catalysts

Catalyst	Size of the aperture, Å	Reaction	Conditions	Critical diameter of molecules		Yield of reaction products, %
				starting substance	product	
0.5% Pd/CaY	~9	Isomerization	350°C, 30 atm;	4.9	5.6	Isohexane: 60.3
0.5% Pd/CaM*	4−5	of n-hexane	v_{vol} = 1 hr^{-1}			2.4
0.5% Pd/CaY*	~9	Hydrogenation	130°C, 30 atm;	5.8	6.1	Cyclo- .80
0.5% Pd/CaM*	4−5	of benzene	v_{vol} = 0.5 hr^{-1}			hexane: 4.2
0.5% Pd/CaY	~9	Isomerization	320°C, 30 atm;	6.1	−	Methyl- 51.5
0.5% Pd/CaM*	4−5	of cyclohexane	v_{vol} = 1 hr^{-1}			cyclo- 2.6
						pentane:
CaY	~9	Alkylation of	300°C, 1 atm;	5.8	−	Isopropyl- 69.6
CaM*	4−5	benzene by propylene	$v_{C_6H_6}$ = 0.3; $C_6H_6:C_3H_6$ = 2:1 (mol)			benzene 1.5
CaY	~9	Dehydration of	170°C, 1 atm,	~6	5.8	Cyclo- 100
CaM*	4−5	cyclohexanol	rate of supply			hexene 3
H−M**	~6.6		3.87 g-mole/l·hr			98
CaY	~9	Dehydration of	250°C, 1 atm,	4.7	4.4	Ethylene 100
CaM*	4−5	ethanol	rate of supply			16
H−M**	6.6		3.87 g-mole/l·hr			100

* CaM — synthetic mordenite in the calcium form.
** H−M — synthetic mordenite in the acid (hydrogen) form.

Our data describing the effect of catalysis on the outer surface of zeolite catalysts are shown in Table 5 and Figure 4.

TABLE 5. Hydrogenation of benzene on the outer surface of
Ca-mordenite:

30 atm, $v_{vol} = 0.5$ hr^{-1}, H_2:C_6H_6 = 5

Catalyst	Yield of cyclohexane, wt %				
	130° C	150° C	170° C	200° C	320° C
0.5% Pd/CaM	4.2	8.8	16.6	37.5	36.7 *
0.5% Pd/CaY	80.0	82.2	—	82.5	63.5 **

* Contains 1.2% methylcyclopentane.

** Contains 20.1% methylcyclopentane.

As is evident from Table 5, the hydrogenation of benzene (for which the critical size of the molecules is greater than the aperture size in the CaM zeolite) occurs only on the outer surface of a 0.5% Pd/CaM catalyst, and an increase in the temperature from 130 to 200° increases the degree of conversion by a factor of nearly 9.

Figure 4 shows that nearly quantitative conversion may be obtained under certain conditions even if the reaction occurs only on the outer surface of the zeolites.

Let us analyze the experimental results. The experimental data show that the activity of zeolite catalysts is determined mainly by the structure of the zeolite and the nature of the cation. Thus, zeolites in the sodium form were inactive (independently of their composition) in the isomerization of hydrocarbons and the alkylation of benzene by olefins under conditions in which the calcium form had the highest activity. The activity of the zeolites increased sharply when the monovalent cation was replaced by a bivalent cation. The decationized form showed a high activity.

Recent data collected by us show that the Pd/NaY catalyst exhibits activity (albeit a rather low one) in isomerization reactions under certain conditions (e.g., at high temperature).

The SiO_2:Al_2O_3 ratio in the zeolites is the second important factor determining the activity of zeolite catalysts. In zeolites of the same structure, an increase in this ratio causes a marked increase in the catalytic activity (see Figure 2). However, in reactions in which the zeolite function is not exhibited in the catalyst (hydrogenation of benzene), the activity of the catalyst is not affected by the above ratio or by the nature of the cation (see Table 3).

The third factor involves the correspondence between the size of the reacting molecules and the size of the pores in the zeolites. In order to carry out a reaction, the size of pores in the zeolites must be greater than the critical size of molecules of the reactants and the reaction products (see Table 4), since these reactions occur mainly in the intracrystalline cavities of the zeolite. However, under more drastic conditions the reactions may occur also on the external surface of zeolite catalysts in which the size of the apertures leading to the cavities is smaller than the size of the molecules, although the external surface of zeolites does not exceed 3 — 5% of the total surface (see Table 5 and Figure 4).

It should be mentioned that the mechanism of the action of zeolite catalysts has not been adequately elucidated. It has been assumed /10, 11,

15/ that reactions catalyzed by zeolites occur in accordance with the carbonium-ion mechanism. It has not been established on which centers the reaction occurs. Rabo et al. /10/ made the most detailed and thorough study of the isomerization of n-pentane and n-hexane and assumed that the negatively charged AlO_4^- tetrahedra act as the active centers in zeolites. According to this assumption, the sodium form of the zeolites is inactive in isomerization since the monovalent cation completely cancels the charge of the AlO_4^- tetrahedron, and the degree of cancellation is independent of the $SiO_2:Al_2O_3$ ratio in the zeolite.

The substitution of Ca^{2+} for Na^+ in the X structure does not affect the activity of the catalyst because of the symmetric arrangement of the Ca^{2+} ions with respect to the two adjacent AlO_4^- tetrahedra and the complete cancellation of their negative charges. It is assumed that in the case of zeolites of type Y in which the $SiO_2:Al_2O_3$ ratio is twice that in type X the Ca^{2+} ions are arranged asymmetricaly with respect to the adjacent tetrahedra, and the bond energy with one of the AlO_4^- tetrahedra is reduced. As a result of such a dislocation of the divalent cation, one of the octahedra bears a negative charge and acts as an active center:

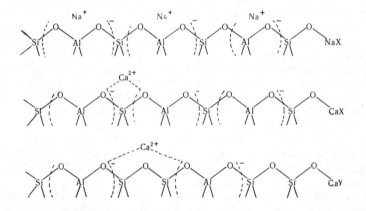

The high activity of zeolites in which the Na^+ is replaced by a cation with a valence higher than two is explained in a similar way. It should be mentioned that after assuming that AlO_4^- tetrahedra serve as the active centers, Rabo does not propose schemes explaining the course of the isomerization reaction. After studying the activity of zeolites in many cationic forms, the authors of /10/ reached the conclusion that the catalytic activity of a zeolite is independent (or depends very little) on the nature of the cation. This conclusion, however, should be regarded as doubtful, since data from the literature as well as our data show that the different cationic forms of zeolites differ markedly in their catalytic properties. Moreover, the possibility of varying the catalytic properties of a given crystal by changing the cation alone is a very characteristic property of zeolites, and according to Weisz /11/ is a unique phenomenon. The nature of the cation affects both the activity and the stability of the catalyst /10/.

The above data show that further research is needed in order to elucidate the mechanism of action of zeolite catalysts by kinetic, isotopic, X-ray diffraction, and adsorption methods as well as methods involving the determination of their acidity, etc. It is quite possible that the action of different cationic forms of zeolites involves different mechanisms.

The use of molecular sieves for the preparation of catalysts is a new stage in the field of heterogeneous catalysis.

BIBLIOGRAPHY

1. DUBININ, M.M., Z.A. ZHUKOVA, and N.V. KEL'TSEV.—In: Sbornik "Sinteticheskie tseolity", p. 7. Moskva, Izd. AN SSSR. 1962.
2. KISELEV, A.V. and A.A. LOPATKIN.—Kinetika i Kataliz, Vol. 4: 786. 1963.
3. TIMOFEEV, D.P. Kinetika adsorbtsii (Adsorption Kinetics).—Moskva, Izd. AN SSSR. 1962.
4. ZHDANOV, S.P.—Vestnik AN SSSR, No. 10: 60. 1962.
5. HERSH, Ch.K. Molecular Sieves. New York. 1961.
6. MINACHEV, Kh.M., V.I. GARANIN, L.I. PIGUZOVA, and A.S. VITUKHINA.—IAN SSSR, seriya khimicheskaya, p. 129. 1966.
7. MINACHEV, Kh.M., V.I. GARANIN, L.I. PIGUZOVA, and A.S. VITUKHINA.—IAN SSSR, seriya khimicheskaya, No. 6. 1966.
8. MINACHEV, Kh.M., V.I. GARANIN, and Ya.I. ISAKOV.—IAN SSSR, seriya khimicheskaya, p. 1722. 1964.
9. RABO, J.A., P.E. PICKERT, and R.L. MAYS.—Ind. Eng. Chem., Vol. 53: 733. 1961.
10. RABO, J.A., P.E. PICKERT, D. STAMIRES, and J. BOYLE. Actes du 2-me Congrès International de Catalyse, Vol. 2: 2055.—Paris, Technip. 1961.
11. FRILLETTE, V.J., P.B. WEISZ, and R.L. GOLDEN.—J. Catalysis, Vol. 1: 301. 1962.
12. WEISZ, P.B., V.J. FRILLETTE, R.M. MAATMAN, and E.B. MOWER.—J. Catalysis, Vol. 1: 307. 1962.
13. TSITSISHVILI, G.V., Sh.I. SIDAMONIDZE, and Sh.A. SEDGENIDZA.—DAN SSSR, Vol. 156: 1395. 1963.
14. MATTOX, Wm.J. and Wm.F. AREY, Jr.—U.S. Patent 2904607. 1959; C.A. 55 970c. 1961.
15. NORTON, C.L.—Chemy. Ind., No. 6: 268. 1962.

Kh. M. Minachev and M. A. Markov

INVESTIGATION OF THE CATALYTIC PROPERTIES OF LANTHANIDE OXIDES IN THE CONVERSION OF HYDROCARBONS AND CYCLIC ALCOHOLS*

The examination of the catalytic properties of little-studied compounds, including the oxides of the rare-earth elements (REE), is part of the important, general problem of catalyst selection, since it extends our knowledge of the relationship between the nature of an element and the catalytic properties of its compounds.

The availability of many rare elements, including the rare earths, is ever increasing as a result of improvements in mining, separation, and purification methods. In some cases, compounds of the REE are obtained as by-products of certain manufacturing processes and are not adequately used. In connection with this, an intensive study is being made of the properties of these elements, and attempts are made to find methods for their use in various branches of the national economy. At present the REE are used in nuclear technology, electronics, and radio engineering, ferrous and non-ferrous metallurgy, the chemical industry, and some other branches of the national economy. Our possible application involves the use of these elements as catalyst or components of catalysts.

In the investigation reported here, we studied the catalytic properties of a large group of REE sesquioxides and catalysts based on these oxides in the dehydrogenation of cyclohexane, the dehydrocyclization of n-heptane, the isomerization and dehydrogenation of cycloolefins, and the dehydration and dehydrogenation of cyclic alcohols.

A continuous apparatus of the conventional type was used in the experiments. The catalyzate was analyzed by gas-liquid chromatography. The surface area of the catalyst was determined by low-temperature adsorption of air.

DEHYDROGENATION OF CYCLOHEXANE

The cyclohexane used in the first part of this investigation was diluted with hydrogen ($H_2:C_6H_{12}$ = 3:1).

The results of these experiments showed that oxides of the elements of the yttrium subgroup (gadolinium, holmium, and erbium oxides) differ little in their activities, but are more active than oxides of elements of the cerium subgroup of REE (samarium and neodymium oxides). Thus, the

---

* Part of the data were published /1−9/.

catalyzate obtained at 560 — 575° on the oxides of the yttrium subgroup contained 7.1 — 12.6% benzene while the product obtained on oxides of the cerium subgroup contained only 0.8 — 2.7% benzene. In the course of the experiment, the amount of coke deposited on oxides of the yttrium subgroup was greater than that deposited on oxides of the cerium subgroup.

In order to reduce the temperature of the process, the second series of experiments on the dehydrogenation of cyclohexane was carried out without using a gas-diluent. The data in Figure 1 (which is a graph of the yield of benzene on REE oxides as a function of the temperature) show that above a certain temperature all curves lie one above the other and do not intersect; the greater the atomic weight of the rare-earth element in the oxide, the higher is the position of the corresponding curve. Thulium oxide is the only exception to this rule. Thus, at temperatures above 545° the total activity of the oxides with respect to the dehydrogenation of cyclohexane to benzene increases with increasing atomic weight of the REE. However, the specific surface of the oxides also increases with increasing atomic weight of the REE. This correspondence between the total activity and the specific surface is shown in Figure 2, which gives the data obtained in the investigation of the dehydrogenation of cyclohexane on oxides of the elements of the yttrium subgroup.

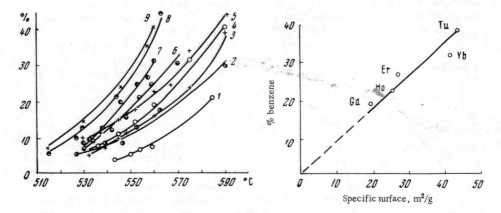

FIGURE 1. Dehydrogenation of cyclohexane (%) on REE oxides as a function of the temperature:

1- La$_2$O$_3$; 2- Nd$_2$O$_3$; 3- Sm$_2$O$_3$; 4- Gd$_2$O$_3$; 5- Ho$_2$O$_3$; 6- Er$_2$O$_3$; 7- Yb$_2$O$_3$; 8- Tu$_2$O$_3$; 9- Y$_2$O$_3$.

FIGURE 2. Agreement between the total activity and the specific surface of oxides of elements in the yttrium subgroup of REE in the dehydrogenation of cyclohexane.

In order to obtain the data in a form suitable for correlation, we calculated the specific activity of the investigated catalysts (Table 1). While on comparing the total activity of the catalysts the degree of dehydrogenation of cyclohexane increased by a factor of more than four in the transition from lanthanum oxide to ytterbium oxide (at 560°), on comparing the specific activities of these oxides the difference was less than 50%. The differences between the activities of oxides of the elements in the yttrium subgroup are even smaller.

TABLE 1. Dehydrogenation of cyclohexane on oxides of the REE ($v = 0.25\,hr^{-1}$)

		La$_2$O$_3$	Nd$_2$O$_3$	Sm$_2$O$_3$	Gd$_2$O$_3$	Ho$_2$O$_3$	Er$_2$O$_3$	Tu$_2$O$_3$	Yb$_2$O$_3$	Y$_2$O$_3$
545 °C:	S' *	17	22	32	20	26	28	44	42	82
	a **	4.1	7.7	10.1	11.0	14.7	11.9	21.3	16.8	22.3
	$a \cdot 10/S$	0.24	0.39	0.31	0.56	0.57	0.43	0.48	0.40	0.27
560° C:	a	8.5	13.9	17.6	19.0	22.2	26.6	39.1	31.5	40.2
	$a \cdot 10/S$	0.50	0.63	0.48	0.96	0.88	0.96	0.88	0.75	0.50

* S — specific surface, m^2/g.
** a — concentration of benzene in the catalyzate, %.

The data on the conversion of cyclohexane were used to plot the straight lines in ln m vs. $1/T$ coordinates (where m is the degree of dehydrogenation in mole-% and T is the absolute temperature). The apparent activation energies for the neodymium, gadolinium, and holmium oxides (determined from the slopes of the straight lines) were 45.2, 46.2, and 39.0 kcal/mole respectively, i.e., the values lay within the range that is characteristic of oxide catalysts. The values for the other oxides were in excess of 50 kcal/mole, which is probably associated with the complicated nature of the high-temperature conversion of cyclohexane. The values of the apparent energies of activation for the investigated series of oxides were inversely proportional to the changes in the effective magnetic moment which reflects the influence of the 4f-subshell (Figure 3).

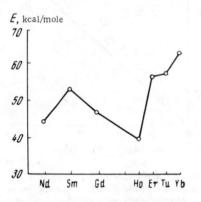

FIGURE 3. Changes in the apparent energy of activation of the dehydrogenation of cyclohexane as a function of the atomic number of the element in the oxide.

In order to collect data on the mechanism of dehydrogenation of cyclohexane on oxides of the REE, a study was made /8/ of the conversion of cyclohexane-cyclohexene mixtures on holmium oxide at 560° at flow rates of 0.01 — 0.09 mmoles/sec; the cyclohexene was labelled with the radioactive carbon isotope — ^{14}C. A determination of the ratio of the rates of formation of benzene formed by direct dehydrogenation of cyclohexane (without desorption of the intermediate products) and by the consecutive scheme involving desorption of the cyclohexene showed that under the selected conditions the two courses are of approximately the same importance. Thus, the results of the above investigation confirmed the validity of the doublet mechanism of dehydrogenation of cyclohexane on oxide catalysts.

DEHYDROCYCLIZATION OF n-HEPTANE

An investigation of the conversion of n-heptane showed that the activity of the oxides in dehydrocyclization reactions is governed by the same rules that govern the dehydrogenation of cyclohexane.

As is evident from the data in Table 2, neodymium and samarium oxides have similar activities, but are much less active than gadolinium, holmium, and erbium oxides.

TABLE 2. Dehydrocyclization of n-heptane on oxides of the REE ($v = 0.25$ hr^{-1})

		Nd_2O_3	Sm_2O_3	Gd_2O_3	Ho_2O_3	Er_2O_3	Y_2O_3
530° C:	a *	3.8	6.2	11.0	14.2	—	—
	$a \cdot 10/S$	0.17	0.18	0.55	0.54	—	—
545° C:	a	8.7	11.9	21.8	23.3	23.4	27.6
	$a \cdot 10/S$	0.39	0.37	1.11	0.91	0.84	0.34
560° C:	a	12.3	21.3	27.4	30.0	35.0	34.5
	$a \cdot 10/S$	0.55	0.64	1.39	1.15	1.26	0.42

a° — concentration of aromatic hydrocarbons in the catalyzate, %

CONVERSION OF CYCLOOLEFINS

In order to determine the catalytic properties of oxides of the REE in isomerization reactions, we studied the transformations of the following cycloolefins (they are more reactive than saturated hydrocarbons): cyclohexene, 1-methylcyclopentene-1, and 1-methylcyclohexane-1. Neodymium and erbium oxides were used as the catalysts.

The experiments with cyclohexene showed that no isomerization of the six-atom ring into a five-atom one occurred on the two investigated catalysts under the experimental conditions (H_2:hydrocarbon = 3:1; $v = 0.25$ hr^{-1}; 350 — 530°). A reaction involving a shift in the position of the double bond in the ring was observed in the case of the transformation of 1-methylcyclopentene-1 and 1-methylcyclohexene-1. At temperatures above 470° the two six-atom cycloolefins were dehydrogenated to the corresponding aromatic hydrocarbons. In the conversion of 1-methylcyclohexene-1 the dehydrogenation started at about 350°, while in the conversion of 1-methylcyclopentene-1 the dehydrogenation started at 400°. At temperatures above 470° there was a decrease in the yield of the 1-methylcyclohexene-2 isomers and of 1-methylcyclohexene-3, because of the rapid increase in the rate of dehydrogenation. The catalytic activity of erbium oxide (in isomerization and dehydrogenation reactions) was somewhat higher than that of neodymium oxide.

CONVERSIONS OF CYCLOHEXANE AND n-ALKANES
ON CATALYSTS CONTAINING THE OXIDES OF REE

Among the mixed catalysts, we carried out a most detailed study of the catalysts prepared by applying oxides of the REE on various activated carbons.

In the investigation of these catalysts (the conversion of cyclohexane was used as an example) we made a detailed study of the influence of various factors such as the temperature of the experiment, the concentration and the nature of the carried oxide, and the type of carbon used.

Data on the effect of the concentration of neodymium oxide on the activity of the catalyst are shown in Figure 4. It is evident that the changes in concentration affect the activity only up to a certain value (5% oxide). It was assumed that the surface area of the oxide in the catalyst also increases only until the above Nd_2O_3 concentration has been reached. The above assumption was confirmed by a separate determination of the surface area of the oxide in the catalyst, which was made at the laboratory of research on catalysts of the IOKh AN SSSR, by the method of selective adsorption of water on the oxide

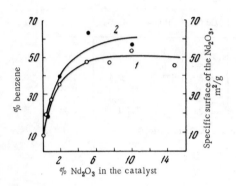

FIGURE 4. Changes in the activity of a Nd_2O_3/ birch carbon catalyst (1) and in the specific surface of the neodymium oxide (2) as a function of the oxide concentration

The data in Figure 4 show the existence of a complete agreement between the changes in these two parameters. Thus, a linear dependence exists between the surface area of the oxide and the activity of the catalyst, and both properties are similarly affected by the concentration.

The investigations of the dehydrogenation of cyclohexane on catalysts containing various oxides showed that the activity of the catalyst is not affected substantially by the nature of the oxide.

For instance, when birch-derived carbon was used as the carrier of 5% R_2O_3/C catalysts (where R = Nd, Ho, Y, and a mixture of REE) the yields of benzene at 500 and 560° were 41 — 48 and 65 — 76% respectively. At 455°, the yield of benzene on a 10% R_2O_3/C_a catalyst (where R = La, Nd, and Y and C_a is high-ash carbon) was 47 — 55%.

It should be noted that the carbons used in the experiments also showed a certain activity in the dehydrogenation of cyclohexane. However, the application of the oxides produced catalysts with a much higher activity. The use of high-ash carbons resulted in a marked increase in the degree of conversion of cyclohexane and made it possible to considerably reduce the temperature required for a high degree of conversion.

As is evident from Table 3, the application of neodymium oxide increases the catalytic activity of carbon with respect to the dehydrocyclization of n-heptane, too. The toluene concentration in the catalyzate obtained with the catalyst containing 5% neodymium oxide decreased from 50% at the beginning to 25% after four hours, while the respective values on carbon alone were 14 and 6%. However, the application of the oxide did not increase the amount of unsaturated hydrocarbons in the catalyzate; on the contrary, within the first hours of operation a higher concentration of unsaturated hydrocarbons was obtained on the oxide-free carbon. The catalytic activity (with respect to the dehydrocyclization reaction) of the oxide-containing catalyst decreased during the course of the experiment, and the amount of heptenes in the catalyzate increased gradually with time and ultimately reached the same value as on pure carbon.

TABLE 3. Yield of reaction products within one hour (%) in the conversion of n-heptane on 5% Nd_2O_3/C and C* catalysts: $v = 0.25$ hr^{-1}; 500°C

Catalyst	Reaction products	Total duration of the experiment, hours			
		1	2	3	4
Nd_2O_3/C	Aromatic hydrocarbons .	52.8	36.3	29.6	26.4
	Olefins	—	3.7	5.6	7.7
C	Aromatic hydrocarbons .	14.4	12.1	8.1	7.7
	Olefins	8.0	8.3	7.6	8.4

* Activated birch carbon.

CONVERSIONS OF CYCLIC ALCOHOLS

The relatively high temperature at which the displacement of the double bond begins (in the conversion of cycloolefins) led us to expect that in the case of cyclic alcohols the conversion conditions may be selected in such a way that the starting alcohols will yield their direct dehydration products. Experiments on the conversion of cyclohexanol showed that both dehydration and dehydrogenation to the ketone take place on neodymium oxide prepared by calcination of the hydroxide, but the first reaction is predominant. For instance, when the temperature is increased from 250 to 500° ($v = 0.83$ hr^{-1}, H_2:$C_6H_{12}O = 2$:1) the concentrations of cyclohexene and cyclohexanone in the catalyzate increased from 6 to 66 and from 2 to 19% respectively. The energy of activation of the dehydration of cyclohexanol (determined at 230 − 286°) was 23 kcal/mole. The hydrocarbon fraction of the catalyzate contained only cyclohexene, i.e., no isomerization of the ring took place, as in the case of the conversion of cyloolefins.

The behavior of different cyclic alcohols was compared at 350°, at $v = 0.83$ hr^{-1} and H_2:$C_6H_{12}O = 2$:1. The results of these experiments showed that the degrees of dehydration and dehydrogenation of cyclopentanol, cyclohexanol, and methylcyclohexanols are approximately the same (30 − 35 and 5 − 6% respectively). Apparently, this indicates the existence of a similarity in the adsorption properties of these compounds under the experimental conditions used by us.

The hydrocarbon fractions of the catalyzates obtained in the dehydration of the three methylcyclohexanols consisted of the products of direct dehydration of the respective alcohols; the dehydration of 1-methylcyclohexanol-2 and 1-methylcyclohexanol-3 produced equimolar mixtures of the two possible methylcyclohexenes. Thus, olefins of a definite structure or the single olefins (in cases in which the water may be detached in only one way) may be obtained under certain conditions by dehydration of alcohols on neodymium oxide produced from the hydroxide.

253

The effect of the calcination temperature was studied by investigating the conversion of cyclohexanol on neodymium oxide samples prepared by the calcination of neodymium oxalate at 500 — 800°. Some of the results are shown in Table 4 and Figure 5. It is evident that catalyst No.1, prepared by calcination at 500°, was the most active and selective in dehydration at all the temperatures used. However, the considerable changes in the calcination temperature did not cause a marked change in the total activity. On the contrary, the data in Table 4 show marked differences between the activities (in dehydration and dehydrogenation) of catalysts No. 1 — 5. Thus, the cyclohexene:cyclohexanone ratio changed from 11.5 — 13.5 to 0.06 — 0.7 (i.e., by a factor of 20) in the transition from catalyst No.1 to No.5. At the same time, the temperature range between 500 and 800° comprised two regions in which sharp changes in selectivity were observed (500 — 550 and 700 — 800°). It was shown that the first change in selectivity corresponds to the removal of the carbon formed in the decomposition of the neodymium oxalate from the catalyst, while in the second region (700 — 800°) the cubic neodymium oxide was transformed to the hexagonal. The presence of a mixed phase in sample No.5 was shown by X-ray diffraction analysis.

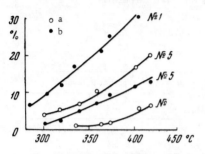

FIGURE 5. Dehydrogenation and dehydration of cyclohexanol on catalysts:

The numbers next to the curves correspond to the numbers of the catalyst samples. a- conversion to cyclohexanone; b- conversion to cyclohexene.

TABLE 4. Conversion of cyclohexanol on neodymium oxide prepared by calcination of the oxalate at 500—800°C ($v = 5$ hr^{-1})

Sample No.	Calcination temperature, °C	300° C		325° C		350° C		375° C		400° C	
		O+K*	$\frac{O}{K}$	O+K	$\frac{O}{K}$	O+K	$\frac{O}{K}$	O+K	$\frac{O}{K}$	O+K	$\frac{O}{K}$
1	500	9.2	—	14.5	13.5	20.0	13.3	26.3	11.5	34.2	5.0
2	550	Not deter.	Not deter.	9.1	4.0	12.2	3.7	17.9	3.1	25.2	2.8
3	600	5.1	2.0	9.4	2.6	14.6	2.6	21.6	2.7	28.3	2.5
4	700	4.7	1.8	8.1	2.4	14.0	2.6	20.4	2.5	31.5	2.7
5	800	6.6	0.54	10.3	0.63	13.6	0.66	19.9	0.70	26.6	0.66

* O — cyclohexene, K — cyclohexanone

BIBLIOGRAPHY

1. MINACHEV, Kh.M., M.A. MARKOV, and O.K. SHCHUKINA. — IAN SSSR, OKhN, p.1507. 1961.
2. MINACHEV, Kh.M., M.A. MARKOV, and O.K. SHCHUKINA. — IAN SSSR, OKhN, p.1665. 1961.

3. MINACHEV, Kh. M., M. A. MARKOV, and G. A. LOGINOV.—Neftekhimiya, Vol. 1: 356. 1961.
4. MINACHEV, Kh. M., M. A. MARKOV, and O. K. SHCHUKINA.—Neftekhimiya, Vol. 1: 490. 1961.
5. MINACHEV, Kh. M., M. A. MARKOV, and O. K. SHCHUKINA.—Neftekhimiya, Vol. 1: 610. 1961.
6. MINACHEV, Kh. M., M. A. MARKOV, and V. I. BOGOMOLOV.—Neftekhimiya, Vol. 2: 144. 1962.
7. MINACHEV, Kh. M., M. A. MARKOV, V. I. BOGOMOLOV, and F. E. ENGLINA.—IAN SSSR, OKhN, p. 13. 1962.
8. DERBENTSEV, Yu. I., M. A. MARKOV, G. V. ISAGULYANTS, Kh. M. MINACHEV, and A. A. BALANDIN.— DAN SSSR, Vol. 155: 128. 1964.
9. See paper in the Collection "Redkozemel'nye Elementy" (The Lanthanides).—Moskva, Izd. AN SSSR. 1963.

K.M. Gitis, V.L. Polinin, G.V. Samsonov, T.Ya.
Kosolapova, and M.I. Rozengart

THE CATALYTIC PROPERTIES OF CHROMIUM AND CHROMIUM CARBIDES IN THE AROMATIZATION OF HYDROCARBONS

It is known that chromium oxide is extensively used as a catalyst for the dehydrogenation and dehydrocyclization of paraffin hydrocarbons. It would be of importance to determine to what extent metallic chromium and other chromium compounds also possess catalytic properties. The chromium carbides — Cr_7C_3 and Cr_3C_2 — were the first oxygen-free chromium compounds selected and tested by us for their catalytic activity, and their activity was compared with that of metallic chromium.

The results of our experiments showed that Cr_7C_3 and Cr_3C_2 catalyze the aromatization of paraffin hydrocarbons. When n-hexane was passed over Cr_7C_3 at 615° we obtained a catalyzate with the maximum concentration of aromatic hydrocarbons (10.8%) and the yield based on the amount of hexane passed was 5.2%; under the same conditions, octane yielded a catalyzate containing 15% aromatic hydrocarbons (at a yield of 4.8%). The other carbide (Cr_3C_2) was much less active, and at 615° the amounts of aromatic hydrocarbons formed from hexane and octane were, respectively, about 1/6 and 1/10 of the amounts formed on Cr_7C_3. At 615° the metallic chromium did not catalyze the dehydrocyclization reaction.

The dehydrocyclization experiments were carried out on a continuous apparatus by the method described in /1/; the starting hydrocarbons were supplied at a rate of 0.7 volumes/hour.

The n-hexane used in the experiments was purified in advance by chromatography on silica gel (the starting substance was commercial n-heptane) and subsequent rectification in a column with an effectiveness of 100 theoretical plates. In some of the experiments we used hexane with a purity of 99.1% (the rest consisted of isohexanes) prepared by passing through silica gel. The n-octane was purified by passing through silica gel with subsequent rectification on the same column; its purity was 99.2%. The hexene-1 and cyclohexane contained 0.5 and 0.6% impurities and were used without additional purification.

The catalyzates obtained from hexane, cyclohexane, and hexene were analyzed on a gas-liquid chromatograph of the SKB IOKh type with a katharometer-detector; a 14-meter column with dioctyl sebacate was used for the chromatography of the hexane catalyzate, and a 8-meter column with triethylene glycol dibutyrate on diatomaceous earth (0.25 — 0.5 mm) was used for the hexene catalyzates. The octance catalyzates were analyzed in a capillary chromatograph with a flame-ionization detector, using a 35-meter capillary column with triethylene glycol dibutyrate /2/.

Chromium carbides (Cr_7C_3 and Cr_3C_2, prepared by the method described in /3, 4/) and electrolytic metallic chromium were used as the catalysts. Some properties of these catalysts are listed in Table 1.

TABLE 1. Physicochemical properties of the catalysts

Property	Catalyst		
	Cr_7C_3	Cr_3C_2	Cr
Crystal structure	hexagonal	rhombohedral	body-centered cubic
Surface, m^2/g	1.0	1.5	0.5
Particle size, mm	0.25—0.5	0.25—0.5	0.25--0.5
Bulk density, g/cm^3........	1.7 (sample 1) 2.3 (sample 2)	1.7 (sample 1) 2.3 (sample 2) }	3.8—3.9

The amount of catalyst used in the experiments with cyclohexane as well as in experiment No.1 (Table 2) with hexane was 10 cm^3; in all other cases it was 5 cm^3. The samples with a bulk density of 2.3 were used only in the experiments with hexenes, while in all other cases we used samples with a bulk density of 1.7. Crushed quartz (10 cm^3) was placed over the catalyst. The catalyst was heated in the reactor to the temperature of the experiment, in a current of oxygen-free and water-free hydrogen. Catalyzate samples were withdrawn at 20-minute intervals, the yield and composition of the catalyzate were determined in each case and the yield of aromatic hydrocarbons was calculated in percent of the starting hydrocarbon. In order to elucidate the role of pyrolytic effect and the possible catalytic action of quartz, we carried out blank experiments in which the catalyst was replaced by quartz of the same particle size and in the same amount as in the experiments with the catalyst.

At first we made an attempt to carry out the aromatization of hexane at 550° (this temperature is used when the reaction is carried out on Cr_2O_3 gel). We found, however, that no benzene was formed (in noticeable amounts) at this temperature. Formation of benzene was observed only at 615°. The data in Table 2 show that when hexane is passed over Cr_7C_3 (experiment No.1), 48.5% of the liquid catalyzate containing 10.8% benzene is formed within the first 20 minutes. In order to determine the stability of the catalyst with time, we carried out one-hour experiments with the two carbides, and the products were withdrawn at 20-minute intervals. In experiment No.2 with Cr_7C_3, the yield of catalyzate within the first 20 minutes was 57% and the concentration of benzene in the catalyzate was 7.1%. Under the same conditions, the Cr_3C_2 showed a much lower activity (experiment No.3): the liquid catalyzate collected over the first 20 minutes (in a yield of 39%) contained only 2% benzene. The activity of both catalysts decreased rapidly, and the benzene concentration in the catalyzate withdrawn in subsequent batches dropped practically to zero (see Table 2).

When hexane was passed over metallic chromium at 615° (experiment No.4) it yielded a catalyzate containing 0.5% benzene, i.e., practically the same as the benzene concentration in the catalyzate obtained in the blank experiment with quartz (0.6%, experiment No.5).

TABLE 2. Aromatization of hexane:
615°C, $v = 0.7$ hr^{-1}

Exp. No.	Catalyst and its volume	From start of exp. to withdrawal of sample, min	Yield of catalyzate, %	Yield of benzene, wt %	Composition of the catalyzate, wt%					
					C_4-C_5 hydrocarbons	isohexanes	n-hexane + hexene-1	other hexenes	hexadienes	benzene
1	Cr$_7$C$_3$, 10 cm^3	20	48.5	5.2	7.3	2.8	72.9	5.5	0.7	10.8
2	5 cm^3	20	57	4.1	15.1	3.2	69.0	4.6	1.0	7.1
		40	56	0.6	2.9	2.4	92.0	1.3	0.4	1.0
		60	42	0.2	3.4	2.8	91.5	1.1	0.6	0.6
3	Cr$_3$C$_2$, 5 cm^3	20	39	0.9	7.1	3.2	82.7	4.3	0.4	2.2
		40	58	0.1	1.8	2.2	95.0	0.7	0.2	0.2
		60	66	0.2	9.9	2.7	85.9	1.0	0.2	0.3
4	Metallic chromium, 5 cm^3	20	62	0.3	3.9	0.6	94.3	0.6	0.0	0.5
5	Quartz, 15 cm^3	20	49	0.3	6.8	0.9	91.1	0.7	0.0	0.6

In the aromatization of n-octane at 615° we observed the same behavior as in the aromatization of n-hexane (Table 3). Thus, in experiment No.6 with Cr$_7$C$_3$ the yield of catalyzate withdrawn with the first batch was 32% and the concentration of aromatic hydrocarbons (total concentration of benzene, toluene, xylenes, and ethylbenzene) was up to 15%. Subsequent batches also showed a sharp decrease in the activity of the catalyst and the concentration of aromatic hydrocarbons in the liquid products did not exceed 1 — 2%. We should mention the extremely high selectivity of the action of Cr$_7$C$_3$, leading to the formation of o-xylene. As is evident from Table 3, the o-xylene concentration in the catalyzate reaches 9% while the concentration of ethylbenene (the second product of the dehydrocyclization of n-octane) was only 0.6%. For comparison, the o-xylene:ethylbenzene ratio in the catalyzates obtained at 528°·over conventional catalysts is 1.4 — 2.0.

The degree of aromatization of n-octane on Cr$_3$C$_2$ and metallic chromium was insignificant. Thus, the catalyzate withdrawn after the first 20 minutes of contact with Cr$_3$C$_2$ (the yield was 35%) contained 1.5% aromatic hydrocarbons (mainly toluene) while the catalyzate formed on metallic chromium (with a yield of 38%) contained 2% aromatic hydrocarbons. The catalyzate from the blank experiments on quartz contained 2% aromatic hydrocarbons.

The data on the aromatization of hexene-1 (Table 4) show that at 550° the degree of aromatization of hexene-1 is low. Thus, the catalyzate yields on Cr$_7$C$_3$ and Cr$_3$C$_2$ under the above conditions were 64 and 32%, and the concentrations of aromatic products in the catalyzates were 1.0 and 0.7% respectively. In addition to benzene, the catalyzate contained products formed as a result of cracking and isomerization (other hexenes) and some unidentified products. At 585° the yield of aromatic hydrocarbons was much higher.   Thus, in the case of Cr_7C_3 the yield of catalyzate in the first withdrawn sample was 47% and the concentration of aromatic products was 10.7%.   On Cr_3C_2 the yield of liquid products was 40% and the concentration of aromatic hydrocarbons was 6.2%.   The collected data show that in the aromatization of hexenes the difference between the activities of the two carbides is less pronounced than in the aromatization of hexane, and in the second batch the activities of the two catalysts become the same.   The yield of catalyzate on metallic chromium at 585° at the end of the first 20 minutes was 47% (the concentration of aromatic hydrocarbons was 3.3%) while the yield on quartz was 37% and the benzene concentration was 4.3% (the yield in both cases was 1.6%).

TABLE 3. Aromatization of octane:
615°C, $v = 0.7$ hr^{-1}

Exp. No.	Catalyst and its volume	From start of exp. to withdrawal of sample, min	Yield of catalyzate, wt%	Yield of aromatic hydrocarbons, wt %	Composition of the aromatic fraction of the catalyzate, wt %					
					benzene	toluene	ethylbenzene	p-xylene	m-xylene	o-xylene
6	Cr_7C_3, 5 cm³	20	32	4.8	3.33	2.13	0.57	0.08	0.06	8.93
		40	48	0.3	—	0.58	0.07	0.003	0.003	0.024
		60	31	0.8	—	1.96	0.34	0.09	0.11	0.09
7	Cr_3C_2, 5 cm³	20	35	0.5	0.13	1.0	0.15	0.05	0.045	0.11
		40	40	0.3	—	0.345	0.16	0.05	0.084	0.09
		60	43	0.3	—	0.49	0.05	0.03	0.04	0.05
8	Metallic chromium, 5 cm³	40	38	0.8	—	1.7	0.15	0.03	0.07	0.07
9	Quartz, 15 cm³	20	50	1.03	—	1.65	0.17	0.05	0.07	0.09

It would be of interest to compare the catalytic activities of Cr_7C_3 in aromatization and dehydrogenation reactions.   To this end, we carried out experiments with cyclohexane which reacts with the formation of the minimum amounts of by-products and coke.   The cyclohexane was used in experiments 16 and 17 at 550 and 615°, at a feed rate of 0.7 volumes/hour. It was found (Table 5) that the benzene concentration in the catalyzate formed at 550° did not exceed 0.6%.   When the temperature was increased to 615° the first batch of catalyzate contained 10.2% benzene, but in the second batch the benzene content decreased to 5.6%.   In addition to benzene, the catalyzate contained products of the incomplete dehydrogenation of cyclohexane: cyclohexene and probably cyclohexadiene.   In order to determine the contribution of pyrolytic effects and the possible catalytic action of quartz on the cyclohexane, we again carried out a blank experiment of quartz.

As is evident from the above table, the yield of catalyzate was 74% and it contained 1% benzene.

Thus, the above carbide shows catalytic activity in dehydrogenation, as found recently by G. V. Samsonov and S. Z. Roginskii et al. /5/ in the dehydrogenation of n-butane.

259

TABLE 4. Aromatization of hexene-1
($v = 0.7$ hr^{-1})

Exp. No.	Catalyst and its volume	Temperature, °C	From start of exp. to withdrawal of sample, min	Yield of catalyzate, wt%	Yield of aromatic hydrocarbons, wt %	Composition of the catalyzate, wt %								
						C$_4$–C$_5$ hydrocarbons	isohexanes	n-hexane	hexene-1	other hexenes	hexadienes	benzene	toluene	nonidentified products
10	Cr$_3$C$_2$, 5 cm^3	550	20	32	0.2	5.7	0.4	0.7	81.7	6.5	0.9	0.7	0.0	3.4
11	Cr$_7$C$_3$, 5 cm^3	550	20	64	0.6	10.5	0.4	0.7	76.0	8.6	0.9	1.0	0.0	1.9
12	Cr$_3$C$_2$, 5 cm^3	585	20	40	2.5	10.1	5.3	0.3	61.5	9.8	3.0	4.3	1.9	3.8
13	Cr$_7$C$_3$, 5 cm^3	585	40	64	3.5	16.4	0.7	Traces	56.6	10.2	4.6	3.7	1.8	6.0
			20	47	5.0	15.5	1.4	0.4	51.6	12.4	2.9	6.3	4.4	5.1
			40	56	3.7	17.8	0.9	0.3	57.6	10.4	2.4	4.3	2.2	4.2
14	Metallic chromium, 5 cm^3	585	20	47	1.6	18.8	1.1	0.4	61.1	9.6	2.2	3.3	0.0	3.6
15	Quartz, 15 cm^3	585	20	37	1.6	6.1	0.9	0.3	65.7	10.4	4.6	4.3	0.0	7.8

TABLE 5. Dehydrogenation of cyclohexane
($v = 0.7$ hr^{-1})

Exp. No.	Catalyst and its volume	Temperature, °C	From start of exp. to withdrawal of sample, min	Yield of catalyzate, wt%	Yield of aromatic hydrocarbons, wt%	Composition of the catalyzate, wt%			
						cracking and isomerization products	cyclohexane	cyclohexene	benzene
16	Cr$_7$C$_3$, 10 cm^3	550	20	Not deter.	—	0.1	98.3	0.5	0.6
17		615	30	71.5	7.3	9.2	76.8	3.7	10.2
			60	68	3.8	4.3	86.5	3.6	5.6
18	Quartz, 20 cm^3	615	30	74	0.7	4.8	92.8	1.4	1.0

A comparison of the courses of some side reactions of the hydrocarbons shows that of the two carbides, Cr$_3$C$_2$ showed a higher activity in the cracking reaction. This can be seen most clearly in the case of hexane and hexene-1. In the case of hexane, the yield of cracking products* on Cr$_3$C$_2$ (experiment No.3) was 64%, and on Cr$_7$C$_3$ it was 52 — 54% (experiments 1 and 2). At 550° the degree of cracking of hexene-1 on Cr$_3$C$_2$ (70%) was higher than on Cr$_7$C$_3$ (42%). In the experiments on Cr$_7$C$_3$ at 615° the yield of cracking products was 35% from cyclohexane (experiment No.17), 52 — 54% from hexane (as we mentioned above, experiments 1 and 2), and 58% from octane.

The catalytic activity of Cr$_7$C$_3$ and Cr$_3$C$_2$ with respect to isomerization was approximately the same (the concentrations of isohexanes were 2.8 and 3.2 respectively). The catalyzates obtained on chromium and quartz contained 0.6 — 0.7% isohexanes (experiments 4 and 5).

The above data show that in dehydrocyclization and especially in dehydrogenation (as an intermediate stage in dehydrocyclization) the chromium must be bound by a valence bond. This is shown by the fact that chromium oxide and to a certain extent, chromium carbides (especially Cr$_7$C$_3$) catalyze the aromatization process while metallic chromium does not act as a catalyst. Apparently, the activity of the chromium compounds is associated with the electron density shifts in these compounds. The formation of chromium carbides occurs through the interaction of chromium and carbon atoms, i.e., through the transfer of valence (including $3d$-) electrons to form a collective with the p-electrons of the carbon. The transfer of some of the electrons towards the atom of the non-metal enhances the acceptor properties of the chromium atom,** and this facilitates the detachment of electrons from the paraffin molecules. The differences in the activities of Cr$_7$C$_3$ and Cr$_3$C$_2$ are due to differences in the nature of the electronic reaction between the chromium and the carbon, and possibly to the difference in the distances between the chromium atoms in these carbides.

* The yield of cracking products was evaluated from the yield of catalyzate and the concentration of C$_4$—C$_5$ hydrocarbons; the data for the first 20 minutes are taken into account.

** As one of the authors showed, the acceptor properties of an atom of a transition metal may be evaluated quantitatively (for details see /6/).

The fact that hexene-1 as well as hexane are not aromatized on metallic chromium, while the degree of aromatization is low on Cr_3C_2 and higher on Cr_7C_3, leads to the assumption that the mechanism of the catalytic action of chromium catalysts with respect to aromatization involves some stage that is common to both paraffins and olefins, i.e., a stage common to the different ones occurring in dehydrocyclization.

To sum up the above data, it should be mentioned that the study of the catalytic activity of a number of binary compounds of chromium and other dehydrocyclization catalysts could elucidate the stages of the dehydrocyclization reaction mechanism, the relationship between the above reaction and dehydrogenation reactions, and the characteristic features of each of these reactions.

BIBLIOGRAPHY

1. ROZENGART, M. I. and B. A. KAZANSKII.—DAN SSSR, Vol. 119: 716. 1958.
2. VITT, S. V., V. B. BONDAREV, V. L. POLININ, and M. I. ROZENGART.—IAN SSSR, seriya khimicheskaya, p. 2043. 1963.
3. KOSOLAPOVA, T. Ya. and G. V. SAMSONOV.—ZhPKh, Vol. 32: 55. 1959.
4. KOSOLAPOVA, T. Ya. and G. V. SAMSONOV.—ZhPKh, Vol. 32: 1505. 1959.
5. LIU CHUNG-HUI, S. Z. ROGINSKII, G. V. SAMSONOV, and M. I. YANOVSKII.—Neftekhimiya, Vol. 3: 845. 1963.
6. SAMSONOV, G. V.—DAN SSSR, Vol. 93: 689. 1953.

G. V. Samsonov

THE CATALYTIC PROPERTIES OF REFRACTORY COMPOUNDS, AND PRINCIPLES OF THE CREATION OF REFRACTORY COMPOUNDS WITH PRESCRIBED CATALYTIC PROPERTIES

One of the first papers that showed the existence of a connection between the catalytic properties and the degree of incompleteness of the d-electron sublevels in transition metal atoms was written by S.Z. Roginskii /1/; the paper indicated that f-elements, and especially the rare-earth metals possess catalytic properties. Many subsequent papers showed the existence of a correspondence between the magnetic properties of transition metals (these properties are a direct function of the incompleteness of the d- and f-shells) and their catalytic properties (for example, see /2 — 4/). Many papers have dealt with catalysis on lanthanide oxides /5 — 10/, and have reported that a certain definite relationship exists between the catalytic properties, the effective magnetic moments, and the bond energies.

In order to carry out a phenomenological discussion of the catalytic properties of the transition metals, their alloys and their compounds, it would be an advantage to use the concepts of the donor-acceptor reaction between the atoms of metallic solids as well as the qualitative criterion of the degree of incompleteness of the electron shells, expressed by

$\xi = \frac{1}{Nn}$ where N is the main quantum number of the unfilled d-sublevel and n is the number of electrons in the d-sublevel of the isolated atom /11 — 13/. At the same time we must take into account the modern theoretical concepts of solid-state physics, according to which little difference exists between the distribution of the d-electron charge in a metal and the distribution of the d-electron charge in a free atom /14/; and also, papers on the ratios of the fractions of collective and covalenty bound electrons in the transition metals /15/ as well as the concepts of stable (from the standpoint of quantum mechanics) electron configurations and hybridizations.

It may be assumed that the catalytic activity of the transition metals can be determined by the number of free d-states remaining after the screening of the sd-levels of isolated atoms during the formation of the metallic crystal. An increase in the degree of incompleteness of the d-shell is accompanied by an increase in the degree of screening of the sd-state in transition metals, which reaches a maximum for the metals with the most pronounced acceptor properties (Table 1) — Ti, V, Zr, Hf, and especially Sc and Y whose catalytic activity has not been adequately investigated. All these metals should exhibit a weak catalytic activity and form the following series in order of relative catalytic activity: Sc, Y, Ti, Zr, V, Hf. A decrease in the acceptor capacity of the d-shell should be accompanied by a decrease in the degree of screening, while the free sites on the d-levels remain and there is a corresponding increase in the catalytic activity. Thus, in the series Sc...Ni, Y...Pd, and Hf...Pt we should expect an increase in the catalytic activity; this increase should not be monotonous, but occur in rather sharp jumps corresponding to the jumps in ξ. For instance, in the first of the above series such a jump can be expected in the transition from V to Cr, from Cr to Fe, etc. It should be noted that a decrease in the degree of screening is accompanied by an increase in the fraction of covalently bound electrons and a decrease in the fraction of collective electrons. For example, according to the data of /15/, niobium has 5 electrons of which 3.8 are covalently bound and 1.2 are collective, while (according to a preliminary communication of the same authors) Zr has 2.6 covalently bound electrons per atom and 1.4 collective electrons per atom, i.e., the ratios of the fractions $\varepsilon_{covalent}$: $\varepsilon_{collective}$ for Zr and Nb are approximately equal to the inverse ratios of the corresponding values of ξ. The increase in the fraction of covalently bound electrons and the decrease in ξ (i.e., the decrease in the degree of screening) are accompanied by a decrease in the probability of formation of spin pairs and by an increase in the paramagnetism of the transition metals until the ferromagnetic metals — iron, cobalt, and nickel — are reached. The ferromagnetism is created as a result of the high values of the exchange energy integral as a function of the ratio of the distance between the atoms to the radius of the unfilled $3d$-shell /16/. Thus, a correspondence should, indeed, exist between the magnetic and catalytic properties of the transition metals; however, the catalytic properties are determined primarily by the degree of screening (characterized by the degree of incompleteness of the d-electron shells in the isolated atoms) while the magnetic properties depend to a great extent on the above-described geometric factors. Evidently, this is the reason why the platinum-group metals which often exhibit a moderate paramagnetism (Figure 1) are good catalysts while the ferromagnetic metals exhibit less pronounced catalytic properties. A review /4/ lists a number of examples of catalysis on transition metals that support the validity of the above considerations. Thus, Figure 2 shows the changes in the rate of hydrogenation and the heat of adsorption of ethylene on films of different metals as a function of the specific contribution of the d-state to the metallic bond. By presenting the same data as a function of the incompleteness criterion (for the d-shell) we obtain a satisfactory correlation, shown in Figure 3.

In dealing with the alloys of the transition metals, we distinguish between the following main groups: 1) alloys of transition metals with similar values of the criteria of incompleteness of the d-electron shells; 2) alloys of transition metals having very different values of the criteria of incompleteness; 3) alloys of transition metals with non-transition metals possessing valence s-electrons; 4) alloys of transition metals with non-transition elements possessing valence p-electrons. In the first case we should expect to observe the same exchange interaction laws as in the case of single transition metals, with a certain increase in the degree of interaction (within the limits of existence of a solid solution). In the case of alloys of transition metals having very different criteria of incompleteness of the d-electron shell, we should expect, in general, an increase in the

264

extent of sd-exchange and a corresponding decrease in the catalytic activity, especially in cases in which the difference between the criteria of incompleteness depends mainly on the number of electrons in the d-shells rather than on the difference between the energy levels of these shells. In this case, the formation of stable electron configurations of the d^5s^2, $d^{10}s^0$ and other types may play an important role, causing sharp increases or decreases in the catalytic activity. The above consideration was correctly mentioned in a recent paper /17/. In the case of alloys of the transition metals with non-transition metals possessing outer s-electrons, we should expect (under favorable energy conditions) a statistical filling of the vacant sites of the d-state with a corresponding decrease in the degree of incompleteness of the d-sublevels and a decrease in the catalytic activity. The probability of such a decrease should evidently increase with decreasing ionization potential of the s-metals, i.e., it should have a maximum in the case of alloys of the transition metals with the alkali and alkaline-earth metals as well as with copper and silver. An example of the catalytic properties of alloys of the above type has been reported in /18/; it shows that the catalytic activity of palladium-gold alloys in the ortho-para conversion of hydrogen decreases sharply at gold concentrations above 60%, when the number of holes in the d-zone of palladium is equal to 0.6 (Figure 4). A similar decrease in activity accompanies the dissolution of hydrogen in the transition metals, as a result of the filling of part of the vacancies in the d-levels by the ls-electrons of the hydrogen /19/. A decrease in the catalytic activity caused by the dissolution of copper in nickel has been reported in another paper /20/ dealing with the decomposition of methanol to $CO + H_2$. This has been confirmed by studies of reactions involving the participation of hydrogen /21, 22/.

TABLE 1. Electron configuration and acceptor capacity of atoms of the d-transition metals

Element	Group	Electron configuration	Acceptor capacity	Element	Group	Electron configuration	Acceptor capacity	Element	Group	Electron configuration	Acceptor capacity
Sc	3	3^14^2	0.333	V	3	$4^14\ 5^2$	0.250	Hf	4	$5^25\ 6^2$	0.100
Ti	4	3^24^2	0.167	Zr	4	$4^24\ 5^2$	0.125	Ta	5	$5^35\ 6^2$	0.067
V	5	3^34^2	0.111	Nb	5	$4^44\ 5^1$	0.063	W	6	$5^45\ 6^2$	0.050
Cr	6	3^44^1	0.067	Mo	6	$4^54\ 5^1$	0.050	Re	7	$5^55\ 6^2$	0.040
Mn	7	3^54^2	0.067	Ru	8	$4^74\ 5^1$	6.036	Os	8	$5^65\ 6^2$	0.033
Fe	8	3^64^2	0.055	Rh	8	$4^84\ 5^1$	0.031	Ir	8	$5^75\ 6^2$	0.028
Co	8	3^74^2	0.047	Pd	8	$4^{10}4\ 5^1$	0.025	Pt	8	$5^95\ 6^1$	0.022
Ni	8	3^84^2	0.041								

Alloys of transition metals with non-transition elements possessing outer p-electrons are characterized by sp-hybridizations that should reduce the probability of sd-hybridization and should reduce the exchange between the d-shells of transition metal atoms in the lattices of such alloys. In general, this should correspond to an increase in the catalytic activity compared to the activity of the starting transition metals, especially in cases in which the acceptor capacity of the d-metals is low (rhenium,

platinum-group metals, iron-group metals) while the energy state of the
p-electrons is fairly high ($3p$- or higher). The validity of the above
assumption is supported, for instance, by the high catalytic activity of
rhenium selenide /23/. As a result, a high catalytic activity should be
exhibited by many aluminides, germanides, arsenides, tellurides,
antimonides, and stannides of metals with a low acceptor capacity of the
d-sublevels.

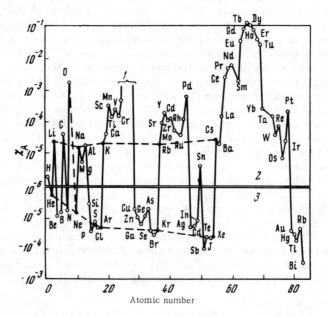

FIGURE 1. Magnetic susceptibility λ_A of the elements as a function of
their atomic number:

1- ferromagnetic (iron, nickel); 2- paramagnetic; 3- diamagnetic
elements.

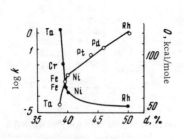

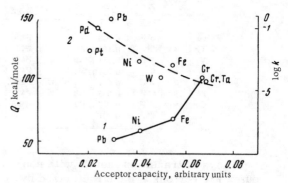

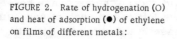

FIGURE 2. Rate of hydrogenation (O)
and heat of adsorption (●) of ethylene
on films of different metals:

k- hydrogenation rate constant; d-
specific weight of the d-state in the
metallic bond, %.

FIGURE 3. Dependence of the heat of adsorption (1) and log k (2)
on the acceptor capacity of the d-shells of the transition metals.

266

Of special importance are cases in which a compound is formed between *d*-metals possessing a high acceptor capacity and typical non-metals possessing $2p$- and $3p$- valence electrons (boron, carbon, nitrogen, silicon, phosphorus, sulfur). The importance of the study of these compounds (nitrides, carbides, hydrides, etc.) from the point of view of the development of the multiplet theory of catalysis was stressed recently by A.A. Balandin /24/. The electron concentration between the cores of atoms in the lattice and the nature of their distribution vary as a function of the value of the criterion of incompleteness of the *d*-electron shell and the value of the ionization of the non-metallic atom. In order to analyze the above case, we may use the following simplified scheme of the chemical bonds in compounds of this type:

$$
\begin{array}{c}
\text{Me} - \text{X} \\
\vdots \quad \vdots \\
\text{Me} \quad \text{X}'
\end{array}
$$

where Me — X is a predominantly metallic bond realized with the participation of collective electrons, Me $\div$ Me is a mixed covalent-metallic bond between atoms of the transition metals, and X: X is a predominantly covalent bond between atoms of the non-metal.

An increase in the acceptor capacity of the transition-metal atom (Me) in compounds with the same non-metal causes an increase in the probability of transfer of p-electrons (as well as of s-electrons) from the atom of the non-metal in the direction of the cores of the transition-metal atoms, and this is accompanied by a displacement of the relative maximum electron concentration in the direction of the same cores. At the same time, an increase in the ionization potential of the non-metal in compounds with the same transition metal displaces the relative maximum electron concentration in the direction of the cores of non-metal atoms. A decrease in the acceptor capacity of the transition metal, expressed by the criterion ξ, is accompanied by a weakening of the Me — X bond, a strengthening of the Me — Me bond up to a certain value (as we noted above, this is associated with a particularly large increase in the relative fraction of Me electrons participating in the covalent bond), and a corresponding strengthening of the X: X bond, which may ultimately lead to a peculiar "isolation" of the Me — Me and X: X bonds with the creation of energy breaks and the consequent appearance of semiconductor properties. Statistic filling of the *d*-state of the transition metal with a corresponding decrease in the electrical resistivity, the magnetic susceptibility and other analogous effects /25, 26/ is possible in the case of very high values of ξ and low ionization potentials of the non-metals. The first ionization potentials of the light non-metals are as follows: B 8.28, C 11.24, N 14.51, O 13.57, Si 8.14, P 10.43, and S 10.42 eV. Thus, we could expect that the valence electrons of boron and silicon would fill most readily the *d*-shells of the transition metals. Hence, the borides and silicides of the transition

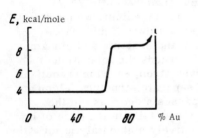

E, kcal/mole

8

6

4

0   *40*   *80*   % Au

FIGURE 4. Conversion of para-hydrogen on palladium-gold alloys

metals should possess the lowest chemisorption and catalytic activities, and the decrease in these activities should become more prounced as the acceptor capacity of the transition metal is increased. In other cases of carbides, phosphides, and sulfides we should expect an increase rather than a decrease in the catalytic activity compared with the activity of the transition metals. This is due to the partial transfer of d-electrons from the metal to the common electron cloud, which is accompanied by a decrease in the degree of incompleteness of the d-shells and a simultaneous polarization displacement of the p-electrons in the direction of the cores of the metallic atoms in the lattice. The above relationships are greatly complicated when the atoms of the non-metals form isolated structural elements in the crystal lattice, as in the case of borides and silicides. As these structural elements become more and more complicated (Figure 5), the p-electrons of the boron become more and more involved in the formation of B — B bonds and this is accompanied by an increase in the degree of sd-screening of the transition-metal atoms (strengthening of the Me — Me bond) and a corresponding decrease in the catalytic activity (within the limits of the relatively low catalytic activity of borides). It has been shown /27/ that one of the lower nickel borides is a satisfactory hydrogenation catalyst, which is in good agreement with the above concepts since the combination of nickel (which is a very weak acceptor) and boron (whose electrons are used-up in the formation of covalent bonds) should lead to a low degree of filling of the d-band of nickel, and hence to a relatively high catalytic activity. Similar data were obtained recently /28/ for the Me_2B borides of palladium, platinum, and ruthenium, which exhibited a high catalytic activity in the low-temperature liquid-phase hydrogenation of cyclopentadiene, cyclohexene, and crotonic and cinnamic aldehydes. In the case of silicides, the trend towards the formation of covalent bonds between the silicon atoms is even stronger, which results in the formation of structures with well-defined separate structural elements of metal and silicon atoms (Figure 6). This causes a decrease in the degree of filling of the d-shells of the metals (especially in the case of low values of ξ) and leads to the appearance of relatively high catalytic activities.

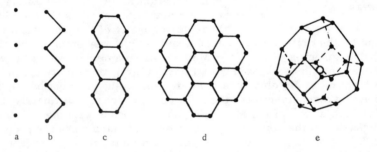

a   b   c   d   e

FIGURE 5. Boron-atom configurations in the structures of borides:

a- isolated boron atoms (Me_4B, Me_2B); b- single chains of boron atoms (MeB);
c- double chains (Me_3B_4); d- grids made of boron atoms (MeB_2); e- skeletons
of boron atoms (MeB_{12}).

The validity of the above conceptions has been confirmed to a certain extent by the results of investigations of the catalytic properties of refractory compounds, that were carried out under the guidance of S. Z. Roginskii /29, 30/. In the dehydrogenation of cyclohexane, borides show a low catalytic activity, while the carbides of titanium, zirconium, and other metals, as well as molybdenum disilicide $MoSi_2$ exhibit a high activity. In the case of carbides, the fact that the ionization potential of carbon is higher than that of boron causes a decrease in the degree of filling of the d-levels of the transition metal; this decrease becomes more pronounced as the value of ξ is reduced. We should mention the characteristic (in the above sense) sharp decrease in the degree of conversion of cyclohexane (Table 2) in the transition from TiC ($\xi = 0.167$) and ZrC ($\xi = 0.125$) to Mo_2C ($\xi = 0.05$). The further increase in activity in the case of $MoSi_2$ may be related to the creation of a substantial fraction of covalent Si — Si bonds with the participation of some of the sd-electrons of the molybdenum. The degree of conversion of cyclohexane decreases sharply in the transition from $MoSi_2$ to Mo_3Si, as a result of the decrease in the fraction of Si — Si bonds and the consequent filling of the d-state by the valence electrons of the silicon. Subsequent research in the same direction revealed that borides show practically no catalytic activity (the borides studied were NbB_2, Mo_2B_5, ScB_2, YB_6, CaB_6, SrB_6, HfB_2, BaB_2, as well as AlB_{12} which is a typical covalent semiconductor /31/). Two silicides — $TiSi_2$ and WSi_2 — exhibited a moderate catalytic activity. Many refractory chromium compounds — carbides ($Cr_{23}C_6$, Cr_7C_3, Cr_3C_2 /30/), a sulfide (Cr_2S_3), silicides (Cr_3Si, Cr_5Si_3, CrSi, $CrSi_2$), nitrides (CrN and Cr_2N) and a phosphide (CrP) — exhibited increased catalytic activity in the dehydrogenation of butane to butenes and butadiene-1,3, while chromium borides (Cr_4B, CrB, CrB_2, and CrB_6) again did not act as catalysts. At the same time, in agreement with the above conceptions, Cr_4B was the only boride that exhibited a certain (albeit insignificantly low) activity; Cr_4B has a crystal lattice with isolated boron atoms, while the chromium atoms are characterized by a relatively low acceptor capacity.

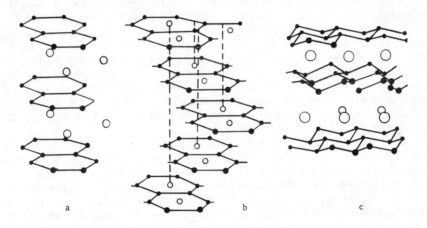

FIGURE 6. Structural elements of silicon atoms in silicide lattices:

a- graphite-like grids of silicon atoms; b- the same grids, centered by metal atoms; c- diamond-like corrugated grids of silicon atoms.

TABLE 2. Results of a study of the catalytic properties of certain refractory compounds with respect to the dehydrogenation of cyclohexane

Sample	Specific surface, m^2/g	Amount of the sample in the catalytic column, g	E, kcal/mole	Degree of conversion X* at 500°C	Temperature of the start of the reaction, °C	Resistivity ohm·cm
TiB_2	0.6	5.8	—	—	600	14.4
ZrB_2	2.4	13.4	—	—	650	16.6
CrB_2	2.9	1.4	—	—	600	56
W_2B_5	1.4	3.5	—	—	650	43
LaB_6	0.5	8.4	—	0.9	400	16.1
CdB_6	1.4	3.0	—	—	600	140
TiC	1.2	5.5	4.0	0.16	350	52.5
ZrC	1.1	7.5	8.9	0.17	450	50.0
Mo_2C	2.2	5.8	10.5	0.52	300	71.0
W_2C	1.1	9.7	—	—	650	—
WC	0.4	11.5	—	0.10	400	19.2
$MoSi_2$	1.7	8.6	18.7	0.65	300	21.6
V_3Si	0.2 **	1.8	9.7	0.25	300	—
Mo_3Si	—	1.2	19.8	0.076	400	—
CaO	42	1.3	11.2	0.08	450	—
Aluminosilicate catalyst	260 †	1.5	21.6	0.12	400	—

* In all cases X corresponds to the same argon flow rate, equal to 20 cm³/min.

** Determined from the adsorption of krypton.

† Determined under static conditions, from the adsorption of heptane.

It should be noted that chromium possesses a stable d^5s^2 -configuration, and the overall $3d^5 4s^1$ configuration has, apparently, a tendency to produce d -electrons with the formation of the stable d^5s^2 -configuration. The crystal lattices of chromium carbides and sulfides (which exhibit the highest catalytic activity) have the most favorable combination of the values of the acceptor capacity of the chromium atoms (medium values) and the ionization potentials of the carbon and sulfur atoms (also medium values). As a result, the relative electron-density maximum occupies a peculiar "central" position, with statistically-free d-positions of the chromium atoms and p-states of the carbon and sulfur atoms. A similar distribution of the electron density is observed in the lattice of scandium nitride (ScN) which combines the exceptionally high acceptor capacity of scandium with the high ionization potential of nitrogen; ScN exhibits a high catalytic activity in the dehydrogenation of butane to butylene.

A comparative study of the catalytic activities of metallic chromium and chromium carbides (Cr_3C_2 and Cr_7C_3) in the aromatization of n-hexane and n-octane has been carried out /32/. Chromium exhibited no catalytic activity, while both carbides caused aromatization (Cr_7C_3 was the more active). The absence of catalytic activity in chromium may be related to the fact that in spite of its formally medium acceptor capacity the stable $d^{10}s^2$ configuration is created when chromium is surrounded by the adjacent atoms in the crystal lattice of the metal. As a result, the acceptance of s-electrons (e.g., hydrogen in dehydrogenation reactions) is strongly hindered or even impossible, as shown by experiment /33/; the donation of s-electrons is much easier and thus a catalytic activity is exhibited in the

270

corresponding reactions. The formation of chromium carbides leads to the destruction of the above stable configuration and to donor-acceptor interaction of the chromium with carbon atoms, which involves the transfer of outer (mainly $4s^1$) electrons from the chromium to become collective with the p-electrons of the carbon. At the same time, because of the relatively low value of ξ for chromium and the high ionization potential of the carbon atoms, in addition to the probability of s-electron transfer from the chromium (in the direction of the core of the carbon atom) there exists the probability of a partial destruction of the $3d^5$-configuration with a corresponding increase in the acceptor capacity. An increase in the relative content of carbon in the chromium carbide phases is accompanied by an increase in the probability of formation of carbon-carbon bonds, which is also a consequence of the complication of the structural elements with carbon atoms, caused by the increase in the C:Cr ratio. The bonds ultimately tend to form a stable configuration of the s^2p^6 (diamond) type (this is equivalent to a sharp increase in the ionization potential of the carbon atoms) and to increase the possibility of disturbance of the $3d^5$.- configuration of the chromium atoms. As a result, a sharp increase in catalytic activity is caused by the transition from chromium to chromium carbides in which the carbon atoms form chains. In the case of chromium oxide, the high ionization potential of the oxygen causes a marked shift in the position of the collective chromium and oxygen electrons (in the direction of the oxygen atoms) which contributes to the destruction of the stable configuration of the chromium d-electrons, increases the acceptor capacity of the core of the chromium atom, and produces the high catalytic activity of chromium oxide (for example, in reactions of the type of the dehydrocyclization of paraffin hydrocarbons). The above data show that oxides in general should have relatively high catalytic activities, especially the lower oxides of the transition metals, since the higher oxides are, as a rule, semiconductors with large forbidden-zone widths that hinder electron transitions. The above is valid also in the case of some other refractory phases (in their homogeneity region), when a decrease in the concentration of the non-metal (within the limits of this region) causes the appearance of energy breaks, as in the cases of titanium and zirconium nitrides /33 —35/.

The compounds of non-metals with lanthanides and actinides (possessing unfilled f-shells) form a special group of refractory compounds. Since the inner f-electrons cannot participate directly in chemical bonding, the determining role in such cases is played by $f \rightarrow d$ electron transitions (of the $4f^n \rightarrow 4f^{n-1}5d^1$ type) that terminate in the formation of the d-state. The theoretical dependence of the number of possible electron transitions is expressed by the curve in Figure 7. According to these data /36/, the maximum multiplicity, and hence the highest degree of electron bonding and the lowest probability of $f \rightarrow d$ transitions correspond to europium and gadolinium which normally have 7 electrons in their $4f$-shells. In general, an increase in the atomic number in the La...Nd series, and a decrease in the Lu...Tb series, should cause a decrease in the number of d-states and a certain corresponding increase in the catalytic activity. This should be exhibited most clearly in the case of compounds of the lanthanides with non-metals possessing high ionization potentials, and especially with oxygen and nitrogen. Interesting observations in this direction were made at the laboratories of A.A.Balandin and Kh.M. Minachev /6 — 9/ during studies on the catalytic activity of oxides of the rare-earth elements, especially in the case of the dehydrogenation of cyclohexane and n-heptane and the isomerization of five- and six-atom cycloolefins (dehydrocyclization). A distinct increase in the catalytic activity was observed in the series $La_2O_3 - Nd_2O_3 - Sm_2O_3 - Cd_2O_3$ (in Cd_2O_3 the catalytic activity is associated with the presence of $5d^1$-electrons) as well as in the series from Yb_2O_3 to Tu_2O_3 (the only exception was Er_2O_3, which according to the data of these authors is less active than Yb_2O_3, while according to the proposed scheme it should be more active than the oxides of yttrium and thulium).

A very important observation was made, namely, that at certain temperatures the oxides of the elements in the yttrium group have similar specific activities that are higher than those of the oxides of the elements in the cerium group and of yttrium oxide (the low activity of Y compounds is attributed to the high acceptor capacity of its d-shell). Evidently, this is due to the fact that the elements in the yttrium group actually have a lower degree of screening of the unfilled levels. A good agreement was found between the bond energies and the effective magnetic moments, which is an expression of the similar influence of the degree of incompleteness and the stability of the $4f$-electron shells on the state (and presence) of outer d-electrons and on the catalytic activity of oxides of the rare-earth elements. Practically the same dependences, but with somewhat reduced activities, should be observed also in the case of the lanthanide nitrides. In accordance with the above, lanthanide borides and silicides should exhibit a low catalytic activity, and this has been confirmed experimentally; a very low activity should be exhibited by scandium and yttrium borides, and possibly by other compounds of these elements, except the nitrides and oxides which should be characterized by a favorable combination of the high acceptor capacity of the metals with the high ionization potentials of oxygen and nitrogen.

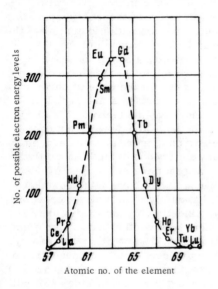

FIGURE 7. Number of possible electron energy levels for the $4f$-levels of lanthanides.

From the point of view of catalytic activity, interesting results could probably be obtained by the introduction of fluorine into the lattices of carbides, phosphides, and sulfides of transition metals with a high acceptor capacity, provided that such carbofluorides, fluorophosphides and fluorosulfides could be prepared on the basis of crystallochemical and thermodynamic considerations.

According to the above conceptions, the lowest catalytic activity should be exhibited by non-metallic refractory compounds formed as a result of various combinations of p-elements. These include, in the first place, the carbides and nitrides of boron and silicon, boron-silicon compounds, etc. /37/ possessing wide forbidden zones. The degree of inactivity of such compounds is determined by the nature of the electron configuration of their bonds and has a maximum when the s^2p^6 configuration (characteristic of the inert gases) is established or approached most closely. The extent to which this configuration is approached depends on the energy state of the s- and p-electrons and on the probability of $s \rightarrow p$ transitions. These stable hybrid configurations may be destroyed mainly by the introduction of transition-metal atoms (possessing a high acceptor capacity) into the composition of the non-metallic refractory compounds; however, this is of theoretical rather than practical interest. For this reason, the practical value of non-metallic refractory compounds in catalysis consists only in their use as inert carriers or supports for active substances.

BIBLIOGRAPHY

1. ROGINSKII, S. Z. — ZhFKh, Vol. 5: 249. 1935.
2. "Solid-State Chemistry". — Collection of translated papers edited by S. Z. Roginskii. Moskva, IL. 1961.
3. PANCHENKOV, G. M. and V. P. LEBEDEV. Khimicheskaya kinetika i kataliz (Chemical Kinetics and Catalysis). — Moskva, Izd. MGU. 1961.
4. GERMAIN, J. Heterogeneous Catalysis. [Russian translation. 1961.]
5. TOLSTOPYATOVA, A. A., I. R. KONENKO, and A. A. BALANDIN. — Kinetika i Kataliz, Vol. 2: 135. 1961.
6. TOLSTOPYATOVA, A. A. and A. A. BALANDIN. — ZhFKh, Vol. 32: 1831. 1958.
7. TOLSTOPYATOVA, A. A. and A. A. BALANDIN. — In: Sbornik "Redkozemel'nye elementy", p. 307. Moskva, Izd. AN SSSR. 1958.
8. TOLSTOPYATOVA, A. A. and A. A. BALANDIN. — DAN SSSR, Vol. 138: 1365. 1961.
9. MINACHEV, Kh. M., M. A. MARKOV, and O. K. SHCHUKINA. — Neftekhimiya, Vol. 1: 482. 1961.
10. BALANDIN, A. A. — Uspekhi Khimii, Vol. 33: 549. 1964.
11. SAMSONOV, G. V. — DAN SSSR, Vol. 93: 689. 1953.
12. SAMSONOV, G. V. — Poroshkovaya Metallurgiya, No. 2: 3. 1962.
13. SAMSONOV, G. V. Tugoplavkie soedineniya (Refractory Compounds). — Moskva, Metallurgizdat. 1963.
14. "Theory of the Ferromagnetism of Metals and Alloys". — Collection of translated papers. Moskva, IL. 1963.
15. KORSUNSKII, M. I. and Ya. E. GENKIN. — DAN SSSR, Vol. 142: 1276. 1962.
16. ZAIMOVSKII, A. S. and L. A. CHUDNOVSKAYA. Magnitnye Materialy (Magnetic Materials), p. 13. — Moskva-Leningrad, Gosenergoizdat. 1957.
17. KRYLOV, O. V. Dissertation. — Moskva, IKhF AN SSSR. 1964.
18. COUPER, A. and D. Eley. — Disc. Faraday Soc., Vol. 8: 172. 1950.
19. SAMSONOV, G. V. — ZhNKh, Vol. 8: 1320. 1963.
20. DOWDEN, P. and R. REYNOLDS. — Disc. Faraday Soc., Vol. 8: 184. 1950.
21. RIENÄCKER, G. — Z. Elektrochemie, Vol. 47: 805. 1941.
22. RIENÄCKER, G. and W. SARRY. — Z. Elektrochemie, Vol. 52: 41. 1948.
23. BALANDIN, A. A., E. I. KARPEISKAYA, and A. A. TOLSTOPYATOVA. — IAN SSSR, OKhN, p. 1365. 1959.
24. BALANDIN, A. A. — Uspekhi Khimii, Vol. 31: 1271. 1962.
25. SAMSONOV, G. V. — ZhETF, Vol. 26: 716. 1956.
26. SAMSONOV, G. V., V. S. NESHPOR, and G. A. KUDINTSEVA. — Radiotekhnika i Elektronika, Vol. 2: 631. 1957.
27. JOSEPH, N. — Ind. Eng. Chem., Vol. 44: 1006. 1952.
28. TABER, A. M., B. D. POLKOVNIKOV, N. N. MAL'TSEVA, V. I. MIKHEEVA, and A. A. BALANDIN. Tezisy dokladov na Pervom soveshchanii po khimii inorganicheskikh gidridov, p. 52. — Moskva, Izd. AN SSSR. 1963.
29. GAZIEV, G. A., O. V. KRYLOV, S. Z. ROGINSKII, G. V. SAMSONOV, E. A. FOKINA, and M. I. YANOVSKII. — DAN SSSR, Vol. 140: 863. 1961.

30. LIU CHUNG-HUI, S.Z. ROGINSKII, G.V. SAMSONOV, and M.I. YANOVSKII. — Neftekhimiya, Vol.3: 843. 1963.
31. SAMSONOV, G.V. and N.N. ZHURAVLEV. — FMM, Vol.1: 564. 1955.
32. GITIS, K.M., V.L. POLININ, G.V. SAMSONOV, T.Ya. KOSOLAPOVA, and M.I. ROZENGART. — In this Collection, p.230.
33. SAMSONOV, G.V. and T.S. VERKHOGLYADOVA. — Zhurnal Strukturnoi Khimii, Vol.2: 617. 1961.
34. SAMSONOV, G.V. and T.S. VERKHOGLYADOVA. — DAN SSSR, Vol.138: 342. 1961.
35. SAMSONOV, G.V. and T.S. VERKHOGLYADOVA. — DAN UkrSSR, No.1: 48. 1962.
36. SAMSONOV, G.V. and V.S. NESHPOR. — DAN SSSR, Vol.122: 1021. 1958.
37. SAMSONOV, G.V. — Poroshkovaya Metallurgiya, No.3: 55. 1961.